FERTILIZER NITROGEN
Its Chemistry and Technology

Edited by
VINCENT SAUCHELLI

Chemical Technologist Consultant
National Plant Food Institute
Washington, D. C.

AMERICAN CHEMICAL SOCIETY
MONOGRAPH SERIES

New York
REINHOLD PUBLISHING CORPORATION
Chapman & Hall, Ltd., London

General Introduction

American Chemical Society's
Series of Chemical Monographs

By arrangement with the Interallied Conference of Pure and Applied Chemistry, which met in London and Brussels in July, 1919, the American Chemical Society was to undertake the production and publication of Scientific and Technologic Monographs on chemical subjects. At the same time it was agreed that the National Research Council, in cooperation with the American Chemical Society and the American Physical Society, should undertake the production and publication of Critical Tables of Chemical and Physical Constants. The American Chemical Society and the National Research Council mutually agreed to care for these two fields of chemical progress. The American Chemical Society named as Trustees, to make the necessary arrangements of the publication of the Monographs, Charles L. Parsons, secretary of the Society, Washington, D. C.; the late John E. Teeple, then treasurer of the Society, New York; and the late Professor Gellert Alleman of Swarthmore College. The Trustees arranged for the publication of the ACS Series of (a) Scientific and (b) Technological Monographs by the Chemical Catalog Company, Inc. (Reinhold Publishing Corporation, successor) of New York.

The Council of the American Chemical Society, acting through its Committee on National Policy, appointed editors (the present list of whom appears at the close of this sketch) to select authors of competent authority in their respective fields and to consider critically the manuscripts submitted.

The first Monograph of the Series appeared in 1921. After twenty-three years of experience certain modifications of general policy were indicated. In the beginning there still remained from the preceding five decades a distinct though arbitrary differentiation between so-called "pure science" publications and technologic or applied science literature. By 1944 this differentiation was fast becoming nebulous. Research in private enterprise

iii

had grown apace and not a little of it was pursued on the frontiers of knowledge. Furthermore, most workers in the sciences were coming to see the artificiality of the separation. The methods of both groups of workers are the same. They employ the same instrumentalities, and frankly recognize that their objectives are common, namely, the search for new knowledge for the service of man. The officers of the Society therefore combined the two editorial Boards in a single Board of twelve representative members.

Also in the beginning of the Series, it seemed expedient to construe rather broadly the definition of a Monograph. Needs of workers had to be recognized. Consequently among the first hundred Monographs appeared works in the form of treatises covering in some instances rather broad areas. Because such necessary works do not now want for publishers, it is considered advisable to hew more strictly to the line of the Monograph character, which means more complete and critical treatment of relatively restricted areas, and, where a broader field needs coverage, to subdivide it into logical subareas. The prodigious expansion of new knowledge makes such a change desirable.

These Monographs are intended to serve two principal purposes: first, to make available to chemists a thorough treatment of a selected area in form usable by persons working in more or less unrelated fields to the end that they may correlate their own work with a larger area of physical science discipline; second, to stimulate further research in the specific field treated. To implement this purpose the authors of Monographs are expected to give extended references to the literature. Where the literature is of such volume that a complete bibliography is impracticable, the authors are expected to append a list of references critically selected on the basis of their relative importance and significance.

AMERICAN CHEMICAL SOCIETY

F. MARSHALL BERINGER
Editor of Monographs

ASSOCIATES

MELVIN CALVIN   HARRY H. WASSERMAN
HENRY EYRING   HAROLD H. ZEISS

Preface

To prevent crops from going hungry, at least sixteen nutrient elements are essential. Of these, some are necessary in relatively small amounts as, for example, the micronutrients; others, the major elements, are required in larger quantities and of the latter, nitrogen is needed in much larger amounts than any of the others. For the purpose of maintaining adequate levels in the soil for optimal crop yields, nitrogen presents a far more serious problem in world agriculture than any of the other plant nutrients. The reason for this stems from the relatively high amounts of this element needed by most economical crops and the relatively higher losses of soil nitrogen caused by crop removal, leaching, and other natural agencies—all of which make multiple applications of nitrogen necessary during the growth cycle of a crop.

This monograph presents reviews of various agricultural and technological phases of the nitrogen industry. The important role played by nitrogen in agriculture is surveyed. A brief description is given of the natural deposits of sodium nitrate in Chile and the latest methods of processing the caliche for commercial uses. Space is given to the process of recovering ammonia from coke-oven gas and its conversion to ammonium sulfate. Soil nitrogen is discussed from several aspects, including its biological fixation and its relationships in plant nutrition. The interesting history of the origin and development of synthetic ammonia is given by two authorities from the organization where it first began.

The technical and economic factors in the industry are presented by authors who have to deal with them first-hand in commercial organizations. Catalysts have made the synthetic process succeed and this phase is presented by an authority from a firm that is eminent in this field. The production of nitric acid is an important development in the industry; its chemistry and manufacture are comprehensively described.

The fertilizer industry is a major consumer of synthetic ammonia and its derived products. Its importance is recognized in this monograph. Considerable space is duly devoted to this major phase of the nitrogen industry. The manufacture and utilization of urea comprise another very important development in all advanced industrial countries. Other pertinent phases of this fascinating, modern and essential industry are properly described.

A monograph of this kind has to be a compilation of chapters by specialists, each competent in his field. This makes it difficult to secure a uniformity in style or manner of presentation in each chapter. The important feature, I believe, is to have each presentation as authoritative and as comprehensive as possible within the assigned space. The Editor has not tried to achieve uniformity of style; rather, it was felt that, with the exception of some obvious editing, it was preferable to publish the chapters essentially as prepared by the authors.

I here express my grateful thanks to the authors for their splendid cooperation in making this monograph possible.

In his preface to Monograph No. 59 on Fixed Nitrogen, issued in 1932, editor Harry A. Curtis commented as follows: "At the beginning of the present century there existed a 'nitrogen problem.' The agricultural and industrial demands for nitrogen compounds were increasing rapidly and the natural sources of supply were limited. Today, the 'nitrogen problem,' if there be one, is to find a market for the output of fixed nitrogen potentially available."

A marketing problem in 1932? In 1963, the industry faces the same problem but how immensely more intense! Plus ça change, plus c'est la même chose.

VINCENT SAUCHELLI

Baltimore, Maryland
April 1964

Contents

1

The Role of Nitrogen in Agriculture

Vincent Sauchelli

Consultant, National Plant Food Institute

Until the turn of the century, the maintenance of the nitrogen supply in farm soils was an urgent problem because agriculture depended entirely upon natural sources of nitrogen. These were mainly animal and vegetable wastes, most of which were from industries other than agriculture per se, e.g., animal manures, seed meals, fish scraps, packing-house wastes, sewage sludges, leather scraps, dried blood, nitrate from Chile, and ammonium sulfate from the coking of coal. Since the supply from these sources was necessarily limited, one can see why Malthus and his followers took such a gloomy view of the world's ability to provide food for future populations. Although natural nitrates from Chile and by-product ammonium sulfate from coking operations contributed substantially to supplies from natural sources, the Malthusian gloom was not lifted until the development of the Haber-Bosch process of synthesizing ammonia in the 1920's. The commercial development of ammonia synthesis can rightly be regarded as among the significant technological advances that have enriched mankind.

NONSYNTHETIC SOURCES OF FERTILIZER NITROGEN

The chief nonsynthetic sources of nitrogen are animal and plant wastes, animal manures, sewage sludges, garbage wastes, industrial and canning wastes, leather scraps, ammonia from the coking industry, nitrate from natural sodium deposits in Chile, and potassium nitrate from animal residues in India. The nitrogen in these materials, originally from the atmosphere, is converted into organic forms through biological and chemical processes. Thus in the form of oxides and ammonia dissolved in snow and rainwater, small amounts (for example, 5 to 7 lb) of nitrogen per acre per year reach many parts of the earth. Another source of nitrogen is the contribution made by soil organisms in symbiotic existence with legumes;

1

under favorable conditions, this source provides 80 to 100 lb of nitrogen per acre per year.

Synthetic ammonia is the principal nitrogenous material from which a variety of nitrogenous compounds needed in the fertilizer industry have been developed. The fertilizer industry uses this ammonia for three major purposes: (1) as raw material for producing nitric acid, which is an intermediate for nitrate fertilizer materials such as synthetic nitrate of soda, nitrate of lime, nitrophos, and ammonium nitrate; (2) to neutralize acidic materials to form ammonium salts such as ammonium sulfate, mono- and diammonium phosphates, ammonium chloride, ammonium nitrate, and ammoniated superphosphates; and (3) to produce urea and allied materials.

Each of about 16 chemical elements essential to the perpetuation of plant life has a unique share in the building up of complex living tissues. Omit any one of these elements and life cannot continue. However, certain of them such as nitrogen play a more significant role. In every living cell, nitrogen is a major and indispensable constituent of protein and of the nucleic acid molecules governing and sustaining life processes, i.e., metabolism, growth, reproduction, and hereditability. What a paradox! Nitrogen is an inert element, chemically considered, and is called "azote," meaning "without life" in some languages; yet it plays a dominant role in the production of the very stuff of life, protein. Most organisms can assimilate nitrogen in a suitably combined form only. The number of species capable of fixing nitrogen into suitable combinations for biological utilization is very small. This ability to fix elemental nitrogen is, however, of great biochemical interest, especially in agriculture, and is justifiably regarded as second in importance only to photosynthesis for the maintenance of life on this planet.

Nitrogen is an inert gas comprising about 75 per cent by weight or 78 per cent by volume of the atmosphere. Despite its inert nature, nitrogen is essential to the existence and perpetuation of life on earth. All chemical reactions involving living organisms require, somehow, the intervention of organic compounds of nitrogen. Without nitrogen, there is no life.

Although the supply of nitrogen in the atmosphere is vast (some 4000 million tons), it is there as a free, inert gas—a form useless to life or industry. In fact, nitrogen is useful only when combined with other elements. How to utilize this immense reservoir of free nitrogen has puzzled man ever since its existence was established. Finally, after 30 yr of tireless chemical and engineering investigations, the feat was accomplished in the 1920's by German research. The history of this remarkable achievement is given in Chapter 4.

The amount of atmospheric nitrogen over each acre of the world's land area is calculated at about 145,000 tons, which is equivalent to about 350,000 metric tons per hectare. The total nitrogen supplies of mineral soils are relatively small, ranging from 2000 to 16,000 lb per 2 million lb of soil. In the United States, the total content of nitrogen in most soils averages about 3000 lb per acre of plow depth (6 in.), except in prairie or Chernozem soils, which contain more. The total fixed nitrogen reserve in the crop-producing land in the United States is estimated at about 500 million tons. Yet, this large amount of soil nitrogen must be supplemented with organic and chemical fertilizers if productivity is to be maintained. Most mineral soils contain 2 to 4 per cent organic matter on an oven-dry basis, the amount being closely related to the nitrogen supply. The organic matter as such cannot be utilized directly by plants; it must be converted first into inorganic ions by soil organisms. The reactions involved in this conversion proceed by stages. If the starting material is protein, the sequence is normally:

$$\text{protein} \rightarrow \text{amino acids} \rightarrow NH_3 \rightarrow NO_2 \rightarrow NO_3.$$

BIOLOGICAL SOIL PROCESSES

The biochemical processes of fixing nitrogen, previously alluded to, have been going on for many thousands of years; they are perhaps the origin of biological processes on our planet. In time, nitrogen-fixing processes created the nitrogenous compounds that are present in coal and petroleum and, indirectly, the caliche of the Chilean desert. In addition, they are responsible for much of the fertility of native soils which, however great, is soon exhausted under heavy cropping. To produce and sustain high crop yields of modern agriculture, this native soil fertility must be supplemented with manures and chemical fertilizers in which nitrogen is a major nutrient element. The biological process of fixing atmospheric nitrogen in soil is still the chief source of plant-nutrient nitrogen in all parts of the agricultural world. (More details are given in a later chapter.)

Soil organic matter comprises a potential source of nitrogen, phosphorus, potassium, and sulfur nutrients. It contains at least 95 per cent of the nitrogen, 5 to 60 per cent of the total phosphorus, and 10 to 80 per cent of the total sulfur in the surface layer. To make these nutrients available to plants, biochemical processes (chiefly bacterial) must convert the organic substances to the ionic state, in which they can be assimilated. The actual path of conversion and uptake is from solid particles to the surrounding liquid phase or soil solution and then ultimate absorption by rootlets. The process involves the creation and movement of positive and negative ions including $(NO_3)^-$, $(H_2PO_4)^-$, $(SO_4)^{2-}$, Cl^-, $(HMoO_4)^-$, $(Ca)^{2+}$, $(Mg)^{2+}$, $(K)^+$, $(Fe)^{3+}$, $(Zn)^{2+}$ and $(Cu)^{2+}$.

All living organisms are composed of tissues built up of units called cells, in which protein is the most vital component. The dominant element in protein and nuclear proteins is nitrogen. It is difficult to visualize the tremendous amounts of protein nitrogen involved in maintaining living organisms of all kinds on earth and the amounts that will continue to be needed in the future. As a simple example to illustrate this, consider the amount of nitrogen required to produce one bushel of shelled corn (maize). An average minimum amount is 2 lb; hence, a harvested crop of 100 bushels will have required about 200 lb. The total amount of nitrogen commonly utilized in bringing such a crop to maturity is derived somewhat as follows: 50 to 75 lb from chemical fertilizers and the remainder from manure, soil organic matter, legume residues, and mineralized soil nitrogen. In 1960, United States agriculture utilized about 2,000,000 tons of chemical nitrogen, and world agriculture, exclusive of China and the Soviet bloc, about 8,000,000 metric tons. Recent estimates by FAO indicate that in 1958–59 eight major world crops removed from the soil a grand total of about 23,000,000 metric tons of nitrogen, the major portion of which was derived from resident fertility. A total of only about 8 to 9 million tons of chemical nitrogen was applied as chemical fertilizer. Data on nitrogen consumption and production are given in Table 1.1 and Table 1.2.

UTILIZATION OF NITROGEN BY PLANTS

A plant may be considered nature's workshop. Its source of energy is derived chiefly from the sun; by photosynthesis, it builds up the complex organic substances of its tissues from raw materials such as air nitrogen, water, phosphates, nitrates, potash, sulfates, and lime. Of the chemical elements known to be essential to plants, nitrogen happens to be deficient in most soils. Moreover, it is relatively costly to supply and difficult to retain in the soil.

Protein

Nitrogen is utilized by the plant in the fabrication of protein, nucleoproteins, amino acids, amines, amino sugars, and various other compounds. It is called the growth element and is present in largest amounts in the more tender, growing tissues such as buds, tips of shoots, and developing leaflets. But, it must be emphasized that for nitrogen to function effectively in plant life a sufficient quantity of other essential elements must be present, among which phosphorus, potassium, sulfur, calcium, magnesium, and many micronutrients are absolutely necessary. A deficiency of any one of these essentials will limit normal functioning. In a plant's early growth

TABLE 1.1. WORLD PRODUCTION AND CONSUMPTION OF FIXED NITROGEN (IN THOUSANDS OF METRIC TONS OF PURE NITROGEN FOR THE RESPECTIVE YEARS ENDED JUNE 30: 1 METRIC TON = 0.9842 LONG TON)

	1953–54	1954–55	1955–56	1956–57	1957–58	1958–59	1959–60	1960–61	1961–62
Production:									
Sulfate of ammonia	2238	2395	2638	2722	2903	3089	3087	3134	3084
Calcium cyanamide	347	359	328	334	328	322	313	302	290
Nitrate of soda	260	281	265	216	247	240	227	186	214
Nitrate of lime	333	368	335	357	368	415	424	462	467
Ammonium nitrate as such for use as fertilizer	517	656	792	879	1047	1144	1419	1669	2124
Lime-ammonium nitrate types	944	1099	1193	1269	1482	1639	1684	1816	1885
Ammonia and solution as direct/ indirect fertilizer	774	936	978	1071	1123	1301	1596	1686	1760
Urea for fertilizer use	109	162	212	343	402	519	578	779	979
Other forms of nitrogen	1442	1707	1883	2082	2439	2615	2984	338.	3722
Total production	6984	7963	8624	9272	10,339	11,284	12,312	13,42	14,525
Increase % on prior year	12.6	14.3	8.3	7.5	11.5	9.1	9.1	9.0	8.2
Consumption:									
World total all forms	6885	7685	8344	9160	10,059	11,147	12,269	13,089	14,395
Increase % on prior year	13.7	11.6	8.6	9.8	9.8	10.8	10.1	6.7	10.0
World total in agriculture	5783	6424	6990	7713	8432	9364	10,267	10,893	12,000
Increase % on prior year	12.7	11.1	8.8	10.3	9.3	11.0	9.6	6.1	10.2
Use in agriculture by continent:									
Europe (incl. USSR)	2846	3130	3416	3777	4016	4412	4764	5045	5303
America	1782	1932	1926	2159	2342	2720	2861	3115	3569
Asia	954	1124	1399	1514	1761	1893	2269	2336	2664
Africa	157	190	198	210	254	282	325	337	401
Oceania (incl. Hawaii)	44	48	51	53	59	57	48	60	63

Source: British Sulphate of Ammonia Federation, Ltd.

TABLE 1.2. NITROGEN CONSUMPTION IN USA BY SPECIFIED YEARS (SHORT TONS)

Year	In Mixtures	In Straight Materials	Total Consumed
1940*	—	—	378,543
1945	334,720	260,593	595,313
1950	467,009	488,630	955,639
1951	545,142	626,276	1,171,418
1952	615,606	750,795	1,366,401
1953	697,071	886,763	1,583,834
1954	745,012	1,044,876	1,789,888
1955	770,945	1,126,402	1,897,347
1956	767,605	1,107,766	1,875,371
1957	808,879	1,256,033	2,064,912
1958	825,943	1,407,473	2,233,419
1959	965,268	1,652,380	2,617,648
1960	983,414	1,702,158	2,685,572
1961	1,012,298	1,941,122	2,953,420

* Calendar year.
Source: U.S.D.A., A.R.S. (W. Scholl, *et al.*).

phases, nitrogen is particularly active and, at this so-called "boom stage" of growth, a steady supply of nitrogen must be available. Such a supply is provided by the action of soil microorganisms on soil organic matter or by applied fertilizers. A second stage in a plant's growth when a nitrogen supply is critical is during the seed-forming period. Thus with the approaching maturity of the plant (say a grain crop), the stored-up nitrogen of the vegetative parts is transported to the developing seed. For example, an average 30-bushel wheat crop will usually contain about 50 lb of nitrogen in the grain and about 20 lb in the remainder of the plant.

SOIL NITROGEN

Soil chemists have shown that all soil nitrogen is in organic forms (largely proteinaceous), and is utilized by soil organisms as a source of food and energy. Complex combinations of organic and inorganic substances form humic and amino acids which become very important constituents of a fertile soil. Crop residues in various stages of decomposition are always present in soil together with varying amounts of inorganic materials, chiefly ammoniates and nitrates. Losses of nitrogen from soil may occur through leaching, denitrification, and fixation. Under waterlogged conditions, dentrification leading to loss of gaseous nitrogen may cause serious losses. Certain types of clays, such as montmorillanite and biotite, have the ability to fix ammonia very tightly within their crystal structure, so that it is released very slowly as plant nutrient. Other factors will influence the potential supply of soil nitrogen, e.g., plowing and the general steps in cultivation hasten the decomposition of organic matter and hence the release of soil nitrogen. When first plowed, many virgin soils in humid regions contained from 0.01 to 1 per cent nitrogen in their surface layer. Leaching and erosion tend to remove top soil and, with it, much of the contained nitrogen. Further losses are caused by cropping. It is estimated that the original reserves of nitrogen in the soils of the North Central Region of the United States declined by about 25 to 50 per cent during the first 75 yr of cultivation. About half of the loss occurred during the first 20 yr; a fourth, in the following 20-yr period.

Availability

If nitrogen is applied to a soil as nitrate, it penetrates that soil quite readily after a rain, because nitrate is not adsorbed by the colloidal complex (clay and humus) of the soil. Thus, excessive rainfall will carry off considerable nitrate nitrogen and move it in the drainage water or, if the structure of the soil is such as to cause water-logging, losses are caused by denitrification, that is, the nitrate is changed to nitrite and then to elemental nitrogen. However, nitrogen applied as ammoniacal nitrogen, penetrates the soil profile less rapidly and drainage losses are reduced. On the other hand, ammonia nitrogen may become fixed chemically or biologically, and it has been estimated that of the total nitrogen in surface soils about 10 per cent (or more in subsoils) of the ammoniacal nitrogen may become fixed. At present, no satisfactory method is accepted universally for assessing the availability of nitrogen in soils or for predicting the probable response of a crop to fertilizer nitrogen.

FACTORS IN CROP PRODUCTION

Crop production is influenced greatly by climate, the nature of the soil, and the system of cultivation with climate playing, perhaps, the dominant role. Man can do much about manipulating the soil to better serve his purposes but, as yet, can do little to modify the climate. In the virgin state, a soil reaches and remains in equilibrium with the climate and the vegetative cover on its surface. Man comes along and, as the history of the United States demonstrates, removes the forests or plows the sod for planting his crops. The old established equilibrium is upset. Within a brief period, the soil fertility and structure deteriorate and the crop yields decline. As previously mentioned, the fertility of Corn-Belt soils declined significantly within the first 75 yr of cropping. Official records reveal that a hectare of land (2.47 acres) under an intensive system of wheat cropping loses 50 to 75 kg (110 to 165 lb) of P_2O_5, 100 to 200 kg (220 to 440 lb) of nitrogen (N), and 120 to 250 kg (264 to 550 lb) of potash (K_2O).

Ancient peoples understood ways and means of restoring worn-out soils to improve their productivity. Roman writers—Virgil, Cato, and Pliny—recorded the farming practices of their day for revitalizing depleted soils and, in fact, those practices remained in vogue in Europe up until the end of the 17th century. Then as chemistry, biology, and the other sciences gradually developed and contributed new insight into the workings of mysterious Nature, the use of agronomic knowledge, better farm equipment, chemical fertilizers, and improved seed influenced the creation of new systems of cultivation. The year 1840 marks a milestone in this progress. In that year, Justus von Liebig announced his famous dictum that plants derive their nutrition from mineral elements in the soil. His researches and writings had a powerful impact on the thinking and subsequent investigations concerned with soil fertility. Before his time, it was believed that plants, like animals, nourished themselves wholly on organic matter and hence that only organic materials could serve to maintain soil fertility.

NUTRIENT REQUIREMENTS OF PLANTS

Although ancient Roman farmers applied ashes and manure to their soils, they did not know definitely why they did it. Furthermore, such empirical practices were expected to merely maintain the former level of productivity. They could not have conceived that proper fertilization and soil-management practices make possible not only return to a soil of the elements removed by crops, but also an increase in yields and the maintenance of the soil's structure and microbiological activities. The modern concept is to fertilize both the soil and the crop under intensive systems of farming. Modern agricultural science embraces chemistry, biology, physics, and engineering. We have learned that a plant requires at least 16 chemical elements for its normal nutrition and growth, and a great deal of knowledge has been accumulated regarding the specific function of these nutritive elements. It is known also that plants obtain their requirements of oxygen, hydrogen, and carbon from the atmosphere and water. The mineral elements such as sulfur, iron, magnesium, and other so-called micronutrients are generally present in most soils in sufficient amounts. In the case of nearly all cultures, however, the soil's supply of nitrogen, phosphorus, potassium, and lime needed to satisfy the crops' requirements is seldom adequate. When they are deficient, it is necessary to supply through fertilizers the required level of these plant nutrients for modern intensive cropping systems. A proper balance between soil and applied nutritional elements has to be maintained. Agronomists have shown that an imbalance will reduce the crop yield. Each element has a specific job to do, and one element cannot be substituted for another.

An excess or deficiency of one nutrient adversely affects the yield and quality of a crop. Nitrogen stimulates the entire vegetative cycle of a plant. Too much nitrogen can overstimulate leaf and stem growth and interfere with the production of seed. Moreover the development of an excess of amino acids and amides accompanied by an inadequate amount of carbohydrates can impair the keeping qualities of fruits and vegetables.

To explain these relationships Liebig proposed his Law-of-the-minimum which states that the yield of a crop is determined by the amount of the growth element present in the least abundance. The "Law" applies to water, heat, and light as well as to the essential nutrients. An example will illustrate this concept.[1] If a soil is seriously deficient in 2 nutrients adding one affects the yield little or not at all. In a field test in which the soil had a very low content of nitrogen and phosphorus the yield of corn was only 4 bu. Adding 40 lb of nitrogen alone resulted in a yield of 12 bu. Adding 40 lb of phosphoric oxide alone gave 21 bu. When 40 lb of each nutrient were both applied the yield was 58 bu. This illustrates how 2 nutrient elements complement each other.

Reference

1. "U.S.D.A. Yearbook of Agriculture," 1957.

2

Nitrogen: Chemical and Physical Properties

Vincent Sauchelli

Consultant, National Plant Food Institute

Nitrogen spans a vast period in the history of chemistry, covering the period of the alchemists to the modern era of 20th-century chemical synthesis. Priestley, Cavendish, Scheele, and Lavoisier played a part in its discovery and identification. Lavoisier published his observations in 1778, in which he disclosed that in calcination only a part of the common air combined with metals and therefore concluded that such air was a mixture of two substances. The purer part was utilized in respiration and in calcination of metals. What was left he called "mofette," but later named it "azote" from two Greek roots meaning "without life." In 1790, Chaptal called this part of the air "nitrogen." Rutherford had designated it as "mephitic air." Priestley named it "phlogisticated air." Lavoisier demonstrated that it was an inert gas. Cavendish showed, however, that it was possible to cause this inert gas to combine with oxygen by means of an electric spark to form oxides. Thus, the colorless, odorless, and relatively inert gas, comprising about 75 per cent by weight of the atmosphere and now recognized as utterly essential to the generation and sustenance of all living organisms, received at one time the paradoxical name "azote," meaning without life; later, it was called "nitrogène," which linked it with saltpeter (or nitrum), believed by the ancients to produce life in plants.

De Saussure, famous in the annals of agricultural science, was led to believe that plants obtained the greater part of their nitrogen from the soil. His contention, however, was not accepted until nearly a half century later, when the brilliant researches of Boussingault, Liebig, and others confirmed de Saussure's experimental data. Boussingault and Liebig believed plants utilized nitrogen in the form of ammonia only. Such was their influence on the thinking of the scientific world of their day that, it is said, when the first shipload of Chilean sodium nitrate arrived in Hamburg, Germany, no one would buy it and it had to be dumped into the harbor.

TABLE 2.1

Processes	Primary Products	Secondary Products
Recovery Process:		
By-product ammonia	crude NH_3 liquor or $(NH_4)_2SO_4$ according to system adopted	other ammonium salts
Chile nitrate process	nitric acid, dilute or concentrated, according to methods of operation	nitrates, e.g., NH_4NO_3
Fixation process:		
Arc	oxides of N, normally recovered as dilute	concentrated HNO_3 or $Ca(NO_3)_2$, $NaNO_3$, or NH_4NO_3
Cyanamide	calcium cyanamide	NH_3 or $(NH_4)_2SO_4$ nitrate or urea, guanidine, and other organic chemicals
Synthetic NH_3-Haber-Bosch (various)	pure NH_3 gas or solution	$(NH_4)_2SO_4$ or NH_4Cl
Cyanide (various)	crude metallic cyanides	finished cyanides, or NH_3 or NH_4 salts

Research in France and Russia later proved conclusively that both ammoniacal and nitrate forms are assimilable under proper soil conditions.

In the 19th century, scientists kept speculating about the feasibility of synthesizing nitrogen compounds from inert atmospheric nitrogen. As late as 1881, knowledgeable men emphatically maintained that it was impossible to cause nitrogen and hydrogen to form ammonia with or without catalysts. Until some 50 yr ago, the only agents which made atmospheric nitrogen available to plant life were lightning and certain bacteria. Then, in 1913, the first of the Haber-Bosch synthetic ammonia plants became a reality. That fateful event is a milestone in man's progress in the conquest of famine. That such an important process could become a commercial success is proved by what today has become a colossal industrial enterprise. In the fiscal year 1961–62, world production of synthetic nitrogen amounted to 14,525,000 metric tons and world consumption, 14,395,000 tons.*

* Source: Messrs. Aikman (London). The figure includes production in the USSR.

NITROGEN

Elemental nitrogen exists in the atmosphere chiefly as diatomic N_2. In the combined form, nitrogen is found as nitrate, represented by sodium nitrate, $NaNO_3$. Two isotopes of nitrogen occur in nature. One is N^{14}, which is abundant (99.63 per cent of the total); the other is N^{15}, which is quite scarce. A third isotope, N^{13}, is known, but it is very unstable, having a half-life of 10.1 min.

Elemental nitrogen is commonly obtained by fractional distillation of liquid air. Its boiling point, $(-195°C)$, is lower than that of oxygen, $(-183.0°C)$, and thus, being more volatile, comes off in the first fractions. Very pure N_2 is obtained by thermally decomposing certain nitrogen compounds, among which is ammonium nitrite, NH_4NO_2.

The atomic weight of N^{14} is 14.008 atomic mass units. Its nucleus has 7 protons and 7 neutrons. N^{14} has a bond energy of 7.5 million electron volts for each of the 14 nuclear elements. This explains why it is difficult to cause it to dissociate into single atoms.

This nitrogen atom, as pictured by the Niels Bohr model, contains two electrons of opposite spin in the first orbit ($1s$) which is closest to the nucleus, and five electrons in the second or peripheral orbit. Since it has only five electrons in the peripheral orbit, the nitrogen atom tends to capture three other electrons from other atoms that may come close to it, making up an octet, or else to release the five electrons to other atoms. It, therefore, behaves, in ionic combinations, as a trivalent or pentavalent element. In combining with metals, the nitrogen atom tends to give up electrons.

The spatial representation of atomic nitrogen is a tetrahedron in which an electron occupies each corner of the base and two electrons, the apex. Dots are used to represent peripheral electrons.

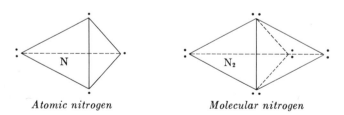

Atomic nitrogen   *Molecular nitrogen*

The N_2 molecule contains a triple bond and is represented by the symbol :N:::N:

The covalent triple bond of the N_2 molecule is particularly stable, re-

TABLE 2.2. NITROGEN CONTENT OF IMPORTANT NITROGEN COMPOUNDS
AND PRODUCTS

Compound	N (%)	Tons of Product per ton of N
NH_4NO_3 (pure 100%)...............	35.00	2.85
$NaNO_3$:		
Pure............................	16.47	6.07
Commercial......................	15.65	6.38
$(NH_4)_2SO_4$:		
100%...........................	21.21	4.71
25% NH_3......................	20.58	4.85
24.5% NH_3....................	20.17	4.95
24.0% NH_3....................	19.76	5.05
Ammonia:		
NH_3 anhydrous liquid..............	82.35	1.21
Conc. liquor:		
25%...........................	20.58	4.85
35.6% (sp gr 0.88)	29.31	3.41
KNO_3 (pure 100%)...................	13.86	7.21
$Ca(NO_3)_2$:		
Pure............................	17.07	5.86
Commercial......................	13.00	7.69
HNO_3 :		
100%...........................	22.22	4.50
96%............................	21.33	4.68
90%............................	20.00	5.00
65%............................	14.44	6.92
$NaCN$ (pure 100%)...................	28.57	3.50
KCN (100%).......................	21.53	4.64
$NaNO_2$ (100%)	20.29	4.92
$CaCN_2$:		
100%...........................	35.00	2.85
Raw furnace products..............	⎰20.00	⎰5.00
	⎱19.50	⎱5.12
Nitrolin........................	⎰18.00	⎰5.55
	⎱16.00	⎱6.25

quiring about 2.2×10^5 kcal/kmol to break it.* (1 kcal $= 2.62 \times 10^{16}$ million electron volts.) It is very difficult to sunder the N_2 molecule by ordinary chemical means. More than 4000°C is required to decompose the N_2 molecule into atoms and at least 10^9 degrees C to decompose the nucleus of atomic nitrogen into its particles.[1]

AMMONIA

In the synthesis process, ammonia is the economical means for the fixation of atmospheric nitrogen and its subsequent conversion to useful compounds. Ammonia is the principal commercial compound of nitrogen. The Haber-Bosch process (described in Chapters 4 and 5) synthesizes ammonia by causing a mixture of nitrogen and hydrogen to pass through a bed of catalyst, comprising essentially iron oxides, under a temperature of about 500°C and a pressure of about 1000 atm. Only about 50 per cent of the nitrogen is converted to NH_3.

The electronic symbol for ammonia is the symbol of the element surrounded by dots which represent the outermost electrons or valence electrons, as follows:

$$\text{H} \atop \text{H} \!:\! \ddot{\text{N}} \!:\! \text{H}$$

The spatial representation of ammonia is a tetrahedron in which the three hydrogen atoms occupy the base of the tetrahedron and an unshared pair of electrons are at the apex, as follows:

* Niels Bohr assumed that the energy of electrons in atoms is a quantum figure and restricted to certain values. This means an electron in an atom can have only specified values, and the only way it can change its quantum of energy is to jump from one discrete level of energy to another. If no lower energy level is available, the electron cannot send out any energy; but if one is available, the electron can emit energy of a definite quantity. The amount of energy thus radiated has to equal exactly the difference between the two levels of energy involved. The energy levels have been numbered and start with the lowest as 1, the next higher as 2, the next higher as 3, and so on. The letter n is used to represent the number of the energy level: thus, $n = 1$; $n = 2$, etc.

Another convention used by the new science and designated as the second principle of quantum mechanics is that the number of electrons that can occupy any energy level in an atom cannot exceed $2n^2$; thus, for the situation where $n = 1$, the maximal number of electrons that can occupy the lowest level is $2(1)^2 = 2$; for the level $n = 2$, the maximum number is $2(2)^2 = 8$; and so on. The lowest energy level is also designated the K shell or orbit; the second of $n = 2$ level is called the L shell or orbit; and as the levels increase, the name of the orbit is lettered consecutively, M, N, etc.

TABLE 2.3. CONVERSION FACTORS. TO FIND THE EQUIVALENT OF ONE MATERIAL
OR ELEMENT, A, IN TERMS OF ANOTHER, B, MULTIPLY THE AMOUNT A (LB) BY THE
FACTOR IN THE COLUMN (A TO B) OR FOR THE REVERSE USE (B TO A)
A × FACTOR = B   B × FACTOR = A

A	B	Factors	
		A to B	B to A
nitrogen	ammonia	1.2159	0.8224
nitrogen	nitrate (NO_3)	4.4266	0.2259
nitrogen	sodium nitrate	6.0683	0.1648
nitrogen	potassium nitrate	7.2179	0.1385
nitrogen	ammonium sulfate	4.7165	0.2120
nitrogen	ammonium chloride	3.8190	0.2618
nitrogen	nitric acid	4.4986	0.2223
nitrogen	protein (crude)	6.2500	0.1600
nitrogen	ammonium nitrate	5.7144	0.1752
nitrogen	urea	2.1437	0.4665
nitrogen	monoammonium phosphate	8.2118	0.1218
nitrogen	diammonium phosphate	4.7138	0.2121
ammonia	nitrogen	0.8224	1.2159
ammonia	ammonium hydroxide	2.0578	0.4859
ammonia	$MgNH_4PO_4 \cdot 6H_2O$	14.410	0.0690
ammonia	ammonium nitrate	4.7000	0.2128
ammonia	ammonium (NH_4)	1.0592	0.9441
ammonia	monoammonium phosphate	6.7566	0.1480
ammonia	diammonium phosphate	7.7566	0.1289
ammonia	ammonium sulfate	3.8793	0.2574
ammonia	nitric acid	3.7000	0.2703

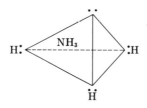

Ammonia gas, as represented by the Bohr model, has 2 electrons in the
first or $1s$ orbit or K* shell and 5 electrons in the second or L orbit.

Formerly, chemistry taught that NH_3 molecules combined with H_2O to
form ammonium hydroxide, a weak base:

* If the shell contains 8 electrons, it is called an octet, and only 8 electrons can occupy a complete shell or orbit except the K shell.

$$NH_3 + H_2O \rightleftarrows NH_4OH \quad \text{or} \quad H:\overset{..}{\underset{..}{N}}:H:\overset{..}{\underset{..}{O}}:$$

Also, that the NH_4OH could dissociate into (NH_4^+) and OH^- ions. It is now believed that when ammonia is dissolved in water, protons move reciprocally so rapidly between nitrogen and oxygen atoms that to distinguish between NH_3 plus H_2O and NH_4OH is quite arbitrary. The basic quality of aqueous ammonia can be shown by the following equations:

$$NH_3 + HOH \rightleftarrows NH_4^+ + OH^-$$

or

$$NH_4OH \rightleftarrows NH_4^- + OH^-$$

Acids can neutralize the ammonia ion to form ammonium salts, and they contain the tetrahedral NH_4^+ ion. An example is ammonium sulfate:

$$2NH_3 + H_2SO_4 \rightleftarrows (NH_4)_2SO_4$$

It gives a slightly acid solution: The reaction may be considered either as an hydrolysis or as a dissociation.

$$(NH_4)^+ + H_2O \rightleftarrows NH_4OH + H^+$$

$$NH_4^+ \rightleftarrows NH_3 + H^+$$

Ammonia and its salts involve nitrogen with a valence or oxidation state of (-3). Nitrogen can have a valence or oxidation of $(+5)$ which is represented by compounds of nitric acid.

In ionic reactions, nitrogen behaves as a trivalent or pentavalent element which is shown by the following ionic symbols, respectively:

$$\overset{\textstyle H}{:\overset{..}{\underset{..}{N}}:H} \qquad\qquad :\overset{..}{O}::N::\overset{..}{O}:H$$
$$H \qquad\qquad\qquad :\overset{}{\underset{..}{O}}:$$

Ammonia
(Trivalent, N)

Nitric acid
(Pentavalent N)

Molecular N_2, at ordinary temperatures, does not react readily with other molecules except biochemically. Once its bond is broken, however, it seems to combine with numerous elements and becomes very important in biological and industrial fixation processes. A brief resumé of its reactions is the following:

reaction with O_2 to yield NO (electric-arc process),

reaction with H_2 to yield NH_3 (catalytic synthesis),

reaction with ozone to yield NO_2 (at about 400°C),

reaction with calcium carbide to produce calcium cyanamide.

Of these and several others not listed, only the reaction with hydrogen to form ammonia is of significant, commercial importance.

References

1. Vancini, C. A., "La Sintesi dell'Ammoniaca," Milan, Hoepli, 1960.

3

Soil Nitrogen

F. J. Stevenson

Department of Agronomy, University of Illinois

Most plants obtain their nitrogen from that which occurs naturally in the soil; this soil nitrogen is supplemented by increments supplied in fertilizers, precipitation, and irrigation waters. Although the primary source of soil nitrogen is the atmosphere, this atmospheric nitrogen (consisting of the stable gaseous molecule N_2) can be utilized directly by only a few bacteria and algae. All other organisms require combined nitrogen for carrying out their life activities.

Systems of agriculture that rely heavily on soil reserves to meet the nitrogen requirements of plants cannot long be effective in crop production. Historically, legumes have been the chief means of maintaining adequate levels of nitrogen in soils; however, in recent years chemically fixed nitrogen has become available, which, when used to augment that supplied by natural processes, can increase yields and improve the quality of crops.

A major concern of present-day farmers is the effective use of nitrogen fertilizers. It has seldom been possible to recover all of the nitrogen added to the crop, for not only have losses occurred through leaching and volatilization but, also, variable quantities have been fixed by clay minerals or have been immobilized by microorganisms during the decay of plant residues. The discussion that follows summarizes our knowledge of the reactions and transformations of nitrogen in soil.

SOURCES OF NITROGEN FOR PLANTS

The Soil

Although plants are capable of utilizing organic forms of nitrogen such as amino acids and amines, practically all of the nitrogen taken up from the soil exists in two inorganic compounds, ammonium (NH_4^+) and nitrate (NO_3^-). In well-aerated soils, the oxidation of ammonium to nitrate proceeds so rapidly that ammonium seldom persists; thus, nitrate is the form normally available to plants.

Chemistry of Soil Nitrogen. The nitrogen in soil occurs almost entirely in combination with organic matter and clay minerals; only a small fraction, generally less than 0.1 per cent, exists in available mineral forms (as nitrate and exchangeable ammonium). It has been pointed out elsewhere[43] that only 100 lb or so of nitrogen per acre may be available to the plant during a growing season, and that only a few pounds may be

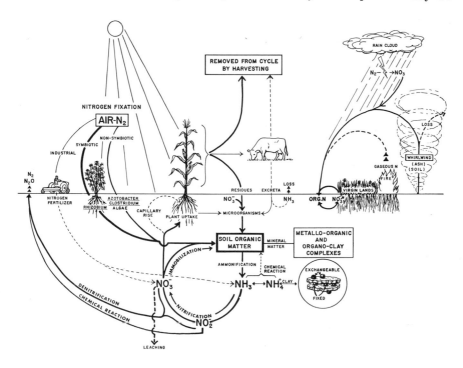

Figure 3.1. Nitrogen cycle.

available at any one time, even though 2 or 3 tons may be present in the organic matter. The inability of microorganisms to decompose the nitrogenous organic compounds in soil has been attributed to their stabilization by lignins, and to the protective action of clay minerals. The formation of stable nitrogen complexes in soil can be considered beneficial, because the nitrogen is protected against loss by leaching and volatilization.

Organic Nitrogen Compounds. At present, not more than one-half of the soil organic nitrogen can be accounted for in known compounds;[10]

approximately one-third exists in amino acids; as much as one-tenth exists in amino sugars. The percentage of nitrogen present in amino acids decreases with increasing depth in the soil profile,[53] whereas the percentage present in amino sugars increases.[52] A small amount of nitrogen, generally of the order of 1 to 2 per cent, occurs in purine and pyrimidine bases.

The modern studies on specific nitrogen compounds in soil commenced soon after Consden, *et al.*[17] gave their first description of paper chromatography in 1944. By using this technique, Bremner[9] isolated 20 amino acids from an acid hydrolysate of soil; among the compounds identified were β-alanine, α-amino-*n*-butyric acid, γ-aminobutyric acid, and α,ε-diaminopimelic acid. The last-named compound is of particular interest, because this amino acid appears to be confined to bacterial organisms, and is widely distributed among them.

Figure 3.2 shows the results obtained in a recent study[54] on the separation of amino compounds from soil by ion exchange chromatography. In all, 36 ninhydrin-reacting compounds were isolated, of which 28 were identified, including the amino sugars glucosamine and galactosamine. Whereas most of these can be considered as naturally occurring compounds, some

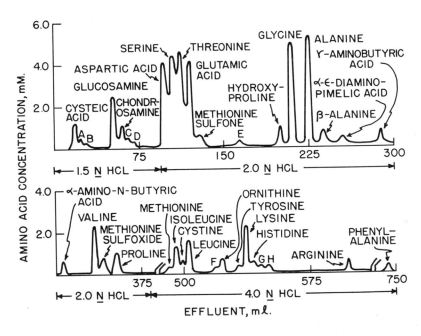

Figure 3.2. Separation of amino compounds from soil using ion exchange chromatography. [*Geochim, et Cosmochim. Acta,* **19,** *261* (*1960*)]

may have been artifacts.[54] Thus, cysteic acid could have evolved from cystine, α-amino-n-butyric acid from threonine, ornithine from arginine, and methionine sulfone and methionine sulfoxide from methionine. Ornithine appears to be a natural soil biochemical.[51]

Very little is known of the remainder of the organic nitrogen in soil. As much as one-fourth is so strongly associated with high molecular weight organic polymers that it cannot be solubilized with hot mineral acids. The nature of this nitrogen has yet to be worked out, but compounds formed by one or more of the following processes are under consideration.

(1) Fixation of ammonia by lignins. Mattson and Koutler-Andersson[36] found that products obtained by autoxidation of lignin in the presence of ammonia contained high percentages of chemically fixed nitrogen. Based on this and other observations, they concluded that humic complexes in soil were derived from lignins through autoxidation and ammonia fixation.

(2) Polymerization of quinones and nitrogen compounds. Some soil scientists[23, 33] support the theory that humic constituents in soil originated through the condensation of quinones with nitrogen-containing compounds, such as amino acids and ammonia. According to this concept, polyphenols, either derived from the biological breakdown of lignins or synthesized by microorganisms, are oxidized enzymatically by phenoloxidases to quinones, which then react with nitrogen compounds to form humic substances. In the process, cyclic nitrogen compounds are formed.

(3) Condensation of sugars and amines. The formation of brown nitrogenous polymers by condensation of carbonyl and amino derivatives occurs extensively in food stored at moderate temperatures, and the reaction has been postulated to be important in soils.[10] The formation of dark-colored complexes by this process takes place through the opening of the ring form of the sugar, addition of the amine to the carbonyl group, and subsequent rearrangement of the molecule to form the N-substituted glycosylamine. After condensation and rearrangement, the sugar moiety is dehydrated, with the formation of the unstable N-substituted 1-amino-1-deoxy-2-ketose. After fragmentation, the intermediates thus formed polymerize, yielding products in which part of the nitrogen occurs in stable linkages.[27]

Occurrence of Fixed Ammonium. For many years, soil scientists assumed that the sole inorganic forms of nitrogen in soils were exchangeable ammonium and nitrates. Now it is known[11, 46, 53, 54, 62] that soils contain fixed ammonium, i.e., ammonium ions that are held within the lattice structures of silicate minerals. This finding affords an explanation for certain natural phenomena relative to the behavior and properties of

TABLE 3.1. DISTRIBUTION OF FIXED AMMONIUM IN SOILS

Soil Horizon	Great Soil Group*					
	Brunizem-chernozem (5)		Gray-brown Podzolic (5)		Others†	
	ppm	%	ppm	%‡	ppm	%
A_1	96.4–128.8	4.3–5.6	112.6–154.6	5.6	57.4–140.6	3.5–7.9
A_2	105.6–131.2	8.2–9.3	109.2–168.0	9.4	70.4–154.0	7.8–10.8
B_2	99.4–155.4	11.5–18.4	142.8–210.0	20.1	54.6–182.0	12.7–17.6
B_3	103.6–173.6	21.4–27.7	184.8–224.0	26.5	84.0–210.0	13.1–17.0
C	98.0–187.6	28.8–44.7	102.2–224.0	34.9	89.6–210.0	27.2–36.1

* Numerals refer to number of profiles examined.
† Include a red-yellow podzolic, a chestnut, and 2 planosols.
‡ For one profile only.

nitrogen in soil, and it accounts for the low C/N ratios observed for sub-surface soils.

The distribution of fixed ammonium in the soils of several great soil groups is shown in Table 3.1. The A_1 horizons contained from 57 to 154 ppm of fixed ammonium, equivalent to from 114 to 308 lb of nitrogen per acre-foot of soil. Taking the soil profile in its entirety (that is, the A, B, and C horizons), the fixed ammonium accounted for a significant part of the total nitrogen.

Availability of Soil Nitrogen. As indicated earlier, nitrogen reserves in the soil are large. In some soils, such as the dark-colored brunizems of the North Central region of the United States, sufficient quantities are present to meet the requirements of plants for a century without any external additions. However, when land is first cultivated, the nitrogen content of the soil declines rapidly, and new equilibrium levels are established which are characteristic of the climate, cultural practices, and type of soil.[20, 32] At equilibrium, all of the nitrogen removed in harvested crops must come from external sources.

A nitrogen-time function curve for the decline of soil nitrogen in the North Central region as a result of cropping is given in Figure 3.3. Under average farming conditions, about one-third of the nitrogen has disappeared in 60 yr of cultivation. During the first few years, sufficient nitrogen was released from the native organic matter to produce bumper crops; since that time, increasing amounts of fertilizer nitrogen have been required to maintain yields at high levels. For these soils, steady-state conditions for nitrogen have been, or soon will be, reached.

According to Mehring,[37] the nitrogen content of the soil has been a factor determining the amount of fertilizer nitrogen used by farmers. Figure 3.4

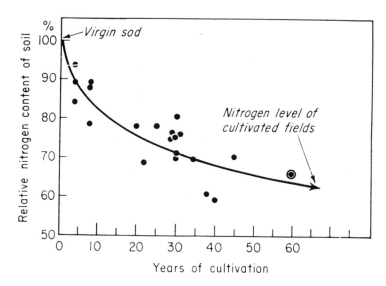

Figure 3.3. Decline of soil nitrogen under average farming practices in the North Central Region of the United States. (From "Factors of Soil Formation" by H. Jenny. Copyright 1941. McGraw-Hill Book Co., Inc. Used by permission.).

shows a soil nitrogen map of the United States. In the Southeast, where the nitrogen contents of the soils are low, commercial nitrogen has been used almost universally. On the other hand, in the Midwest, where the soils are rich in nitrogen, comparatively little nitrogen has been used, although recent trends in this region have been toward higher nitrogen fertilization. Other factors influencing nitrogen fertilizer consumption are the kinds of crops that are grown, the quantities of animal manures available for application to cultivated crops, and the climate.[37] Where moisture is the over-all limiting factor in crop production, such as in the dry-land areas of the Great Plains and the Mountain States, fertilizer nitrogen will be used sparingly, irrespective of the quantity of nitrogen present in the soil.

Biological Nitrogen Fixation

Symbiosis of Root Nodule Bacteria with Leguminous Plants. The symbiotic relationship between members of the bacterial genus *Rhizobium* and leguminous plants has had a comprehensive development. The importance of this relationship is emphasized by the fact that, even with the tremendous expansion in facilities for producing fertilizer nitrogen since World War II, legumes are still the main source of fixed nitrogen for the majority of the world's soils. On the conservative estimate of an average

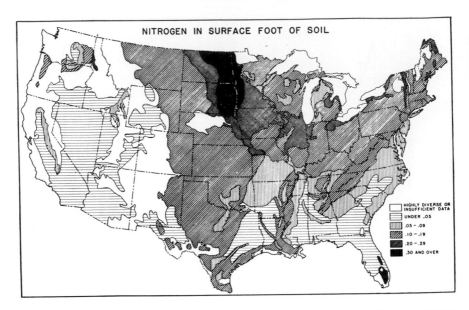

Figure 3.4. Soil nitrogen map of the United States. [*Ind. Eng. Chem.*, **37**, *289* (*1945*)]

fixation of 50 lb of nitrogen per acre for the 75 million acres of legumes planted each year in the United States, a total of over 1.8 million tons of nitrogen, or 2 to 3 times the amount sold as chemical fertilizer, are fixed annually.

Present-day botanists estimate that the Leguminosae family contains from 10 to 12 thousand species, most of which are indigenous to the tropics.[44] Only 1196 species (or about 10 to 12 per cent of the total) have been examined for nodulation; of these, 1063 (or about 89 per cent) have been found to bear nodules.[2] Approximately 200 species of Leguminosae are cultivated by man; about 50 species are grown commercially in the United States.

The bacterial symbionts, all members of the genus *Rhizobium*, are gram-negative, nonspore-forming mobile rods which measure 0.5 to 0.9μ by 1.2 to 3.0μ. At present, the following species are recognized: *R. meliloti, R. leguminosarum, R. phaseoli, R. japonicum, R. lupini,* and *R. trifolii*. A collection of leguminous plants which exhibit specificity for a common *Rhizobium* species is referred to as a "cross-inoculation group." The validity of these bacterial-plant associations has been severely challenged because the boundaries between the groups overlap, and because some strains of rhizobia form nodules on plants occurring in several different groups. A list of the important legumes with which the above-mentioned species of *Rhizobium* are associated is given in Table 3.2.

The rhizobia are generally capable of prolonged independent existence in the soil; however, nitrogen fixation takes place only when symbiosis is established with leguminous plants. The maintenance of a satisfactory population of any given *Rhizobium* species in the soil depends largely upon the previous occurrence of the appropriate leguminous plant. High acidity, lack of necessary nutrients, poor physical condition of the soil, and attack by bacteriophages contribute to their disappearance. The desirability of legume inoculation to insure nodulation with host-specific effective rhizobial strains is well known.

Influence of Available Nitrogen on Fixation. Maximum expression of the nitrogen-fixing capabilities of the *Rhizobium*-legume symbiosis is obtained only when the amount of mineral nitrogen in the soil is low. However, during the early stages of plant growth, small amounts of fertilizer nitrogen may improve nodulation and nitrogen fixation, especially on nitrogen-poor soils. Presumably, the added nitrogen alleviates the nitrogen starvation period which occurs between the exhaustion of seed nitrogen and

TABLE 3.2. CLASSIFICATION SCHEME OF *Rhizobium*-LEGUME ASSOCIATIONS

Rhizobium Species	Cross-inoculation Group	Host Genera	Legumes Included
R. meliloti	Alfalfa	*Medicago* *Melilotus* *Trigonella*	Alfalfa Sweet clover Fenugreek
R. trifolii	Clover	*Trifolium*	Clovers
R. leguminosarum	Pea	*Pisum* *Vicia* *Lathyrus* *Lens*	Pea Vetch Sweetpea Lentil
R. phaseoli	Bean	*Phaseolus*	Beans
R. lupini	Lupine	*Lupinus* *Ornithopus*	Lupine Serradella
R. japonicum	Soybean	*Glycine*	Soybean
	Cowpea*	*Vigna* *Lespedeza* *Crotalaria* *Pueraria* *Arachis* *Phaseolus*	Cowpea Lespedeza Crotalaria Kudzu Peanut Lima bean

* This group has not attained species status.

the onset of symbiotic nitrogen fixation. The optimum amount of combined nitrogen required varies with the leguminous species.

The presence of sufficient available nitrogen in the soil to support the prolonged growth of plants depresses nodule formation severely, a result that appears to be associated with a low carbohydrate-nitrogen ratio in the plant and, consequently, an inadequate supply of carbohydrates to the roots. Numerous studies have shown that the quantity of nitrogen fixed by rhizobia decreases as the ability of the soil to provide mineral nitrogen increases. However, the amount of nitrogen released from the soil organic matter is rarely adequate to suppress nitrogen fixation entirely.

Legume Nitrogen versus Fertilizer Nitrogen.   In the United States, and elsewhere, the availability of cheap fertilizer nitrogen has prompted a reevaluation of the importance of legumes in crop production. It now appears that, under certain circumstances, legumes in a rotation can be replaced effectively by commercial nitrogen. Thus a greater production of plant material is brought about through adequate fertilization with nitrogen. Provided the residues are returned to the soil following harvesting of the crop, this increased production of plant material may allow nonlegumes to assume some of the functions historically assigned to legumes, namely, to improve soil tilth, to prevent erosion, to increase the storehouse of soil nitrogen, and to enhance the activities of desirable microorganisms in such a way that they can accentuate the soil as a dynamic medium for the growth of plants.

The extent to which fertilizer nitrogen will eventually replace legumes in crop rotations will depend upon the availability of inexpensive nitrogen fertilizers, the need for increased acreage of nonleguminous crops, and the ability of legume-free cropping systems to maintain soil fertility and prevent erosion.

Nodulated Nonlegumes.   Symbiosis of a nature similar to that of the *Rhizobium*-Leguminosae relationship has been demonstrated for the nonleguminous families Betulaceae, Elaeagnaceae, Myricaceae, Coriariaceae, Rhamnaceae, and Casuarinaceae.[2, 7] In addition, nodulation has been reported for certain species of the families Zygophyllaceae and Cycadaceae. In all, 65 species of trees and shrubs, many of them adapted to growth on poor soils, have been reported to bear nodules.[2]

A list of the nonleguminous families for which reasonable proof of nitrogen fixation has been obtained, along with some notes regarding their geographical distribution, is given in Table 3.3. Very few quantitative data are available regarding the amounts of nitrogen fixed by these plants, although fixation of a magnitude equivalent to that of many legumes has been reported for several species of *Alnus*.

Free-living Bacteria.   The classical examples of nitrogen fixation by

TABLE 3.3 DISTRIBUTION OF NODULATED NONLEGUMES

Family	Genus	Number of Species Nodulated	Geographical Distribution
Betulaceae	*Alnus*	15	Cool regions of the northern hemisphere
Elaeagnaceae	*Elaeagnus*	9	Asia, Europe, North America
	Hippophae	1	Asia and Europe, from the Himalayas to the Arctic Circle
	Shepherdia	2	Confined to North America
Myricaceae	*Myrica*	7	Temperate regions of both hemispheres
Coriariaceae	*Coriaria*	1	Discontinuous distribution
Rhamnaceae	*Ceanothus*	7	Confined to North America
Casuarinaceae	*Casuarina*	12	Tropics and subtropics, extending from East Africa to the Indian Archipelago, Pacific Islands, and Australia

free-living bacteria are by the photosynthetic *Rhodospirillum*, the aerobic heterotroph *Azotobacter*, and the anaerobic heterotroph *Clostridium*.[60] To this list should be added *Beijerinckia*, an organism classified originally with *Azotobacter*, but now relegated to generic rank.[56] *Beijerinckia* appears to be the tropical counterpart of *Azotobacter*, as the former normally is not found in soils of the temperate regions of the earth.

Under natural conditions, the nitrogen-fixing capabilities of free-living bacteria are greatly restricted. Nitrogen fixation by *Rhodospirillum* is of negligible ecologic significance because the requirement for both irradiation and anaerobiosis confines the organism to shallow, muddy ponds or estuarine muds. *Azotobacter*, *Beijerinckia*, and *Clostridium* require a source of available energy, a factor which limits their activities to environments with relatively high organic-matter contents. Current estimates are that no more than 6 lb of nitrogen per acre are added to the soil each year through the combined activities of free-living nitrogen-fixing microorganisms.

There are conflicting reports regarding fixation of nitrogen by organisms living in the rhizosphere of plant roots. Considerable quantities of decomposable organic matter occur in this zone through secretion of organic compounds by plant roots, and by the sloughing off of root materials; thus, the conditions in this zone should be favorable for fixation to occur.

Russian scientists have claimed for many years that inoculation of soils and seeds with *Azotobacter* and *Clostridium* resulted in improved growth of plants through nitrogen fixation, and extensive programs of inoculation have been carried out in Russia for many years. Soil scientists associated with the United States Department of Agriculture have made repeated tests in attempts to confirm the Russian claims, but, as yet, the findings have failed to show increases in growth that could be ascribed positively to nitrogen fixation.[5]

Blue-green Algae. There is now satisfactory evidence for nitrogen fixation by more than a dozen species of blue-green algae, all of which belong to the family Nostocaceae.[24]

The blue-green algae occur in almost every environmental situation where sufficient sunlight is available for photosynthesis, including barren rock surfaces and frozen wastelands. Their ability to colonize virgin landscapes is due to the fact that they are completely autotrophic, being able to synthesize all of their biochemical requirements from carbon dioxide, free nitrogen, water, and mineral salts. The blue-green algae form symbiotic relationships with a variety of organisms, the most important being the lichen fungi.

Geographically, the lichens are widely distributed over the land masses of the world. In the semi-arid regions of Western Australia and along the Great Plains of the United States, their favorite habitat is the undersurface of light-colored pebbles, where the combination of adequate moisture and penetration of light rays permits them to thrive. Lichens are also common in the desert areas of the southwestern part of the United States, where they form surface crusts with high nitrogen contents.

The importance of blue-green algae as a source of soil nitrogen is limited to the early stages of soil formation. Nitrogen fixation by these organisms occurs only in the presence of sunlight, so their activity is confined largely to the most superficial layers of the earth's crust.

The blue-green algae may play an important role in the nitrogen economy of rice soils. In India, the ability to produce rice on the same land for many years without applying nitrogen fertilizer is believed to be due to nitrogen fixation by algae.[24]

Biochemical Aspects of Fixation. There appears to be a striking similarity in the over-all process of nitrogen fixation irrespective of the organism involved. However, most of the studies have been done with *Azotobacter*, primarily because this organism is convenient to work with. In the case of *Rhizobium*, nitrogen fixation occurs only when the organism is living in association with its appropriate host, and, while some success has been obtained by using excised root nodules, fixation of a magnitude equivalent to that obtained in the natural environment has not been possible.

The classical work on the mechanisms of nitrogen fixation has been done by research groups associated with P. W. Wilson of the University of Wisconsin and A. I. Virtanen of Finland. On the basis of isotopic studies, Wilson[60, 61] proposed that ammonia was the key stable intermediate; from studies on products excreted from the roots of leguminous plants (presence of aspartic acid, β-alanine, and oximes) Virtanen[58] postulated that hydroxylamine was the "key intermediate."

The following evidence has been presented by Wilson and his group in support of the ammonia hypothesis: (1) ammonia is utilized preferentially by *Azotobacter;* (2) ammonia is assimilated rapidly by cells previously supplied with molecular nitrogen only; (3) in studies using N^{15}, highly-labeled ammonia is excreted from *Clostridium* and *Azotobacter;* (4) kinetic studies of nitrogen fixation by *Azotobacter* show that ammonia is an early product and, when plotted against time, a negative slope characteristic of a primary product is obtained.

Virtanen's evidence in support of the hydroxylamine theory includes: (1) the occurrence of high amounts of aspartic acid and β-alanine in the excretion products from leguminous plants; (2) the presence of oximino-succinic acid in the excretion products; (3) the detection of oxalacetic acid in leguminous plants; (4) the stimulation of nitrogen fixation by excised nodules upon addition of oxalacetic acid.

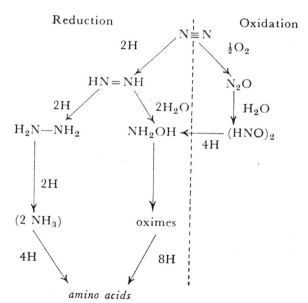

amino acids

(From Nutrition of the Legumes, ed. by E. G. Hallsworth. Copyright 1958.
Butterworth's Medical & Scientific Publications.
Used by permission)

Some possible pathways of biological nitrogen fixation are outlined on page 29.[40]

Evidence that the initial step is one of reduction is supported by the absence of any oxidized products in cultures of nitrogen-fixing organisms, and by the finding that nitrous oxide is a specific and competitive inhibitor of nitrogen fixation.

Atmospheric Precipitation

Combined nitrogen, consisting of ammonia, nitrite, nitrate, and organically bound nitrogen, is a normal constituent of atmospheric precipitation. Nitrite, which occurs in trace amounts only, is usually ignored or included with the nitrate determination. The organically bound nitrogen is associated with cosmic dust; thus, this nitrogen does not represent a new addition to the land masses of the world.

Eriksson[21] has summarized the measurements made for the nitrogen in atmospheric precipitation. For Europe and the United States, the values for ammonia and nitrate range from 0.7 to 19.6 lb per acre per year. However, it is probable that many of the higher values represent analytical or sampling errors; the estimate generally accepted for the maximum amount of mineral nitrogen returned to the soil each year in atmospheric precipitation is 6 to 7 lb per acre.

The mineral nitrogen content of precipitation is highest during the warmer periods of the year, and for any given rainfall the concentration descreases progressively with the duration of precipitation.

The following represent possible sources of combined nitrogen in atmospheric precipitation[28]: (1) from the soil and the ocean, (2) from the fixation of atmospheric nitrogen (electrical, photochemical, and in the trail of meteorites), and (3) from industrial contamination.

The relative contribution of each source to the nitrogen in precipitation is unknown. The view that nitrogen is fixed by electrical discharge during thunderstorm activity runs into the difficulty that nitrate distribution patterns have seldom correlated well with thunderstorm activity. The ratio of ammonia to nitrate is remarkably constant (of the order of 2:1), a fact which suggests that the two are formed by a similar mechanism. As yet, there is no satisfactory explanation for this phenomenon.

Other Sources

Dhar,[18, 19] working in India, has claimed that nitrogen fixation occurs in soil as a result of photochemical activity. According to Dhar[19] " ... sunlight or artificial light is appreciably absorbed by a mixture of soil and organic matter and is readily utilised in increasing nitrogen fixation in the soil and improving its nitrogen status."

Equally revolutionary is the recent claim by Ingham[29, 30] that cellulose and other organic colloids in the soil absorb sufficient ammonia from the atmosphere to maintain soil fertility.

Neither Dhar's claim nor that of Ingham can be reconciled with results observed under field conditions. Until their theories have been tested adequately by the use of N^{15}, they cannot be taken seriously.

FACTORS AFFECTING THE AVAILABILITY OF SOIL NITROGEN AND FERTILIZER NITROGEN TO PLANTS

Mineralization of Nitrogen

The *conversion* of organic nitrogen to the more available mineral forms, a process referred to as mineralization, encompasses two distinct microbiological processes: (1) ammonification, in which organic nitrogen is converted into ammonia; and (2) nitrification, in which ammonia is oxidized to nitrate. The over-all reaction is illustrated below.

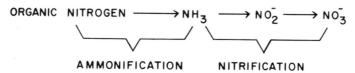

Both aerobic and anaerobic organisms are involved in the ammonification process, whereas only aerobic organisms oxidize ammonia to nitrate. Therefore, conditions which restrict the supply of oxygen in the soil permit ammonia (as the ammonium ion) to accumulate, such as in rice fields. In cultivated, well-aerated soils, nitrate is the predominant available mineral form of nitrogen. For reasons which are not clear, grassland soils contain rather high levels of exchangeable ammonium.

Seasonal variations in the production of mineral nitrogen in soil have been described by Harmsen and Van Schreven.[26] In temperate climates, mineralization of nitrogen is optimum in the spring and decreases gradually during the summer. The spring optimum may result from a "partial sterilization effect" of freezing during the winter. In uncropped soil, the mineral nitrogen content is lowest during the winter, rises rapidly in the spring, maintains itself at rather high levels during the summer, and drops rapidly to the low winter level with the onset of autumn rains. In cropped land, a second minimum observed in midsummer is thought to be caused by absorption of mineral nitrogen by plants.

Nitrification. The oxidation of ammonia to nitrate in soil is brought about by two groups of bacteria, one deriving energy through the oxidation of ammonia to nitrite, the other through oxidation of nitrite to nitrate.

Bergey's "Manual of Determinative Bacteriology"[8] lists five genera of ammonia oxidizers and two genera of nitrite oxidizers; however, only one genus of each is considered important, *Nitrosomonas* and *Nitrobacter*, respectively. A single species of *Nitrosomonas* (*N. europaea*) is involved, whereas two species of *Nitrobacter* (*N. winogradskyi* and *N. agile*) are important.

The nitrifying bacteria are obligate autotrophs; not only does the carbon for cell synthesis come from inorganic sources, but inorganic forms of nitrogen are used as the sole sources of energy.

The initial nitrification, catalyzed by *Nitrosomonas*, involves the consecutive removal of three pairs of electrons from ammonia, with the formation of hydroxylamine, hyponitrite, and nitrite.

$$NH_3 \xrightarrow{\frac{1}{2}O_2} HO\text{-}NH_2 \xrightarrow{-2H} \frac{1}{2}\left[HO\text{-}N\text{:}N\text{-}OH\right] \xrightarrow{\frac{1}{2}O_2} HO\text{-}N\text{:}O$$

AMMONIA	HYDROXYLAMINE	HYPONITRITE	NITRITE
−3	−1	+1	+3

Members of the genus *Nitrobacter* remove two electrons from nitrite. A dehydration reaction may characterize this reaction.[1]

$$HO\text{-}N\text{:}O \xrightarrow{H_2O} \left[HO\text{-}N\begin{matrix}OH\\OH\end{matrix}\right] \xrightarrow{-2H} HO\text{-}N\begin{matrix}O\\O\end{matrix}$$

NITRITE	NITRATE
+3	+5

In normal soil, the rate of oxidation of nitrite to nitrate is considerably higher than that of the formation of nitrite from ammonia; thus, nitrites are seldom found. However, nitrites may accumulate in alkaline soils, a result that appears to be due to ammonia toxicity of *Nitrobacter*.[1]

The production of nitrates from ammonia decreases with decreasing temperatures below 30 to 35°C; below 5°C very little nitrate is formed. In the northern section of the United States, farmers are encouraged to wait until the soil temperatures fall below 5°C (about 40°F) before applying ammoniacal fertilizers in the fall.

Immobilization of Nitrogen

The C/N ratio of organic residues added to the soil is of primary importance in regulating the quantity of mineral nitrogen available to plants. Residues which have C/N ratios greater than about 30, such as mature corn stalks, result in a lowering of mineral nitrogen reserves because the nitrogen is immobilized by microorganisms. On the other hand, residues with C/N ratios below about 20 lead to an increase in mineral nitrogen.

The changes in nitrate levels attending the addition of low-nitrogen crop residues to the soil are illustrated diagrammatically in Figure 3.5. Under conditions suitable for microbial activity, rapid decomposition of the residues occurs, with the liberation of considerable quantities of carbon dioxide. To meet the nitrogen requirements of the microorganisms, mineral nitrogen is consumed; that is, there is a net immobilization of nitrogen. However, when the C/N ratio of the decomposing residue has been decreased to about 20, mineralization predominates and nitrate levels increase.

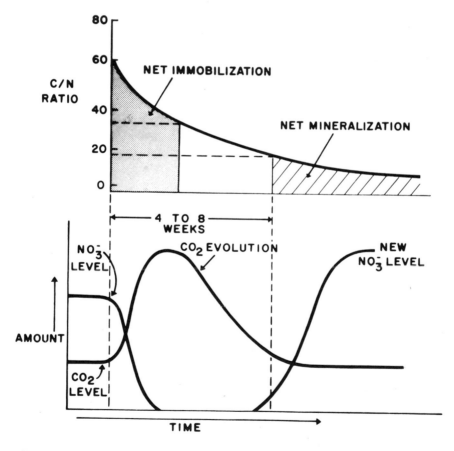

Figure 3.5. Changes in nitrate levels attending the decomposition of carbonaceous residues in soil. (*Courtesy B. R. Sabey, Department of Agronomy, University of Illinois*)

The time required for microorganisms to decrease the C/N ratio of plant residues to the point where mineral nitrogen accumulates depends upon such factors as the rate of plant residue addition, lignin content of the material, degree of comminution of the residues, and the level of respiration of the soil microflora. A reasonable estimate is that, under conditions favorable for good microbial activity, net mineralization will begin after 4 to 8 weeks of decomposition. Therefore, if low-nitrogen crop residues are added to the soil immediately prior to planting, sufficient fertilizer nitrogen should be added to meet the needs of both the microorganisms and the crop.

Fixation of Ammonium

The ammonia produced in soil through microbial activity, or added as anhydrous ammonia, reacts readily with soil water and hydrogen ions on the exchange complex to form the positively charged ammonium ion. The ammonium ion can then enter into fixation reactions with certain clay minerals; that is, it can become inaccessible to other ions during the normal process of cation exchange.

The mechanism whereby ammonium is held in difficultly exchanged form by clay minerals is presumed to be similar to that of potassium fixation. Specifically, fixation results from a replacement of ammonium for interlayer cations in the expanded lattice of clay minerals. The fixed ammonium can be replaced by cations that expand the lattice (Ca^{2+}, Mg^{2+}, Na^+, H^+), but not by those that contract the lattice (K^+, Rb^+, Cs^+). The minerals in soil that are responsible for ammonium fixation are vermiculite, illite, and montmorillonite.

With regard to the availability of fixed ammonium to higher plants, various studies[3, 34] have shown that under normal fertilizer practices fixation is not a serious problem. However, when large amounts of potassium are added simultaneously with the ammonium, all of the fixed ammonium may not become available immediately.[42] The blocking effect of potassium can be avoided, if desired, by applying the potassium well in advance of the ammonium.

Ammonium can be fixed by reaction with lignins and humic substances.[36, 38, 49] Fixation is associated with a simultaneous oxidation reaction, and is favored by an alkaline reaction. In the application of ammonium salts to soils having pH values below 7, very little ammonium would be fixed. On the other hand, with the application of aqueous solutions of ammonium or of anhydrous ammonia, considerable fixation might result because of the alkaline pH in the zone of fertilizer application. The ammonium fixed by organic matter is not immediately usable by plants, although it does become available eventually through the mineralization process. The low uptake of nitrogen reported for the fall application of anhydrous ammonia to highly organic soils may have been caused by chemical fixation by organic matter.[38]

Losses of Nitrogen From Soil

Quantitative recovery of soil nitrogen and fertilizer nitrogen by growing plants has seldom been obtained under field conditions; usually, a maximum of two-thirds of the nitrogen has been accounted for by crop removal. Numerous studies have been made in an attempt to account for the low recoveries, and it is now known that mineral nitrogen, whether added as fertilizer or produced during decay of organic matter, will not remain very long in the soil. It is apparent, therefore, that any mineral nitrogen not absorbed by plants, or immobilized by microorganisms, will be lost by one or more of the processes listed below.

Leaching. Nitrogen is lost by leaching mainly as nitrate, although ammonium may be lost from sandy soils. Under cropping, the loss is greatly reduced, for the reason that the nitrate content of the soil is lower and less water passes through the soil.

Direct evidence for nitrogen losses through leaching has come from lysimeter experiments. Allison[4] prepared nitrogen balance sheets for a large number of lysimeter experiments conducted in the United States. He reported the following findings:

(1) Crops commonly recovered only 40 to 75 per cent of the nitrogen that was added or made available from the soil. Low recoveries were usually obtained where large additions of nitrogen were made, where the soils were very sandy, and where the crop was not adequate to keep the nitrogen low.

(2) The nitrogen content of most soils decreased regardless of how much was added as fertilizer unless the soil was kept in uncultivated crops.

(3) A large proportion of the nitrogen not recovered in the crop was found in the leachate, but substantial unaccounted-for losses occurred in most lysimeters. Nitrogen gains were few.

(4) The magnitude of the unaccounted-for nitrogen was largely independent of the form in which the nitrogen was supplied, whether as nitrate, ammonium, or organic nitrogen.

(5) Unaccounted-for nitrogen was commonly slightly higher in cropped soils than in fallow soils.

In addition to leaching, considerable nitrogen may be lost from the soil as a result of erosion.[20] Sheet erosion is highly selective in that the eroded fraction contains several times more nitrogen than the original soil.

Volatilization of Ammonia. Under suitable conditions, ammonia is lost rapidly from soils by volatilization.[4, 26, 38] The facts concerning ammonia volatilization can be summarized as follows:

(1) Losses are of greatest economic importance on calcareous soils, especially when ammonium-containing fertilizers are used. Only slight losses occur in soils of pH 6 to 7, but the losses increase markedly as the pH of the soil increases.

(2) Losses increase with temperature, and they may be appreciable when neutral or alkaline soils containing ammonium near the surface are dried out.

(3) Losses are greatest in soils of low cation-exchange capacities. Clay and humus absorb ammonium and prevent its volatilization. In soil with an alkaline reaction, very little ammonia is lost provided adequate moisture is present.

(4) Losses can be high when nitrogenous organic substances, such as farmyard manures, are permitted to decompose on the surface of a soil, even one that is acid, because of the localized increase in pH resulting from ammonia formation.

The use of anhydrous ammonia as a fertilizer has become widespread in recent years. Losses through volatilization are not serious as long as the gas is injected below the surface of the soil (preferably 2 in. or more) and the sorption capacity of the soil is not exceeded. Jackson and Chang,[31] in a study of absorption of anhydrous ammonia in soil, found that alkalinity resulting from $CaCO_3$ or Na_2CO_3 did not prevent retention of ammonia by field-moist soil when placement was to a depth of 2 to 4 in.

Bacterial Denitrification. The consensus of soil scientists is that most of the gaseous loss of nitrogen from soil (excluding volatilization of ammonia) comes about through reduction of nitrate by denitrifying bacteria.[1, 4, 26, 41] The process of *nitrate respiration* differs from *nitrate assimilation* in this respect; in the former, nitrate replaces molecular oxygen as the final hydrogen acceptor during respiration; in the latter, nitrate is reduced to ammonia prior to being incorporated into amino acids.

Under anaerobic conditions, such as occur frequently in soils following heavy rains, nitrate-nitrogen can be volatilized quantitatively in a comparatively short time, particularly when sufficient energy is available in the form of organic matter. Losses are generally negligible at moisture levels below two-thirds of the water-holding capacity of the soil; above this value the magnitude of nitrogen loss is correlated directly with the moisture regime. Soils which have pH values below about 5.5 contain such a sparse population of denitrifying organisms that losses of nitrogen by denitrification may be negligible.

Biological denitrification is of considerable importance in well-drained and actively nitrifying soils which become partially anaerobic during wet periods, or through additions of large quantities of decomposable organic matter.

The ability to reduce nitrates and nitrites to gaseous products appears to be limited to a few bacteria, most of which belong to the genera *Pseudomonas, Micrococcus, Achromobacter,* and *Bacillus.* Four species of *Pseudomonas* have received the greatest attention in denitrification studies—*P. denitrificans, P. stutzeri, P. aeruginosa,* and *P. fluorescens.* Several autotrophs, such as *Thiobacillus denitrificans* and *T. thioparus,* are also capable of reducing nitrates to nitrogen gases.

The following biochemical pathway represents the probable mechanism of bacterial denitrification.

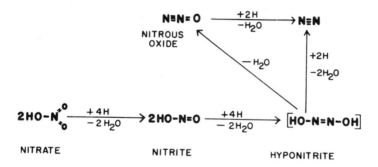

The relative proportions of the two gases in a system undergoing denitrification depend upon pH, temperature, and degree of anaerobiosis.[1, 41]

Chemical Reactions of Nitrites. Three reactions have been suggested for loss of nitrogen from soil as a result of the degradation of nitrites. They are: (1) double decomposition of ammonium nitrite ($NH_4NO_2 \rightarrow 2H_2O + N_2$), (2) the Van Slyke reaction ($RNH_2 + HNO_2 \rightarrow ROH + H_2O + N_2$), and (3) decomposition of nitrous acid ($3HNO_2 \rightarrow 2NO + HNO_3 + H_2O$). All three reactions require low pH values (<5.0); thus losses are possible only from acid soils.

The intermediate accumulation of nitrites following the application of urea to near-neutral soils has recently been found to lead to volatile loss of nitrogen.[14, 50] An unknown component of the soil organic matter has been postulated to be the activating agent.[13]

Loss of Ammonia from Urea. Because of the rapid hydrolysis of urea to ammonia in soils, together with the fact that urea may be adsorbed (admittedly weakly) by clay colloids, or chemisorbed to organic matter,[12] losses due to leaching are negligible and the rules governing volatilization of ammonia should apply.

Fertilizer trials have often shown that urea is inferior to ammonium sulfate or ammonium nitrate when applied as a topdressing on grass sods, but not when incorporated into the soil.[48, 59] Subsequently, it has become accepted that losses of urea nitrogen from plant tissues are possible. According to present concepts, the urea is lost as free ammonia after hydrolysis by the enzyme urease.

Controlled Release of Fertilizer Nitrogen

For reasons which were discussed earlier, the period of availability of fertilizer nitrogen to plants is limited. Losses resulting from leaching and volatilization are particularly troublesome, and since nitrate is the main offender, it is clearly desirable to regulate the quantity of this ion in the soil solution.

The interest in nitrogen fertilizers with controlled availability is evident from the new products that have been developed in recent years. Among them are synthetic organic polymers,[15, 16, 39] coated fertilizers,[35, 45] and ammoniated natural products, such as peat,[47] sawdust,[22] and lignite.[6]

Ureaform fertilizers are recognized as desirable sources of slowly available nitrogen; unfortunately, their high costs limit their use to turf grasses and ornamentals.

The control of nitrification with 2-chloro-6-(trichloromethyl) pyridine has been proposed as an economical way of reducing nitrogen losses from ammoniacal fertilizers.[25, 55, 57] This chemical is highly toxic to the organisms which convert ammonia to nitrite, but not those which convert organic nitrogen to ammonia, or nitrite to nitrate. Initial tests look promising.

References

1. Alexander, M., "Introduction to Soil Microbiology", New York, John Wiley & Sons, Inc., 1961.
2. Allen, E. K., and Allen, O. N., "Handbuch der Pflanzenphysiologie," vol. 8, p. 48, Berlin-Göttingen-Heidelberg, Ed. W. Ruhland, Springer-Verlag, 1958.
3. Allison, F. E., *Agr. Ammonia News*, **19**, (1958).
4. Allison, F. E., *Adv. Agron.*, **7**, 213 (1955).
5. Allison, F. E., *et al.*, *Soil Sci.*, **64**, 489 (1947).
6. Anonymous, *Chem. Eng. News.*, **41**, 82 (1963).
7. Bond, G., "Nutrition of the Legumes", Ed. E. G. Hallsworth, USA edition, p. 216, New York, Academic Press, Inc., 1958.
8. Breed, R. S., *et al.*, "Bergey's Manual of Determinative Bacteriology," Baltimore, The Williams & Wilkins Co., 1957.
9. Bremner, J. M., *Biochem. J.*, **47**, 538 (1950).
10. Bremner, J. M., *J. Soil Sci.*, **2**, 67 (1951); **5**, 214 (1954).
11. Bremner, J. M., *J. Agr. Sci.*, **52**, 147 (1959).
12. Chin, W., and Kroontje, W., *Soil Sci. Soc. Am. Proc.*, **26**, 479 (1962).

13. Clark, F. E., and Beard, W. E., *Proc. 7th. Intern. Congr. Soil Sci.*, **2**, 501 (1960).
14. Clark, F. E., *et al.*, *Soil Sci. Soc. Am. Proc.*, **24**, 50 (1960).
15. Clark, K. G., *et al.*, *Ind. Eng. Chem.*, **40**, 1178 (1948).
16. Clark, K. G., *et al.*, *J. Agr. Food Chem.*, **4**, 135 (1956).
17. Consden, R., *et al.*, *Biochem. J.*, **38**, 224, (1944).
18. Dhar, N. R., *Nature*, **151**, 590 (1943).
19. Dhar, N. R., *Trans. 7th Intern. Congr. Soil Sci.*, **3**, 314 (1960).
20. Ensminger, L. E., and Pearson, R. W., *Adv. Agron.*, **2**, 81 (1950).
21. Eriksson, E., *Tellus*, **4**, 215 (1952).
22. Farber, E., and Hind, R. R., *Forest Prod. J.*, **9**, 340 (1959).
23. Flaig, W., *Proc. Royal Dublin Soc., A.*, **1**, 149 (1960).
24. Fogg, G. E., *Endeavour*, **6**, 172 (1947).
25. Goring, C. A. I., *Soil Sci.*, **93**, 211, 431 (1962).
26. Harmsen, G. W., and Van Schreven, D. A., *Adv. Agron.*, **7**, 299 (1955).
27. Hodge, J. E., *J. Agr. Food Chem.*, **1**, 928 (1953).
28. Hutchinson, G. E., *Am. Scientist*, **32**, 178 (1944).
29. Ingham, G., *J. Agr. Sci.*, **40**, 55 (1950).
30. Ingham, G., *Soil Sci.*, **70**, 205 (1950).
31. Jackson, M. L., and Chang, S. C., *J. Am. Soc. Agron.*, **39**, 623 (1947).
32. Jenny, H., "Natural Resources", Eds. M. R. Huberty and W. L. Flock, p. 184, New York, McGraw-Hill Book Company, Inc., 1959.
33. Kononova, M. M., "Soil Organic Matter", New York, Pergamon Press, 1961.
34. Legg, J. O., and Allison, F. E., *Soil Sci. Soc. Am. Proc.*, **23**, 131 (1959).
35. Lunt, O. R., and Oertli, J. J., *Soil Sci. Soc. Am. Proc.*, **26**, 584 (1962).
36. Mattson, S., and Koutler-Andersson, E., *Lantbrucks-Högskol Ann.*, **11**, 107 (1943); **12**, 70 (1944).
37. Mehring, A. L., *Ind. Eng. Chem.*, **37**, 289 (1945).
38. Mortland, M. M., *Adv. Agron.*, **10**, 325 (1958).
39. Musser, H. B., and Duich, J. M., *Agron. J.*, **50**, 381 (1958).
40. Nicholas, J. D. H., "Nutrition of the Legumes," Ed. E. G. Hallsworth, USA edition, p. 239, New York, Academic Press, Inc., 1958.
41. Nömmik, H., *Acta Agr. Scand.*, **6**, 195 (1956).
42. Nömmik, H., *Acta Agr. Scand.*, **7**, 395 (1957).
43. Norman, A. G., *Soil Sci. Soc. Am. Proc.*, **11**, 9 (1946).
44. Norris, D. O., *Empire J. Exp. Agr.*, **24**, 247 (1956).
45. Oertli, J. J., and Lunt, O. R., *Soil Sci. Soc. Am. Proc.*, **26**, 579 (1962).
46. Rodrigues, G., *J. Soil Sci.*, **5**, 264 (1954).
47. Scholl, W., and Davis, R. O. E., *Ind. Eng. Chem.*, **25**, 1074 (1933).
48. Simpson, D. M. H., and Melsted, S. W., *Soil Sci. Soc. Am. Proc.*, **26**, 186 (1962).
49. Sohn, J. B., and Peech, M., *Soil Sci.*, **85**, 1 (1958).
50. Soulides, D. A., and Clark, F. E., *Soil Sci. Soc. Am. Proc.*, **22**, 308 (1958).
51. Stevenson, F. J., *Soil Sci. Soc. Am. Proc.*, **20**, 201 (1956); **20**, 204 (1956).
52. Stevenson, F. J., *Soil Sci.*, **84**, 99 (1957).
53. Stevenson, F. J., *Soil Sci.*, **88**, 201 (1959).
54. Stevenson, F. J., *Geochim. et Cosmochim. Acta*, **19**, 261 (1960).
55. Swezey, A. W., and Turner, G. O., *Agron. J.*, **54**, 532 (1962).
56. Tchan, Y. T., *Proc. Linnean Soc., New South Wales*, **78**, 85 (1953).
57. Turner, G. O., *et al.*, *Soil Sci.*, **94**, 270 (1962).
58. Virtanen, A. I., *Ann. Rev. Microbiol.*, **2**, 485 (1948).
59. Volk, G. M., *Agron. J.*, **51**, 746 (1959).
60. Wilson, P. W., "Handbuch der Pflanzenphysiologie", vol. 8, p. 9, Berlin-Gottingen-Heidelberg, Ed. W. Ruhland, Springer-Verlag, 1958.
61. Wilson, P. W., and Burris, R. H., *Bact. Rev.*, **11**, 41 (1947).
62. Young, J. L., *Soil Sci.*, **93**, 397 (1962).

4

History of Nitrogen Fixation Processes

BERNHARD TIMM AND WILLI DANZ

Badische Anilin- & Soda-Fabrik AG, Ludwigshafen am Rhein

Although in ancient times certain nitrogen compounds were known in the form of their salts (e.g. ammonium chloride), J. Priestley produced ammonia gas for the first time in 1754 by distilling ammonium chloride with quicklime. He called this reaction product "alkaline air." In 1784 C. L. Bertholet demonstrated that ammonia consists of nitrogen and hydrogen; moreover, his conception of its quantitative composition was almost correct.

In 1795 G. F. Hildebrand carried out the first systematic experiments for the production of ammonia by synthesis of the elements at normal pressure; I. B. Biot and F. de Laroche even tried the reaction of nitrogen and hydrogen under pressure of up to 50 atm. However, all of these early experiments gave negative results because the theory of chemical equilibrium was not yet known.

J. W. Döbereiner (1823) was the first chemist to envisage the possibility of combining nitrogen and hydrogen by the aid of a catalyst. His theory terminated a long period of discussion on the special properties of hydrogen in *statu nascendi*—work which previously bore no fruit because the principle of catalysis still had not been recognized. In 1784 Cavindish carried out an interesting experiment in order to force nitrogen to react chemically. He demonstrated that with the help of electrical discharges all of the nitrogen in an air-filled tube can be converted into oxides of nitrogen.

RESEARCH (1850–1900)

All of these older experiments for synthesizing ammonia were doomed to fail because of the underlying basic assumption that ammonia will be decomposed completely at higher temperatures. However, since 1850 the science of physical chemistry has developed considerably. C. M. Guldberg and P. Waage discovered the law of mass action; H. Le Chatelier, I. H. van't-Hoff, W. Ostwald, W. Nernst and F. Haber studied successfully the principle of chemical equilibrium and formulated a sound theory which allowed a correct explanation regarding the influence of pressure, temperature, and concentration on the reaction equilibrium. An important conclusion from these theories was that an exact study of the decomposition of ammonia would give valuable information on the possibility of its synthesis from the elements. W. Ramsay (1884) and S. Young investigated the decomposition of ammonia in the temperature range from 500 to 830°C and came to the conclusion that the reaction must be reversible. They also referred to the catalytic influence of iron and copper on the reaction velocity.

Intensive studies on the fixation of nitrogen from the air were greatly promoted by Liebig's famous book "Organic Chemistry in Its Application to Agriculture and Physiology." It was published in 1840 and stressed the economic consequences which a synthesis of nitrogen compounds would have in the field of agriculture.

In 1900 three possibilities existed for fixing the nitrogen of the air: (1) the direct oxidation of the nitrogen from the air under formation of nitric acid and nitrates; (2) the fixation of nitrogen to metals or metalloids with the possibility of converting these intermediate products finally into ammonia; and (3) the direct reaction of nitrogen and hydrogen to ammonia. At that time the production of electric energy was already developed to such an extent that it seemed attractive to repeat Cavendish's experiment on a larger scale and with the intention of commercially producing oxides of nitrogen.

W. Nernst studied the reaction:

$$N_2 + O_2 \rightleftarrows 2NO - 43.2 \text{ kcal} \qquad (4.1)$$

which according to the principle of Le Chatelier does not depend upon the pressure but shows a marked influence of the temperature. The calculations of the equilibrium by Nernst which were later confirmed by H. Pauling gave the following equilibrium concentration for the formation of nitric oxide:

Temperature °C	1227	1527	2227	3227	4127
Formation of NO, vol. %	0.1	0.5	1.79	5.9	10.0

From these studies it was concluded that economical yields could only be obtained in the temperature range above 3000°C and that it would be necessary to cool the reaction products quickly and drastically to prevent the decomposition of the nitrous oxide into its elements according to Eq. (4.1).

Birkeland and Eyde developed a process by which an AC electric arc is spread in the shape of a disk under the influence of a DC electromagnet. Air is pumped through this furnace at high speed, and the reaction takes place in the electric arc at 3200°C. At the exit of the furnace the gas contains 1.8 to 2.5 vol. % of NO. In order to freeze the equilibrium the gases are quenched to 1500°C. They are cooled further in a heat exchanger to produce steam until below 600°C nitrogen dioxide is formed according to the following equation:

$$2NO + O_2 \rightleftarrows 2NO_2 + 33.4 \text{ kcal} \tag{4.2}$$

A Norwegian company, Norsk Hydro-Elektrisk Kvaelstofaktieselskab (Norsk Hydro), Oslo, was formed to exploit the large resources of hydro-electric power for the purpose of nitrogen fixation. At Norsk Hydro the air must be pumped through the electric arc at very high speed (approximately 400 m/sec). This is necessary to obtain a concentration of 1.8 to 2.5 vol. % in the outgoing gases behind the burner. The subsequent conversion of NO to NO_2 is a slow reaction carried out in large oxidation towers at a gas speed of less than 0.5 m/sec. After cooling, these gases are condensed in absorption towers to form nitric acid.

Schönherr and Hessberger of Badische Anilin & Soda-Fabrik AG (BASF), Ludwigshafen am Rhein, carried out the reaction to NO in a vertical electric arc built up in the center of a tube and around which the air passes through the tube in a spiral flow. The economics of the two processes are comparable. A joint company of Norsk Hydro and BASF for the development of these processes did not last long. BASF preferred to concentrate its efforts on the direct catalysis of ammonia from nitrogen and hydrogen when it became evident that such a process would in the long run be superior to the electric-arc process.

But until recently many efforts have been undertaken to carry out the direct oxidation of the nitrogen from the air on a large scale. In modified electric arc processes, low or high frequency electric discharges are used; in Mont Louis in the Pyrenees the sun's rays were utilized as the energy source for the production of high temperatures. Research work of Hartek and Dondes in the Brookhaven National Laboratory led to experiments with nuclear energy as a source for the reaction between nitrogen and oxygen. The Wisconsin Research Foundation developed a process to heat a layer of magnesium oxide pebbles to more than 2100°C by combusion of natural gas and liquid hydrocarbons. By passing air through this layer of hot pebbles, concentrations of 1 to 2 vol. % of NO may be obtained. The quenching of the hot gases to freeze the equilibrium is carried out in a second layer of cool pebbles. As a result of this development work, a pilot plant was erected by Food Machinery and Chemical Corporation in San José, California.

Since it has long been known that cyanides react with water with formation of carbonates and ammonia, experiments were undertaken to use a cheap cyanide as an intermediate route for ammonia. Since Wilson's experiments in 1892 calcium carbide became abundantly available by the reaction of quicklime and carbon in the electric furnace. In 1898 A. Frank, N. Caro and F. R. Rothe discovered that contrary to expectations calcium carbide and nitrogen reacted to form calcium cyanamide instead of calcium cyanide according to the equation:

$$CaC_2 + N_2 \rightleftarrows CaCN_2 + C + 67 \text{ kcal} \qquad (4.3)$$

In the soil, calcium cyanamide is converted through various steps into calcium carbonate and ammonia, and may thus be used as a fertilizer. The production of calcium cyanamide rose quickly during the first decades of this century, and then gradually came to a standstill. Calcium cyanamide is still the starting material exclusively used for melamine, but in the fertilizer field its relative importance (as compared with other nitrogenous fertilizers) is decreasing. Today calcium cyanamide fertilizers contribute only 2.5 per cent to the world consumption of nitrogenous fertilizers. The main reasons for the limited progress of calcium cyanamide as a fertilizer are high production costs and the requirement of very large amounts of electric power. Hence, only a small number of calcium cyanamide plants have been erected in the world, and the markets for this product are localized. It should be noted here that calcium cyanamide continues to have widespread application as a fertilizer in Germany where it is still being produced in three plants.

Serpek devised a costly experiment for the production of ammonia by way of a metal nitride. It was carried out by the Société Générale des Nitrures, Paris, and seemed very promising in the beginning because it produced simultaneously ammonia for the fertilizer industry and pure alumina for the quickly growing aluminum industry. In this process bauxite is brought to reaction with carbon at 1600°C and aluminum nitride is formed by passing nitrogen through the reaction furnace. Aluminum nitride is decomposed under pressure with water to produce ammonia and alumina according to the following equations:

$$Al_2O_3 + 3C + N_2 \rightarrow 2AlN + 3CO \qquad (4.4)$$

$$2AlN + 6H_2O \rightarrow 2NH_3 + 2Al(OH)_3 \qquad (4.5)$$

Although the Péchiney group spent large funds for a plant on an industrial scale in Alsace, this development failed mainly because no refractories were available to withstand the very hard reaction conditions in the furnace.

DEVELOPMENT OF CATALYSTS

As a consequence of new theories of mass action and chemical equilibrium, many scientists since the beginning of this century undertook research work to synthesize ammonia directly from the elements. The chemical formula for ammonia showing the electronic configuration of hydrogen and nitrogen is shown in Chapter 2.

In 1904 Fritz Haber and van Oordt carried out a comprehensive study on the equilibrium of the ammonia reaction; they were the first to measure accurately the formation of a chemical equilibrium of pure dry hydrogen, nitrogen, and ammonia at temperatures up to 1000°C.

In the course of these experiments, Haber described one case where an iron wire is heated to 1000 to 1100°C and a stream of nitrogen and hydrogen is passed continuously over the wire by means of a recirculating pump. Ammonia was formed in a concentration of 1/200 per cent and recovered as ammonium sulfate by passing the gas stream through a vessel with sulfuric acid. A. Mittasch later described this experiment of Haber as a "timid first step into a new technique which was to be carried out later under high pressure on an industrial scale."

In order to produce larger quantities of ammonia, W. Nernst and others investigated the formation of ammonia under elevated pressures and with the application of catalysts. They used pressures between 40 and 75 atm and temperatures from 685 to 1040°C. With a manganese catalyst they could obtain 0.896 vol. % of ammonia at 685°C and 50 atm.

However, Nernst was primarily interested in the scientific investigation of the ammonia equilibrium in the light of his own research work on thermodynamics which is generally known as "Nernst's theorem." He found the yields of the ammonia reaction to be too low for industrial exploitation. On the other hand, F. Haber devoted his research work to the development of better, more efficient catalysts. In his letter of March 23, 1909 to BASF, he stated,

"We have discovered in osmium a catalyst, which surpasses by far all the other catalysts which we know or which have been checked until now."

He then points out that under a pressure of 200 atm he had been able to obtain a concentration of 6 vol. % of ammonia. This remarkable result was the beginning of a close cooperation between Haber and BASF in the field of the synthesis of ammonia from its elements.

Even at this early stage of the research work, Haber had conceived of the idea of a recirculating process, e.g., the reaction components were to be recirculated through the reactor and the reaction product ammonia was to be extracted without reducing the pressure of the system. A patent was filed which in its English version contains the following claims:

(1) The manufacture of ammonia by passing nitrogen and hydrogen, or a gaseous mixture containing nitrogen and hydrogen, over a catalytic substance at a high temperature and removing, at a lower temperature, a part, or the whole, of the ammonia contained in the gases leaving the catalytic substance, and afterwards passing the gases from which ammonia has been removed over the catalytic substance, the process being carried on under pressure and nitrogen and hydrogen, or gases containing them, being supplied in accordance with the quantity of ammonia removed from the gases.

(2) In the manufacture of ammonia as claimed in the preceding claiming clause, causing the hot gases leaving the catalytic substance to preheat the cooler gases about to pass over the catalytic substance.

(3) In the manufacture of ammonia in accordance with the preceding claiming clauses, causing the cooling effect produced by the evaporation of the produced ammonia to cool the gases leaving the catalytic substance.

On July 2, 1909 C. Bosch and A. Mittasch paid a visit to Haber's laboratory at Karlsruhe, in the course of which a small metal apparatus was put into operation; on this day it was possible for the first time to produce larger quantities of ammonia under conditions which were promising as a first step to the industrial development of the process. The apparatus contained 98 g of osmium catalyst, was operated at a pressure of 185 atm, and produced 80 g of liquid ammonia per hour (Figure 4.1). But it still was a long way from this laboratory experiment to industrial realization of the process, and the solution of the difficult technological problems involved required the technical genius of Carl Bosch and the support of a large staff of chemists and engineers.

Bosch at once recognized that osmium and uranium were not available in sufficient quantities to be employed as catalysts in an industrial process for the production of ammonia. He drew the attention of his staff to iron, which was known to have a certain catalytic effect on ammonia, and suggested the use of modified iron compounds as catalytic agents. One of his chemists was fortunate enough to find that red iron oxide, known commercially as crocus martis, gave yields almost as good as osmium and that

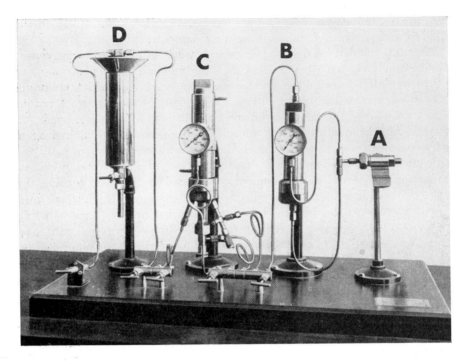

Figure 4.1. Original laboratory apparatus used to produce liquid ammonia in 1909 at Dr. Haber's laboratory in Karlsruhe. The pressurized gas containing nitrogen, hydrogen, and traces of oxygen is passed through heated platinum asbestos catalysts (A) in order to complete conversion of the oxygen to water which in turn is removed in a drying column (B). Provision is made to measure the pressure, temperature, and composition of the purified reactant gas mixture prior to its introduction into the reactor (C) which is water jacketed in order to remove the excess heat of reaction. Provision is made to sample the gas leaving the reactor which is passed through a cooler condenser (D), where the ammonia is condensed, the unreacted nitrogen and hydrogen being returned to the suction side of the circulation pump.

magnetite from Gellivara even surpassed the effect of uranium. But A. Mittasch soon discovered that pure iron oxide quickly lost its activity because of a change of its surface structure by sintering together under the reaction conditions. He detected that small amounts of alkali increased the yield, that magnesium and aluminum had a favorable influence on the reaction, and that sulfur, arsenic, and phosphorus acted as poison. The result of broad research by Mittasch and his associates led to the development of a catalyst system of iron with alkali, magnesium, aluminum, and calcium as promoting agents. In his Nobel lecture in Stockholm on May 21, 1932 Carl Bosch disclosed that more than 20,000 experiments had been necessary to develop a useful catalyst for industrial application. Today, promoted catalysts on the basis of iron are used in all ammonia synthesis plants throughout the world (for further discussion of catalysts see Chapter 6).

REACTORS

Just as important as the development of the catalyst was the construction of the reactor. There was still no technology for chemical reactions at temperatures of 600°C and pressures of several hundred atm. First it was necessary to study the properties of steel and alloys for these conditions. Moreover, a period of serious setbacks had to be mastered when it became evident that normal steel is destroyed by hot hydrogen. Figure 4.2 describes the form and dimensions of the reactor tube, which was used in 1910 in the first pilot plant for the ammonia synthesis. This plant consisted of only one reactor tube, one circulating pump, and one stripper for the removal of the ammonia from the gas circle. The tube of the reactor was of normal steel, the only available material which had sufficient mechanical strength for the pressure of 200 atm. But after 80 hr of operation the

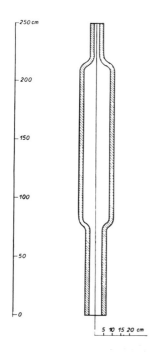

Figure 4.2. Reactor tube used in May 1910.

tube cracked. It was soon detected that the hot hydrogen had decarbonized the steel completely, thus destroying its mechanical strength. C. Bosch therefore suggested the use of soft iron as an inner lining of the reactor instead of steel and the utilization of a thick steel vessel as the outer wall in order to provide the necessary mechanical support. Thus the inner vessel will not be destroyed by hydrogen attack. Since a small amount of hydrogen would diffuse through the inner lining and come in touch with the outer steel wall, Bosch drilled small holes in the outer wall—small enough not to weaken the body. By allowing the hydrogen to escape into the atmosphere, Bosch safely avoided decarbonization of the outer vessel.

Figure 4.3 shows a reactor built in 1910. The catalyst is contained in a series of iron tubes through which the synthesis gas is passed; this system fills the larger part of the reactor. In the lower part is a built-in heat exchanger which serves to cool down the gas after its passage over the catalyst and to heat the oncoming fresh gas to reaction temperature. The first heat exchangers were very unreliable and offered many engineering problems. The reaction was started by heating the whole reactor with gas flames from the outside. However, since this treatment led to distortions of the wall

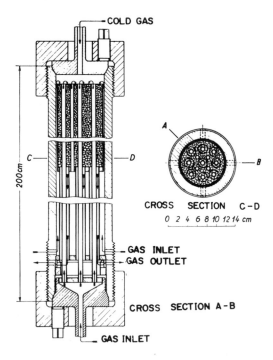

Figure 4.3. Reactor built in July 1910.

and to leaks at the joints, it had to be abandoned because of the permanent risk of explosions. Later, an electrical heating element was developed which is installed as a coil in the upper part of the reactor parallel to the flow of the gases; the red hot element is switched off once the reaction has been started. The construction of reliable heating elements offered many engineering problems over a long period of time. In certain modifications of the Haber-Bosch process and in the related synthesis of methanol from carbon monoxide and hydrogen, the heaters are installed as part of the piping system outside the reactor. In the beginning the reactors had to be protected against heat losses by heavy insulation on the outside; today the insulation within the reactor is so effective that no outside insulation is required. With these achievements the daily output per reactor was raised to 20 to 21 tons of nitrogen during the first years of industrial application of the Haber-Bosch process. The first ammonia synthesis at Ludwigshafen-Oppau went on stream on September 9, 1913 and soon produced 30 tons of nitrogen per day.

Considerable effort went into the improvement of the construction, safety, reliability, and performance of the reactors, heat exchangers, circulating pumps, and control instruments. The introduction of stainless steel contributed not only to a higher degree of perfection of the equipment but also paved the way for considerable progress in the operational conditions of ammonia reactors. Now maximum yield and reduction of operational costs by better temperature control within the reactor became a vital target for development work. Besides the tubular reactors other types were developed which contain 5 to 6 layers of catalyst with diaphragms between these layers to introduce cool gas for the control of the temperature in such a way that the reaction takes place under optimum equilibrium conditions. During recent years mathematical models of ammonia reactors have been derived from modern results in the field of chemical kinetics. These models are very helpful for the design of ammonia plants and have greatly spread the knowledge of the ammonia synthesis all over the world.

Between 1921 and 1927 certain modifications of the Haber-Bosch process became known in connection with the names of Fauser, Casale, and Claude. The origin for these modified versions of the process was the desire to use certain special raw materials for the synthesis. Fauser started from hydrogen by electrolysis and developed a special electrolytic cell for that purpose. The nitrogen was taken from the off-gas of the oxidation of ammonia with air to nitrogen oxides in the production of nitric acid. After due purification over a copper catalyst, sufficiently pure nitrogen could be obtained. In the beginning the Fauser reactor was very similar to the original

Bosch reactor. However, later Fauser developed a reactor with several layers of catalyst and a system for indirect water cooling with subsequent steam production for more effective temperature control.

The Casale process operates at pressures of 700 to 800 atm and uses injectors instead of circulating pumps for the introduction of the fresh gas into the reaction circle. The final cooling of the reaction product is done with water only. It leads to liquefaction of most of the ammonia of the circulating gas, but leaves a higher ammonia content in it than the Haber-Bosch process where the cooling is done at the temperature of liquefied ammonia.

The Casale reactor consists of one big reactor volume without any tube system in it and an annular heat exchanger between the inner lining and outer wall of the reactor. The Claude process operates at still higher pressures, i.e., between 900 to 1000 atm. In its original version it used hydrogen from coke oven gas as raw material. The coke oven gas is passed over a catalyst by which the carbon monoxide is hydrogenated to methane and methanol, which are absorbed with water and eliminated. This process gained a certain importance for relatively small production units.

In the United States the Nitrogen Engineering Corporation developed a system for ammonia synthesis which was later commercialized by Chemical Construction Corporation and found widespread application in many ammonia plants in America and abroad.

Although the development of ammonia reactors has reached a high degree of perfection, even today this development has not come to a standstill. A comparison of the different types of reactors shows that each development has its own merits according to the circumstances of its use and its combination with the preceding plants for synthesis-gas production. But in general it has been found that the ammonia reaction offers optimum economical results when it is operated in a pressure range between 200 and 450 atm. In fact, approximately 90 per cent of the synthetic ammonia plants in the world use this pressure range with a marked preference for 350 atm.

PRODUCTION OF SYNTHESIS GAS

C. Bosch early recognized the fundamental importance of a cheap hydrogen source if the ammonia synthesis were to become a commercial success. He therefore saw to it that parallel to the ammonia synthesis, development work was carried out on a large scale for the production of synthesis-gas. In the beginning coal or coke was the only available raw material. Their gasification always led to a mixture of hydrogen and carbon monoxide, from which the carbon monoxide must be removed in the so-called conversion reaction according to the equation:

$$CO + H_2O \rightleftarrows H_2 + CO_2 + 9.8 \text{ kcal.} \tag{4.6}$$

This process, invented by W. Wild at BASF in 1915, uses an iron catalyst and operates at normal pressure or at elevated pressures of approximately 25 atm. Other important problems were the elimination of the carbon dioxide from the converted gas and the removal of traces of sulfur and carbon monoxide. All these steps were of great importance for the ammonia synthesis, but most important was certainly the process of the gasification of the solid fuels. In the beginning coke was gasified with steam in a discontinuous operation in water-gas generators. In order to overcome the disadvantages of this process, Fritz Winkler developed in 1921 at BASF a continuous process to gasify lignite in a turbulent layer, through which oxygen and steam were passed.

This gasification process gained great importance only after cheap oxygen had become available from the Linde-Fränkl process of air distillation. In 1930 the Leuna works introduced the Winkler process on a gigantic scale. Later similar plants were built at several places in Europe and Japan. In recent years BASF built a nitrogen plant in Turkey, where coal with high ash-content is gasified in a Winkler generator.

There are other processes for the use of solid fuels. The method of Koppers-Totzek employs coal dust and has a high degree of flexibility with regard to the ash-content of the coal. Lurgi has developed a process for gasification of coal under pressure, which found industrial application for the production of town gas for heating purposes and of synthesis gas for the Fischer-Tropsch process. Finally BASF has transformed its synthesis gas production in recent years and abandoned completely the former discontinuous water-gas process. With coke serving as raw material, BASF has built large tapping generators similar to the blast furnaces of the iron industry in which coke is converted into synthesis gas in a continuous process by the addition of oxygen and steam. Such generators can be built in large sizes. At BASF they have an intake of 24 tons of coke per hour and 12,000 cubic meters of oxygen per hour. The production of synthesis gas is 55,000 cubic meters per hour, which corresponds to a daily production of 475 tons of pure nitrogen per generator. A special feature of these new generators is their high degree of flexibility which makes it possible to adapt the operation within limits to the requirements of succeeding plants. Another consequence of this flexibility is that these generators can also gasify, together with the basic feed of coke, powdered fuels, liquid fuels, and even methane. This process is therefore particularly well adapted to the raw material situation in Europe where at present a marked shift is occurring from solid fuel to oil derivatives from new refinery operations of crude oil. The tapping generators of BASF work at present at a ratio of 60 per cent oil input and only 40 per cent coke.

The use of petrochemical raw materials for fixed nitrogen production is increasing all over the world. This is above all true for natural gas wherever it is available. It may be of historical interest that soon after the practical achievement of ammonia synthesis, research work was done at BASF to make methane from carbon monoxide and hydrogen. On the basis of those results many catalysts were examined which found application later in the development of processes for the cracking of methane to synthesis gas. A cracking process with the catalysts in a system of tubes was developed at BASF and introduced in the United States at the end of the 1920's. It became the standard process for the conversion of methane to synthesis gas in the United States during the last war. Today 77 per cent of the ammonia production of the United States is based on natural gas. This is equivalent to more than 3,750,000 tons of nitrogen per year. In Europe, natural gas plays an important role in Italy and in France and will do so in the near future in the Netherlands.

Recently, there has been a gradual shifting away from the tubular cracking process. BASF has developed a process for the thermal cracking of methane in a special burner with a flame, which may be carried out so that it leads either to synthesis gas alone or to a mixture of synthesis gas and acetylene. The synthesis gas is available only after the extraction of the acetylene. A third development finally led to the use of catalysts for the conversion of methane with oxygen and steam in a very large uniformly-heated contact volume without the formation of a flame. An industrial unit following this principle has been built, probably for the first time, by the French company ONIA in a nitrogen plant in the Pyrenees. Later, similar systems have been used in Italy. BASF has built during the last few years fully automatic furnaces on the same principle, but for far larger throughputs. In recent times ICI has developed a synthesis-gas process based on catalytic steam reforming of light naphtha in a tube system under elevated pressure.

The desire to use higher boiling oil fractions as raw material for synthesis gas led to the development of special cracking processes for that purpose of which the Texaco process and the Shell/BPM process are examples. The introduction of these processes and the use of oil derivatives as raw material is of great economic importance because ammonia plants can now be erected in the neighborhood of the ammonia markets, whereas when solid fuels were used as a base it was generally necessary to build the ammonia plants close to the raw material source. Recently BASF has added a new version to its process of cracking methane to acetylene which starts from light gasoline fractions and produces synthesis gas besides acetylene.

The final processing of the synthesis gas normally requires several steps before the gas is pure enough for admission to the ammonia converters, e.g., the removal of sulfur or carbon dioxide and the last traces of carbon monoxide. Formerly these purification steps were carried out in corresponding washing towers with absorbing solutions such as pure water or aqueous solutions, inorganic and organic salts, or copper salt liquor. In recent years the washing of the synthesis gas at low temperatures with liquid nitrogen has found growing application. The desire to simplify the ammonia plants has led to the increase of the dimensions of the individual pieces of equipment so that an ammonia synthesis plant consists today in principle of the combination of a small number of large and very efficient individual systems arranged in series. Unfortunately it is not possible to build compressors for gas intakes larger than 16,000 cubic meters per hour; therefore a certain number of compressors is always necessary.

The inner parts of ammonia converters are now almost always made of stainless steel. All these improvements made it possible to increase the daily production of an ammonia reactor of 1,000 mm in diameter and 18,000 mm in length to more than 300 tons per day. Furthermore, the gas recirculators are no longer piston pumps but a special type of centrifugal pump in which the motor and the pump are contained in a pressure vessel, working there under the pressure of the synthesis (Figure 4.4). Because of

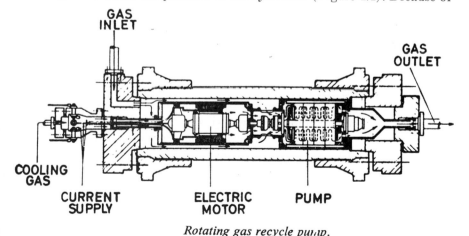

Rotating gas recycle pump.

Figure 4.4. Rotating gas recycle pump.

this special form, this pump is usually called the "mole pump." Modern ammonia converters are discussed in more detail in Chapter 5.

CONCLUSION

Before the development of ammonia synthesis, the processes for conversion of ammonia into different nitrogen compounds were already known in their essentials. The main problem was to adapt such processes to large production volumes once ammonia was available in large amounts. With the gradual increase of the ammonia output, the production of fertilizer salts such as ammonium sulfate, ammonium nitrate, and calcium nitrate grew correspondingly. In this connection the scientific research work by Ostwald on the oxidation of ammonia to nitrogen oxides must be mentioned; it was the basis for ammonia oxidation and the subsequent production of nitric acid. This reaction was originally carried out at normal atmospheric pressure. Later the oxidation of ammonia under pressure was developed in the United States. At present there is a tendency to carry out the oxidation to nitrogen oxides at normal pressure and to convert these gases in absorption towers under elevated pressure into nitric acid.

Unlike the previously mentioned nitrogen salts, the industrial production of urea from ammonia and carbon dioxide has offered many technological difficulties. This reaction takes place under high pressure and at elevated temperatures. For this reason it could be carried out only after the technology of the ammonia synthesis under high pressure had been in operation for several years. In 1922 the BASF urea process came into production on a large scale. Today urea is available in large quantities from several closely related processes.

The development of the ammonia synthesis has had far-reaching consequences in the economic and technological fields. The economic importance of the ammonia synthesis lies in the fact that nitrogen fertilizers became abundantly available all over the world. Nitrogen fertilizers provide an effective means for increasing agricultural production and for protecting burgeoning humanity against starvation. Table 4.1 indicates impressively the growth of the fertilizer production in the world and demonstrates at the same time the importance of the Haber-Bosch process as the primary industrial source for the production of nitrogen compounds.

Ammonia synthesis is indeed the beginning of a new era of chemical technology, leading as it did to the widespread application of high pressures and high temperatures in many chemical processes. Thus chemists were able to carry out processes and reactions that could not be developed industrially before. Moreover, the continuous operation of the ammonia

TABLE 4.1. DEVELOPMENT OF WORLD NITROGEN PRODUCTION IN 1000 TONS

Fertilizer Year	Chile Saltpetre	Coke Oven Nitrogen	Cyanamide	Total	Synthesis Nitrogen	Grand Total
	1	2	3	4 = 1 − 3	5	6
1913/14	402	269	59	730	4	734
1919/20	324	274	125	723	97	820
1924/25	303	352	114	769	400	1169
1929/30	362	459	202	1023	904	1927
1934/35	178	368	232	778	1294	2072
1938/39	230	476	290	996	2098	3094
1947/48	280	500	209	989	2622	3611
1949/50	272	500	307	1079	3650	4729
1954/55	232	600	359	1191	6772	7963
1956/57	185	600	347	1132	8099	9272
1957/58	200	639	328	1176	10,164	11,340
1958/59	196	642	322	1160	10,838	11,998
1959/60	185	653	331	1169	11,843	13,012
1960/61	145	—	304	—	—	13,422
1961/62	140	—	—	—	—	14,525

synthesis had a profound influence on the layout of modern chemical plants and of their equipment. The first two ammonia plants of the world in Ludwigshafen and at Leuna were industrial combines of gigantic dimensions.

The new technique of high pressure reactions was quickly extended to other branches of chemical engineering. In the early 1920's the methanol synthesis was ready for industrial use. Shortly afterwards the synthesis of isobutanol from carbon monoxide and hydrogen was introduced on a large scale in Germany. The hydrogenation of coal tar or coal to produce liquid hydrocarbons found widespread industrial use in Europe until 1945; later these big plants were gradually converted into oil refineries. But the refinery technique too has made ample use of the high pressure chemistry, e.g., in the hydrofining process for the removal of sulfur. The purification of benzene with sulfuric acid has been replaced by the modern BASF-Scholven process in most of Europe's benzene plants. These few examples are enough to prove that the modified versions of the technique of the ammonia synthesis have had a great influence on the modern development of organic chemistry. And even such reactions as the polymerization of ethylene under pressures of 2000 atm or more became possible only because the study of the ammonia synthesis paved the way for these new processes also.

The ammonia process is a continuous operation which must be maintained over a long period of time without interruption; in order to control

Figure 4.5. Dr. Fritz Haber.

Figure 4.6. Carl Bosch.

the reaction new instruments had to be developed. Thus the instrumentation of chemical plants received valuable impulses from the experience of the operation of ammonia plants. In fact, the ammonia synthesis and its instrumentation are the real forerunners of the technique of automation, which has found nowadays widespread application in all parts of modern industrial life. It therefore is not astonishing that complete automatic operation of large chemical plants by the help of computers was demonstrated for the first time in an ammonia plant and is being extended now also to more complicated organic syntheses.

For the steel industry the forging of large vessels for pressures of several hundred atmospheres brought with it many difficult problems. Many efforts were undertaken to reduce the weight of these vessels. In the Schierenbeck-BASF process a steel coil is wound around a core tube; the prestressing of the windings gives higher strength than a corresponding solid steel volume and thus considerably diminishes the weight of these reactors. A similar technique has been developed in the United States by the A. O. Smith Corporation. The desire to operate such equipment over a long period of time led quite logically to the development of special alloys which can withstand even very aggressive chemical reactions. These results of the chemical industry found later widespread application in many other industries and have had a large influence on many branches of modern technical life.

The scientific work of Fritz Haber (Figure 4.5) and the technological importance of the work of Carl Bosch (Figure 4.6) were justly interpreted as a very big advance in the science of chemistry during the first phase of the industrial introduction of the ammonia synthesis. The Nobel Committee in Stockholm bestowed the Nobel prize on Fritz Haber in 1918 and on Carl Bosch in 1931. By doing this it honored the scientific work of two men who despite the expanding world population are virtually responsible for banishing the specter of world-wide famine.

5

Production of Synthetic Ammonia

L. C. AXELROD AND T. E. O'HARE

The M. W. Kellogg Company

The properties of nitrogen and the initial attempts at isolation and combination with other elements have been reported in many historical references. Briefly, in order of effectiveness, it has been found that atmospheric nitrogen can be reduced, oxidized, and selectively reacted. Today, by far the most important of these three processes is reduction with hydrogen. However, this is not due to advanced fixation techniques, but to the advent of processes and availability of raw materials for the production of cheap hydrogen. As has been previously indicated, the arc processes (along with the cyanamide process, the cyanide process, and the nitride process) have faded into technical obscurity when compared to the direct synthesis route. For direct synthesis, nitrogen is fixed most easily by reaction with hydrogen by the use of a catalyst to produce ammonia. The use of catalysts is discussed in Chapter 6.

The chemistry and the thermodynamics of hydrogen fixation are long established and well documented. As shown in Table 5.1, once ammonia is produced, it is utilized in various combinations with forms of phosphorus and potassium to make a broad range of multi-nutrient fertilizer materials and mixtures. The quantities of fertilizers shown in this table were based on the production of about 3,000,000 short tons of ammonia which was almost three quarters of the U. S. synthetic production for that year.

Population growth figures are frequently used to project fertilizer demand. Table 5.2, prepared from various types of United Nations source material, compares population increase and nitrogen nutrient consumption per unit of population for selected countries for the years 1953 and 1959. The yearly average increase in nitrogen nutrient consumption per unit of population represents the increased rate of consumption over and above

TABLE 5.1. AMMONIA USAGE IN MAJOR FERTILIZER PRODUCTS

Raw Material	Primary Reactant	Primary Product	Secondary Reactants	Secondary Product	Tertiary Reactant	Tertiary Product	Fertilizer Materials	U.S. Consumption for Year Ended June 1959 (short tons*)
hydrocarbons	steam, air	ammonia					*As Nitrogen:* anhydrous ammonia	681,073
			water	aqua ammonia			aqua ammonia	482,818
			carbon dioxide	urea			urea solids	110,176
			air	nitric acid	ammonia	ammonium nitrate	ammonium nitrate and, nitrate limestone solids	1,579,148
			sulfuric acid	ammonium sulfate			ammonium sulfate	549,945
							Fertilizing solutions	504,440
							As Phosphorus:	
			phosphoric acid	ammonium phosphate			ammonium phosphates	182,508
			phosphoric acid sulfuric acid	ammonium phosphate sulfate			ammonium phosphate sulfate	336,759
			phosphate rock nitric acid	ammonium phosphate nitrate			ammonium phosphate nitrate	20,334
							Fertilizer Mixtures: nitrogen-phosphorus-potassium	14,843,274
							nitrogen-phosphorus	418,130
							nitrogen-potassium	279,301

* Figures selected from Scholl, W., *et al.,* "Consumption of Commercial Fertilizers and Primary Plant Nutrients in the U.S.," ARS, Annual Reports, U.S. Department of Agriculture, Fiscal Year 1959.

TABLE 5.2. POPULATION INCREASE AND NITROGEN NUTRIENT CONSUMPTION FOR SELECTED COUNTRIES (YEARS 1953 AND 1959)

	Population in Millions			Nitrogen Nutrient Consumption (1000 metric tons/million population)		
	1953	1959	Average Yearly Increase (%)	1953	1959	Average Yearly Increase (%)
World..............	2436	2695	1.75	2.15	2.97	6.2
Brazil*..............	58	64	2.50	0.23	0.68	32.5
Canada..............	15	17	2.85	2.5	3.6	7.3
France..............	43	45	0.92	6.3	10.7	16.9
India..............	373	403	1.20	0.28	0.45	10.1
Japan..............	87	93	1.10	4.6	7.4	10.1
Mexico..............	28	33	3.10	0.56	4.2	108.2
United Kingdom......	51	52	0.42	4.6	6.6	7.3
United States.........	160	177	1.50	10.2	13.2	4.9
West Germany........	49	53	1.20	8.5	10.9	2.1

* Complete data available from 1955 only.

that due to population increase. This pattern for nitrogen nutrient consumption which is shown gives every indication of continuing at an equal or increased rate.

AMMONIA: THE PRIMARY NITROGEN PRODUCT

Prior to the successful commercial operation of the Haber process for directly synthesizing ammonia, the principal sources of fertilizer nitrogen were the Chilean nitrate deposits and ammonium sulfate obtained as a by-product in the coking of coal. According to estimates reported in *Nitrogen*,[2] Chilean nitrate supplied about 70 per cent of the fertilizer nitrogen from 1850 to 1900 and about 50 per cent up to 1914. The production of synthetic nitrogen which had been about 1.4 per cent of the total in 1910 rose to around 10 per cent by 1914. In 1918, at the end of World War I, the market share for Chilean nitrate and that of synthetic nitrogen were equal, at approximately 33 to 35 per cent of the world output. From that date, the proportion of fertilizer nitrogen derived from Chilean nitrate gradually declined to a level of about 2 per cent in 1958–59. During this same period, the amount of synthetic ammonia manufactured rose rapidly. In 1960–61, it represented about 93 per cent of the production of nitrogen for all purposes.[6]

Since 1921 when the first successful synthetic ammonia plant went on stream in the United States, ammonia production capacity has grown in spurts. By 1932, there were 10 plants in the United States with an aggregate annual capacity of about 316,500 tons.[26] In 1943, there were 17 plants and by January 1962, there were 64 plants operating with a combined annual capacity of around 6,200,000 tons; in addition, there were 11 new plants proposed or under construction which would increase the annual capacity of the United States by 750,000 tons of ammonia.[19] These plants are listed in Table 5.3.[20] Although a similar listing is not available on a world-wide basis, the many references scanned indicate that the United States accounted for more than 35 per cent of the total synthetic ammonia produced in the world in 1960. From a plant-economics viewpoint this is noteworthy because, as is well known, most of the plants outside the United States have smaller unit capacities and better than 50 per cent use coal and/or coke as the hydrogen raw material.

In retrospect, the tremendous growth that has occurred in the United States synthetic nitrogen industry resulted from the needs of World War II and the Korean conflict. However, starting in the early 50's, certain nitrogen fertilizer practices appeared which provided the momentum for the industry's accelerated growth. Included in these were introduction of direct application ammonia, acceptance of direct use of ammonium nitrate, use of multi-nutrient fertilizers, stress on nutrient concentration or analysis, start of planned seasonal fertilizer programs, and use of specific crop fertilizers and mixes. Some of these market practices led to developments in manufacturing technology, but many were the result of improved processes.

AMMONIA PROCESSES

In reflecting on the development of process technology for the manufacture of ammonia, it is necessary to think of the total process as being composed of three steps: synthesis gas preparation, purification, and ammonia synthesis. Synthesis gas preparation encompasses the generation of hydrogen and the suitable introduction of nitrogen. Purification involves the removal of CO_2 and CO, the elimination of catalyst poisons, and the preparation of the required stoichiometric ratio of hydrogen and nitrogen ($3H_2/1N_2$). Ammonia synthesis covers the catalytic fixation of nitrogen at elevated temperature and pressure and the recovery of the ammonia product. Although there have been numerous modifications and improvements in all of these steps, the most outstanding have been in synthesis gas preparation. These developments were aided greatly by the dramatic rise in the supply of natural gas and the availability of fuels derived from petroleum, which have made possible an increase in the hydrogen source for ammonia processes.

TABLE 5.3. ANHYDROUS AMMONIA PLANTS, JANUARY 1, 1962.

Name of Company	Plant Location	NH₃ Capacity (thousand tons/year)
1. Allied Chemical Corporation	Hopewell, Virginia	400
2. Allied Chemical Corporation	LaPlatte, Nebraska	76
3. Allied Chemical Corporation	South Point, Ohio	320
4. American Cyanamid Company	Fortier, Louisiana	53
5. Apache Powder Company	Benson, Arizona	11
6. Armour Agricultural Chemical Company	Festus, Missouri	86
7. Armour Agricultural Chemical Company	Cherokee, Alabama	126
8. Atlantic Refining Company	Philadelphia, Pennsylvania	60
9. California Ammonia Company	Lathrop, California	45
10. California Chemical Company	Richmond, California	115
11. California Chemical Company	Fort Madison, Iowa	105
12. Calumet Nitrogen Products Company	Hammond, Indiana	108
13. Coastal Chemical Corporation	Pascagoula, Mississippi	70
14. Collier Carbon and Chemical Corporation	Brea, California	115
15. Commercial Solvents Corporation	Sterlington, Louisiana	144
16. Consumers Cooperative Association	Hastings, Nebraska	70
17. Cooperative Farm Chemicals Association	Lawrence, Kansas	147
18. John Deere Chemical Company	Pryor, Oklahoma	72
19. Diamond Alkali Company	Deer Park, Texas	40
20. Dow Chemical Company	Freeport, Texas	115
21. Dow Chemical Company	Midland, Michigan	36
22. Dow Chemical Company	Pittsburg, California	11
23. E. I. duPont de Nemours and Company	Belle, West Virginia	250
24. E. I. duPont de Nemours and Company	Gibbstown, New Jersey	75
25. E. I. duPont de Nemours and Company	Niagara Falls, New York	11
26. Escambia Chemical Corporation	Pace, Florida	81
27. FMC Corporation	Charleston, West Virginia	24
28. Grace Chemical Corporation	Memphis, Tennessee	160
29. Hercules Powder Company	Hercules, California	55
30. Hercules Powder Company	Louisiana, Missouri	43
31. Hooker Electrochemical Corporation	Tacoma, Washington	22
32. Ketona Chemical Corporation	Ketona, Alabama	45
33. Mississippi Chemical Corporation	Yazoo City, Mississippi	117
34. Monsanto Chemical Company	El Dorado, Arkansas	224
35. Monsanto Chemical Company	Luling, Louisiana	184
36. Northern Chemical Industries	Searsport, Maine	45
37. Olin Mathieson Chemical Corporation	Lake Charles, Louisiana	131
38. Olin Mathieson Chemical Corporation	Niagara Falls, New York	6
39. Pennsalt Chemicals Corporation	Portland, Oregon	15
40. Pennsalt Chemicals Corporation	Wyandotte, Michigan	34
41. Petroleum Chemicals, Incorporated	Lake Charles, Louisiana	100
42. Phillips Chemical Company	Etter, Texas	208
43. Phillips Chemical Company	Pasadena, Texas	219
44. Phillips Pacific Chemical Company	Kennewick, Washington	73
45. Pittsburgh Plate Glass Company, Chemical Division	Natrium, West Virginia	27
46. Rohm and Haas Company	Deer Park, Texas	50
47. St. Paul Ammonia Products Company	Pine Bend, Minnesota	110
48. San Jacinto Chemical Division, Smith-Douglass Company	Houston, Texas	40
49. Shell Chemical Corporation	Pittsburg, California	110
50. Shell Chemical Corporation	Ventura, California	73
51. Solar Nitrogen Chemicals, Inc.	Lima, Ohio	133
52. Solar Nitrogen Chemicals, Inc.	Joplin, Missouri	108
53. Southern Nitrogen Company	Savannah, Georgia	150

TABLE 5.3.—*Continued*

Name of Company	Plant Location	NH₃ Capacity (thousand tons/year)
54. Southwestern Nitrochemical Corp.	Chandler, Arizona	28
55. Spencer Chemical Company	Henderson, Kentucky	76
56. Spencer Chemical Company	Pittsburg, Kansas	184
57. Spencer Chemical Company	Vicksburg, Mississippi	74
58. Sun Oil Company	Marcus Hook, Pennsylvania	108
59. Tennessee Corporation	Tampa, Florida	123
60. Tennessee Valley Authority	Wilson Dam, Alabama	90
61. The Texas Company	Lockport, Illinois	65
62. U. S. Steel Corporation	Geneva, Utah	72
63. U. S. Industrial Chemicals Division, National Distillers Corporation	Tuscola, Illinois	70
64. Valley Nitrogen Producers	Fresno, California	65
Tota capacity		6,203

Anhydrous Ammonia Plants Proposed or Under Construction

1. Amoco (American Oil Company)	Texas City, Texas	165
2. Central Nitrogen, Inc.	Near Terre Haute, Indiana	115
3. Dow Chemical Company	Plaquemine, Louisiana	50
4. E. I. duPont de Nemours Company	Victoria, Texas	—
5. Farmers Chemical Association	Chattanooga, Tennessee	60
6. Grace Chemical Company	Big Spring, Texas	60
7. Hawkeye Chemical Company	Clinton, Iowa	105
8. Monsanto Chemical Company	Muscatine, Iowa	70
9. Pure Oil Company	Worland, Wyoming	11
10. Shamrock Gas and Oil Company	Dumas, Texas	53
11. Tenneco Chemical Company	Houston, Texas	53
Total known reported capacity of plants proposed and under construction		742

Raw Material Aspects

Prior to World War II, coal and coke accounted for over 90 per cent of the world ammonia capacity. As can be seen from Tables 5.4 and 5.5,[3] natural gas and petroleum fuels have supplanted coal and coke as the principal feedstocks.

Synthesis-Gas Preparation

Specific feedstocks, some of their characteristics, and applicable synthesis-gas-preparation processes, are shown in Tables 5.6 and 5.7. It can be seen from the applications column of Table 5.7 that the processes of greatest current interest are noncatalytic partial oxidation and steam-hydrocarbon reforming. Usually, low temperature processes as a primary means of production and catalytic partial oxidation as a single-step hydrogen-producing method are utilized only for special situations. Some examples of

TABLE 5.4. TRENDS IN WORLD-FEEDSTOCK UTILIZATION
FOR SYNTHETIC AMMONIA MANUFACTURE

Feedstock	Usage as Per Cent of World Capacity	
	Feb., 1959	Feb., 1962
Natural gas......................	31	38
Fuel oil.........................	15	13
Refinery gas.....................	9	7
Coal and coke...................	40	40
Other...........................	5	2
	100	100

TABLE 5.5. PRESENT TRENDS IN FEEDSTOCK UTILIZATION FOR SYNTHETIC-AMMONIA
MANUFACTURE IN SELECTED COUNTRIES

Feedstock	Usage as Per Cent of Total For:								
	Belgium	France	Italy	Nether-lands	Norway	West Ger-many	USA	USSR	Japan
Natural gas........	—	30	61	12	—	—	77	29	15
Refinery gas and naphtha..........	14	12	17	—	—	2	8	—	7
Fuel oil............	22	3	2	10	—	11	2	—	10
Coke-oven gas......	59	48	15	55	—	46	2	34	32
Water gas..........	5	6	3	23	—	41	8	24	—
Electrolytic hydro-gen..............	—	1	2	—	100	—	—	—	11
Other..............	—	—	—	—	—	—	3	13	25*
	100	100	100	100	100	100	100	100	100

* Not included in cited source material but from other references judged to be crude oil.

these are: hydrogen-rich refinery gas and instances where surplus oxygen is available at little or no cost. It is interesting to note that while 10 years ago there appeared to be an abundance of refinery hydrogen, today, many oil refiners install hydrogen manufacturing units to increase their market flexibility. These units utilize the same basic processes and feeds which are used for the preparation of ammonia synthesis gas.

The steam-hydrocarbon reforming process has gained wide acceptance. Recently, it was reported that about 65 per cent of the United States synthetic ammonia is manufactured via steam reforming of natural gas.[4] The growth of this process since the advent of noncatalytic partial oxidation

TABLE 5.6. FEEDSTOCKS FOR SYNTHESIS-GAS PRODUCTION

Feedstock	Characteristics	Synthesis Gas Preparation Processes*
1. Electrolytic hydrogen	Impurities are trace quantities of oxygen and chlorine.	Purification by absorption and catalytic deoxidation or combustion.
2. Hydrogen-rich refinery gas	Contains 80–95% hydrogen plus aliphatic hydrocarbons; generally no heavier than butane.	Low temperature purification or more hydrogen may be produced, if required, by reforming.
3. Coke-oven gas	Wide range of impurities including NO, COS, and heavy hydrocarbons.	Absorption and low temperature purification or catalytic partial oxidation.
4. Natural gas	Easily removed sulfur compounds are usually the only impurities.	Steam reforming or partial oxidation.
5. Petrochemical and cracked refinery gas	Composition variable with time, contains olefins and sulfur; petrochemical gas may contain acetylenes and diolefins.	Steam reforming or partial oxidation.
6. Liquified petroleum gas	Largely propane and butane, but may contain olefins, COS, and sulfur compounds.	Steam reforming or partial oxidation.
7. Light gasoline fractions	Refractory sulfur requires special treatment for reforming.	Steam reforming or partial oxidation.
8. Crude and residual oils	Ash, metals, and high sulfur.	Partial oxidation.
9. Coal and carbonaceous materials	Ash, metals, high sulfur, tars; solids handling required.	Water-gas reaction and/or partial oxidation.

* Nitrogen is introduced in the air or as a purified gas, depending on the feedstock and method of hydrogen preparation.

TABLE 5.7. SYNTHESIS-GAS-PREPARATION PROCESSES

Type Process	Application	Remarks
Low temperature	Hydrocarbon-rich gases. Also used as purification step with other processes.	Commercial operation generally at 200–400 psig. Residual methane level essentially zero.
Noncatalytic partial oxidation	Hydrocarbons containing less than 65% H_2 + CO, but otherwise full range including crude and residual oils.	Commercial operation at pressures in excess of 500 psig. Treatment required for carbon in the effluent gas.
Catalytic partial oxidation (secondary reforming)	Hydrogen containing hydrocarbon feeds up to and including light gasoline fractions.	Commercial operation at pressures up to 350 psig. Feed must be desulfurized.
Steam-hydrocarbon reforming	Hydrocarbon feeds up to and including light gasoline fractions.	Commercial operation at pressures up to 300 psig. Catalyst sensitive to sulfur compounds and olefins.

is based on coupling competitive investment and utilities cost with the relative ease of operation afforded by the elimination of the air-plant and carbon-removal problems. The noncatalytic partial oxidation process is now employed mainly in areas where reformable feeds are not available, i.e., where only heavy oils and solid carbonaceous materials can be used or in situations where special conditions exist which provide favorable economics.

Generally, as molecular weight increases, the difficulty and cost of processing increases. With few exceptions (notably coke-oven gas), it can be stated that the most economic feedstock will likely be the one with the highest H_2/C ratio. This may be demonstrated by consideration of the following reactions:

$$C + \tfrac{1}{2}O_2 \rightarrow CO \qquad \text{(partial oxidation)}$$

$$C + H_2O \rightarrow H_2 + CO \qquad \text{(water gas)}$$

$$C_nH_{(2n+2)} + (n/2)O_2 \rightarrow nCO + (n + 1)H_2 \qquad \text{(partial oxidation)}$$

$$C_nH_{(2n+2)} + nH_2O \rightarrow nCO + (2n + 1)H_2 \qquad \text{(reforming)}$$

$$CO + H_2O \rightarrow H_2 + CO_2 \qquad \text{(shift conversion)}$$

As a greater portion of the hydrogen is produced from carbon, the requirements for reaction, for catalyst, and for carbon dioxide removal increase, leading to higher investment and operating costs.

The processes listed in Table 5.7 are diagramatically represented in Figures 5.1A, B, C, and D. They are typical schemes and show the usual methods for synthesis gas generation. Purification and heat recovery sequences will vary in accordance with the specific case.

Noncatalytic Partial Oxidation. In a typical unit for preparation of raw hydrogen by partial oxidation, the hydrocarbon feedstock and oxygen or oxygen-enriched air are preheated separately and injected into a refractory lined chamber where reaction takes place at temperatures between 2000 and 2700°F and pressures up to 500 psig. With heavy hydrocarbons, steam is added to maintain flow velocity, inhibit cracking during preheat, control carbon formation, and reduce the high adiabatic flame temperature which would result from the low hydrogen to carbon ratio of these fuels.

The basis for this process is the exothermic reaction of oxygen and methane. As reported in the literature,[17] this reaction was studied by Padovani around 1933, at atmospheric pressure in the presence of a nickel catalyst. The process was commercialized somewhat later by Schiller, *et al.*, at Oppau in Germany. Like Padovani, they carried out the reaction at atmospheric pressure using a nickel catalyst. Oxygen and methane were premixed and fed to a reactor through small openings in a refractory burner block at velocities above the rate of flame propagation. Hydrocarbon Research worked on a pressurized version of the same process subsequent to World War II.

In the 40's, Texaco developed a noncatalytic process at high pressure with simplified equipment which involved the use of a specially designed burner permitting all of the mixing to be done within the reaction zone. Natural gas was used as the feed material. Later, light oil and heavy fuel oils were utilized. The Texaco partial oxidation process was first operated at the Texaco Laboratory in Montebello, California from 1946 through 1954 to produce synthesis gas for a pilot unit on a modification of the Fischer-Tropsch process. Since then, the process has been installed to generate synthesis gas at many ammonia and hydrogen plants throughout the world. Similar processes have been developed by Shell, Koppers-Totzek, Fauser-Montecatini, Oesterreichische Stickstoff Werke A.G., and others.

Parallel to these developments, gasification of coal by partial oxidation was investigated. The principal incentive was the prospect for the manufacture of heavy hydrocarbons through Fischer-Tropsch in oil-short areas. These activities were impeded by the problems encountered in coal gasification which included the introduction of solids to the pressurized gasifier, the removal of the ash or slag, and the economical completion of conver-

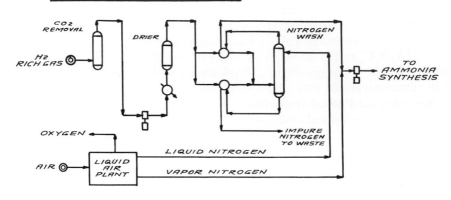

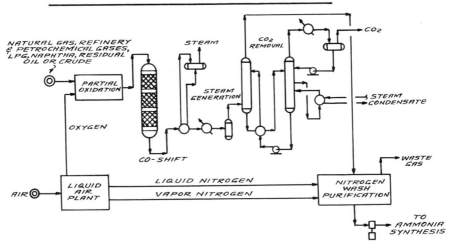

Figure 5.1. Synthesis gas preparation and purification.

sion over a wide range of coal characteristics such as ash content, composition, and high temperature plasticity. Despite these problems, coals ranging from peat and lignite to anthracite have been gasified successfully, and operating pressures as high as 400 psig have been achieved. Winkler, Lurgi, De Mag, Koppers, Texaco, the U. S. Bureau of Mines, the American Gas Association, the Institute of Gas Technology, the British Coal Utilization Research Association, and a host of others made significant contributions which have been reported in detail.

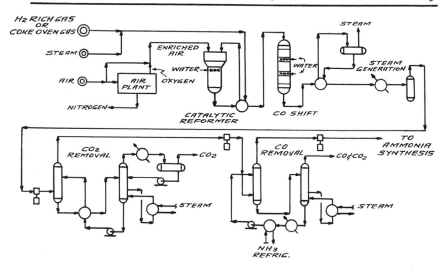

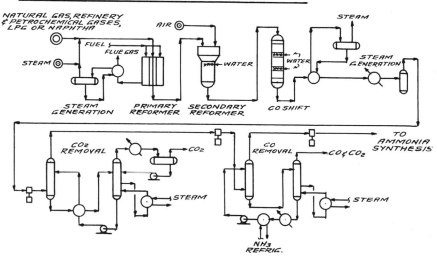

Figure 5.1. *cont'd.*

In conventional operations, the make gas in partial oxidation units has a high CO/CO_2 ratio, i.e., from about 18 for natural gas to about 9 for fuel oil. The CO/H_2 ratio is high and is dependent on the feedstock. The carbon make also varies with the feedstock and may go from negligible quantities for natural gas to as high as 2 to 4 per cent of the feed for fuel oil. In some early partial oxidation plants running on heavy feeds, unconverted carbon particles in the effluent gas from the generator have been a recurrent problem. Because of this, considerable emphasis has been placed on the development of designs for scrubbing the carbon from the gas, for recovering the water, and disposing of the carbon. A method is now available for recovering and recycling all carbon so that there is no longer any net production of unconverted carbon in the process.

The treatment of the generated gas in partial oxidation units varies in commercial practice. For example, in the Texaco process, the generator effluent usually is water quenched and water scrubbed and delivered saturated at 300 to 500 psig and approximately 400°F. However, in some Texaco plants, as well as in the Shell and Montecatini processes, part of the heat in the gas is used to make steam and the gas is cooled to about 100°F. If shift conversion is necessary, these gases must be reheated and resaturated.

In presenting data, it must be noted that comparisons should not be made between processes unless hydrocarbon compositions are identical. Hydrocarbon composition is easily recognized for gases and light hydrocarbons where analyses are usually given, but is often disregarded for heavy oils. Some typical performance data for the Texaco partial oxidation system are shown in Table 5.8 for natural gas, naphtha, and fuel oil.

Steam-hydrocarbon reforming. The steam-hydrocarbon reforming process operates through the endothermic reaction of steam and hydrocarbons over a catalyst, usually nickel on a refractory base. The reaction heat may be supplied by the sensible heat of the reactants; external firing of the catalyst-filled reaction chamber; internal combustion of a portion of the gas using air, oxygen-enriched air, or high purity oxygen; or by a combination of these methods. Composition of the effluent gas is a function of the reactant ratio, the pressure, the temperature, and the time spent in contact with the catalyst.

Steam reforming was introduced to the Western Hemisphere at Baton Rouge in 1931. The technology and catalysts used were largely those developed by I. G. Farben in Germany. Synthesis gas so produced was used to obtain hydrogen for refinery operations. Later, one or two other units were constructed for the same purpose, but it was not until 1941 at the Imperial Chemical Industries' unit in Canada that a reforming unit was operated for the preparation of ammonia synthesis gas. Prior to 1953, when Kellogg engineered and constructed the first pressure reformer for Shell at Ventura, California, all of the plants that had been built operated at about 10 to 20 psig. This is generally referred to as atmospheric reforming, since the effluent gas after secondary reforming, shift, heat recovery, and cooling is at or near atmospheric pressure.

TABLE 5.8.* TYPICAL PERFORMANCE DATA FOR THE
TEXACO PARTIAL OXIDATION SYSTEM

	Natural Gas	64° api Naphtha	9.7° api Fuel Oil
Feed composition (wt,%)			
Carbon.	73.40	83.8	87.2
Hydrogen.	22.76	16.2	9.9
Oxygen.	0.76	—	0.8
Nitrogen.	3.08	—	0.7
Sulfur.	—	—	1.4
	100.00	100.0	100.0
Gross heating value (btu/lb)	22,630	20,300	18,200
Product gas composition (mole,%)			
H_2.	61.1	51.2	45.8
CO.	35.0	45.3	47.5
CO_2.	2.6	2.7	5.7
N_2.	1.0	0.1	0.2
C_1.	0.3	0.7	0.5
H_2S.	—	—	0.3
COS.	—	—	0.0
	100.0	100.0	100.0
Operating conditions			
Pressure (psig).	340	350	350
Fuel and steam preheat (°F).	900	665	630
Oxygen feed temperature (°F).	260	105	72
Flow rates, per mmcf of dry-product gas			
Fuel (lb).	16,354	18,524	19,486
Steam (lb).	none	4625	11,043
Oxygen (mcf).	248	239	240
Net carbon produced (lb).	none	112	none—1034 lb recycled
Performance data			
Oxygen consumed, ft³/mcf of H_2 + CO. . .	255	248	258
Cold gas efficiency expressed as:			
(Higher heating value of H_2 + CO as % of fuel used).	83.8	82.7	84.7

* Presented with permission of Texaco, Inc.

The Shell plant was designed for 60 psig normal operation and was ultimately operated with reforming at 90 psig. After the success of this plant, a series of synthesis-gas, reducing-gas, and hydrogen plants were designed and constructed by Kellogg, Chemico, Girdler, and others for pressures up to 150 psig. The significance of operation at increased pressure can best be understood by referring to the reaction equation and noting that the theoretical expansion of dry gas volume across the reaction is $(2n + 1)$. Since the gas is ultimately required at a higher pressure, much of the compression can be done on the smaller volume of gas at a considerable saving in both capital investment and operating cost. Heat recovery is also improved and simplified through pressure operation. Because of these advantages, the trend was to higher and still higher pressure. Present practice is to set primary reformer outlet pressure near 300 psig. This represents an approach to an optimized situation with current technology and is achieved by balancing the decrease in synthesis-gas compression against the increase in air compression and equipment cost in the synthesis-gas-preparation sections.

Feed materials used in steam-hydrocarbon reforming units often need pretreatment, since the catalysts used are sensitive to sulfur and may crack olefins under certain conditions, resulting in carbon formation. Hydrogen sulfide can be removed by reaction with iron oxide. Mercaptans are removed by adsorption on activated carbon. Hydrodesulfurization is required for feedstocks containing refractory sulfur compounds.

After desulfurization, the gas is joined with steam and preheated in the convection section of the reforming furnace. The preheated steam gas mixture then enters the tubes in the radiant section of the furnace and passes over the catalyst where the reaction takes place. The hot gas from the primary reformer flows directly to the secondary reformer where it is joined with air over a bed of catalyst. The quantity of air used is that required to make a 3 to 1 H_2/N_2 ratio in the purified synthesis gas. Combustion of a portion of the gas with oxygen in the air supplies heat for further reaction and raises the temperature to permit very low methane content in the effluent gas.

Some typical operating data for steam-hydrocarbon reforming of natural gas are shown in Table 5.9. The cases illustrate the change in operating variables as a function of design pressure and feed-nitrogen concentration. As the pressure is increased, low residual methane is retained by increasing the steam rate and/or the reforming temperature. Comparing the high and low nitrogen cases, it can be noted that the amount of air which may be added to the secondary reformer is limited by the necessity for maintaining synthesis stoichiometry. This increases the primary reforming load which is reflected in increased steam content and primary reforming temperature.

Synthesis Gas Purification

After the generation of synthesis gas by noncatalytic partial oxidation or steam-hydrocarbon reforming, various combinations of purification processes accomplishing the same objectives are used. These consist of the

TABLE 5.9.* TYPICAL OPERATING DATA FOR STEAM-
HYDROCARBON REFORMING PROCESSES

	Natural Gas Feed		
	Low Pressure (Low Nitrogen)	Intermediate Pressure (High Nitrogen)	Intermediate Pressure (Low Nitrogen)
Ammonia capacity (ton/day)	300	300	300
Feed (mph)			
CO_2	4.1	.23	1.30
N_2	2.3	127.91	16.87
C_1	642.0	564.83	645.23
C_2	28.7	49.79	49.74
C_3	5.4	27.23	6.49
C_4	1.4	7.78	.07
C_5	0.3	.08	.58
C_6	0.6	.08	.43
C_7	0.5	.08	.22
H_2O	1605.5	3114.29	2714.23
Total	2290.8	3892.39	3435.15
Primary effluent (mph)			
H_2	1647.9	2122.88	1988.40
CO	322.4	319.27	304.26
N_2	2.3	127.91	16.87
CO_2	187.0	323.67	287.38
C_1	224.5	135.92	181.12
H_2O	917.3	2148.15	1837.81
Total	3301.4	5177.72	4615.84
Primary outlet pressure (psig)	125	220	220
Primary outlet temperature (°F)	1470	1491	1481
Air to secondary reformer (mph)	1003.9	884.30	1010.99
Secondary effluent (mph)			
H_2	1890.9	2143.01	2096.96
CO	530.6	441.36	466.07
N_2	785.3	811.53	804.43
A	10.1	15.38	11.12
CO_2	197.0	330.01	299.32
C_1	6.3	7.50	7.37
H_2O	1110.7	2384.79	2076.74
Total	4530.9	6133.18	5762.01
Secondary outlet temperature (°F)	1760	1729	1754

* Presented with permission of the M. W. Kellogg Company.

catalytic reaction of carbon monoxide and water to produce hydrogen and carbon dioxide in the water-gas shift reaction, removal of carbon dioxide and any sulfur compounds, and removal of residual carbon monoxide.

Since ammonia-synthesis gas should consist exclusively of a 3 to 1 mixture of hydrogen and nitrogen, the contaminants which must be either eliminated or reduced to economic proportions are:[27]

(1) Solids or materials which can become solid and block equipment, pollute solutions, and foul catalysts. These include carbon, oil vapors, unsaturated hydrocarbons, water vapor, and ash and metal oxides.

(2) Gases which are corrosive to equipment and poisonous to catalysts. These include sulfur compounds, oxygen, water vapor, and carbon oxides.

(3) All gases other than hydrogen or nitrogen which can accumulate as inerts in the ammonia-synthesis recycle system. The synthesis recycle system must be purged in proportion to the presence of these materials which include methane, argon, and helium.

Carbon dioxide and any trace amounts of H_2S can be removed by many scrubbing methods some of which are circulating regenerative monoethanolamine, water washing, hot potassium carbonate, and Giammarco-Vetrocoke solution. Residual carbon monoxide can be removed by using a regenerative solution of cuprous ammonium acetate, cuprous ammonium formate, or a combination of the two in a scrubbing step which is carried out at pressures ranging from 1600 to 4700 psig. This is followed by caustic washing for removal of trace amounts of carbon dioxide. Other systems used for removal of carbon monoxide are catalytic methanation and liquid nitrogen scrubbing. In methanation, carbon monoxide, carbon dioxide, and oxygen are catalytically reacted with hydrogen at high temperatures to produce methane and water. The water produced is condensed prior to delivering synthesis gas to the ammonia-conversion system. Liquid nitrogen scrubbing is used normally in conjunction with partial oxidation processes, since the nitrogen is available from the air separation plant. This system not only removes carbon monoxide but also reduces inerts as well.

Although inerts do not deactivate the ammonia-synthesis catalyst, their presence in the synthesis system reduces the partial pressure of the reacting hydrogen and nitrogen, thereby decreasing the rate of the synthesis reaction. The purified synthesis gas feed in plants using copper liquor and/or catalytic methanation contains from 0.4 to 2.0 per cent inerts consisting of residual methane plus argon from the incoming air and any helium present in the hydrocarbon feedstock. Carbon oxides as well as other oxygen-bearing compounds normally are maintained at 10 ppm or less. With liquid nitrogen scrubbing, argon is controlled to about 250 ppm. Otherwise, it is not controlled and is purged from the synthesis loop along with the other inerts.

Ammonia Synthesis

Ammonia synthesis is carried out through the exothermic reaction of hydrogen and nitrogen at elevated pressure for high equilibrium conversion, at elevated temperature for high rate of reaction, and over a catalyst in order to activate the reaction and improve the approach to equilibrium. As previously mentioned, the reaction was first achieved commercially in Germany by Haber-Bosch some 50 years ago. In this commercial unit,[14] the converter containing iron catalyst was operated once through at about 3000 psig and 1000°F. The 5 to 10 per cent ammonia in effluent gas was recovered by water scrubbing. Later, the unit was modified to include recirculation of the unreacted gas. This basic processing concept is still employed in present plant designs. Improvements have been made in the selection of operating conditions, design of converter internals, method used for recovering product ammonia, type of recirculation system, and choice of synthesis catalyst.

Increasing the operating pressure beyond Haber's, improves liquid-product recovery and increases the ammonia content of the effluent gas. However, higher pressure reduces the thermodynamic efficiency* and raises synthesis-gas-compressor horsepower. Increasing the operating temperature, improves the reaction rate and the thermodynamic efficiency but favors the decomposition of ammonia. It also reduces the life of the catalyst and increases the cost of the high alloy heat-exchange equipment. According to current design practice, the range of temperature for satisfactory catalyst performance is from 900 to 1050°F. On the other hand, commercial operating pressure extends from 1500 to 15,000 psig, depending on the system used, though the intermediate pressure processes (from 3700 to 5300 psig) account for about 50 per cent of capacity in both the U. S. and Europe.[5]

Converters

Present ammonia converters consist of a cartridge comprising a catalyst section or basket and a heat exchanger or interchanger, which serves to preheat incoming synthesis gas to the initiation temperature of the reaction. The converter cartridge, which is of alloy construction and usually insulated, fits into and can be withdrawn from a multi-layered or forged carbon steel pressure shell. The pressure shell is maintained below the reaction temperature by allowing cold feed gas to flow through the annular space between the pressure shell and the cartridge. Converter designs can be divided into two groups: those using a single continuous catalyst bed which may or may not have transfer surfaces or cooling tubes for control-

---

* Defined as 100 times the actual percentage of ammonia in the effluent gas divided by the theoretical or equilibrium percentage.

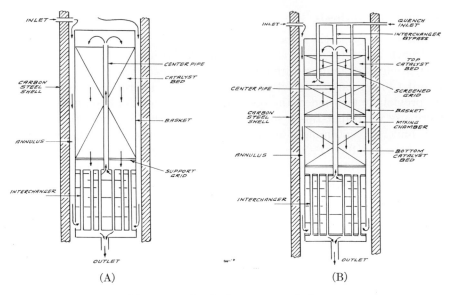

Figure 5.2. Synthesis converter design.

ling reaction heat, and those having several catalyst beds with provision for removing or controlling reaction heat between the beds.

A converter in its simplest form, consisting of a single charge of catalyst located above the interchanger, is illustrated in Figure 5.2A. The flow of cold incoming gas enters between the converter shell and the basket and leaves through the outlet nozzle. This converter does not possess any means for controlling reaction temperature. Because the exothermic heat of reaction must be dissipated through controlled temperature rise in this type of design, the converter must be operated at low over-all conversion efficiency limiting the concentration of ammonia in the effluent gas. Even so, the temperature gradient will be quite steep and will be a function of the catalyst volume and the inlet ammonia concentration. TVA, Chemico, and Claude converter designs,[1] among others, use cooling tubes in the catalyst bed to surmount this problem.

Both TVA and Chemico employ converters containing a single catalyst bed with imbedded cooling tubes. In the TVA type design, the catalyst temperature is controlled by means of countercurrent flow cooling tubes in the catalyst bed while in the Chemico design, this is done by using co-current cooling tubes in the catalyst mass. The flow pattern is the essential difference between these two converter designs. They both use an interchanger for preheating the inlet gas and have means for bypassing this interchanger with cold feed gas. The Claude converter design[21] differs from these in that it does not contain an interchanger. Before reaching the catalyst, gas from the catalyst cooling tubes passes over an electric heater which is energized if the temperature is too low; cold feed is admitted if the temperature is too high. Other designs (Mont Cenis, Lummus, and Casale) also make use of a single catalyst bed with heat transfer surfaces.

Kellogg and Fauser-Montecatini converters[1] are typical of those using several layers of catalyst while controlling the temperature between the layers. The details of the Kellogg design[29] are shown in Figure 5.2B. In the Kellogg converter, the catalyst section contains several layers of catalyst, and provision is made to inject cold gas as quench between the layers in order to maintain the entire charge of catalyst at optimum temperature. An interchanger bypass tube is provided to permit the introduction of feed gas without preheating and to control the temperature in the top catalyst bed. A principal feature of this design is that it permits more precise control of the temperature profile at the inlet and outlet of each catalyst layer and for the converter as a whole. In the Fauser-Montecatini converter,[18] the catalyst temperatures are controlled by the removal of reaction heat between the catalyst layers by the generation of high pressure steam. The design of the closed cycle cooling system is based on operation at a minimum differential pressure between the circulating coolant and the synthesis gas to allow the use of thin-walled cooling tubes. Without this feature, the cost of the coolant system would be uneconomic.

A recent development by Oesterreichische Stickstoff Werke A.G.[7] is based on cooling partly converted gases by indirect heat exchange between catalyst beds plus the injection of cold feed gas at the catalyst inlet. As yet, no operating figures are available for this converter, but it is said that the temperature of the gas at the inlet and outlet of each catalyst zone is held at levels which permit high over-all conversion and that the total heat-exchange surface is small.

Ammonia-Synthesis Systems

A comparison of some of the currently available ammonia-synthesis systems is presented in Table 5.10. This table shows individual approximate operating conditions, method of product recovery, and type of recirculation equipment for each process. The material given in the table, therefore, illustrates the general outline and background for the various ammonia systems but is not applicable for detailed specific design cases.

Save for the Mont Cenis process, the ammonia-synthesis systems presented in the table operate at higher pressures than the original Haber unit. The Claude process[14, 30] was one of the first high pressure systems and it involved a radical departure from the Haber design in that it operated at

TABLE 5.10. COMPARISON OF SOME AMMONIA-SYNTHESIS PROCESSES

System	Pressure Category	Basic Converter Features	Approximate Catalyst Conditions		Approximate Hydrogen Conversion (mole, %)	Approximate Converter Ammonia Concentrations*		Method of recovering product	Method of Recycling
			Press (psig)	Peak Temp Range (°F)		mole, % (in)	mole, % (out)		
Haber-Bosch[13, 31, 24] (original)	low	Single catalyst charge with feed preheat.	3000	930-1100	9-18	nil	5-10	Water scrubbing.	compressor
Claude[15, 30] (original)	high	Single catalyst charge with preheat of feed in converter annulus. Series-parallel operated converters.	15,000	930-2100	80 (overall)	—	25	Water cooling and single stage condensation followed by water scrubbing.	none
Claude (present)[10, 21] Grande Paroisse	high	Single catalyst charge with heat exchange in catalyst bed.	5000-9500	1000-1100	30-34	3-4.5	20	Water cooling and single stage condensation. Also water cooling and refrigeration for two stage condensation.	compressor
Casale[1, 32]	high	Single catalyst charge with preheat via internal heat exchange. Use of special catalyst.	9000	850-1000	30	3-5	23	Water cooling and single stage condensation.	ejector
Mont Cenis[1, 16, 22, 25, 31]	low	Internal heat exchange in catalyst bed. Use of high activity low temperature catalyst.	1500-2400	750-800	9-20	—	5-12	Water scrubbing and also low temperature refrigeration.	compressor
TVA[1]	low	Single catalyst charge with counter-current cooling tubes. Interchanger to preheat feed.	3700-5200	900-1000	25	5	17.5	Water cooling and refrigeration. Two stage condensation.	compressor
Chemico[1, 9]	low	Single catalyst charge with co-current cooling tubes. Interchanger to preheat feed.	3700-5200	900-950	25	3	17	Water cooling and refrigeration. Two stage condensation.	compressor
Fauser-Montecatini[1, 12, 18, 22]	low	Interchanger to preheat feed. Catalyst temperatures controlled by steam generation between catalyst beds.	4000-5000	950	30	1.5	20	Water cooling and refrigeration. Two stage condensation.	injector
Kellogg[28]	low	Interchanger to preheat feed. Catalyst temperatures controlled by introduction of cold feed between catalyst beds.	3500-4700	900-950	25	3	17	Water cooling and refrigeration. Single and two stage condensation.	compressor

UHDE[8]	low and high	Interchanger to preheat feed. Catalyst temperatures controlled by introduction of cold feed between catalyst beds.	4600–6400	950	25–30	3	17–20	Water cooling at high pressure. Water cooling and refrigeration at low pressure.	compressor
Lummus[23]	low	Interchanger to preheat feed. Single catalyst charge with countercurrent cooling tubes.	4000–5000	930–950	25	3	14–18	Water cooling and refrigeration. Two stage condensation.	compressor

* Conversions estimated from trade information.

near 15,000 psig and used multiple converters in a series-parallel arrangement without benefit of a synthesis gas recycle compression system. The present design,[9, 21] uses a single converter operating at 5000 to 9500 psig with a recycle compression system. Initially, the converter inlet pressure will be about 5000 psig. Usually, the pressure is raised gradually until it reaches 9500 psig to compensate for catalyst aging and loss in activity. The high partial pressure of ammonia permits its simple condensation in a

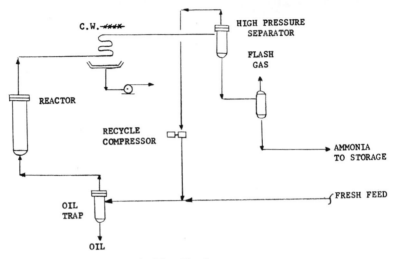

A. The Claude process.

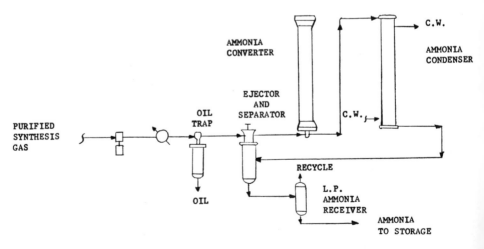

B. The Foster Wheeler-Casale process.

Figure 5.3. Ammonia synthesis processes.

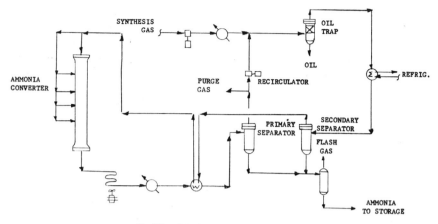

C. The M. W. Kellogg process.

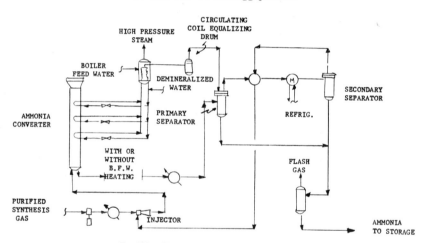

D. The Fauser-Montecatini process.
Figure 5.3. *cont'd.*

water-cooled condenser. In this system, it is not necessary to take a purge stream from the loop because the inerts enter at the same rate as they leave in the ammonia product. In recently constructed units, it has been reported that reaction heat is removed as steam at the rate of one pound of steam produced at pressure up to 400 psig/lb of ammonia. The Claude-synthesis system is shown in Figure 5.3A.

Another example of a high pressure conversion system is the Casale process.[11, 32] In the Casale system, as in the present Claude system, the ammonia in the converter effluent may be condensed by water cooling only. High pressure operation also permits greater per pass conversion of hydrogen to ammonia. Reaction temperatures in the order of 850 to 1000°F are maintained by balancing the heat of reaction by internal heat exchange. One of the main features of the Casale process is that the ammonia converter and the product condenser are designed to retain a certain amount of ammonia in the unconverted recycle gas. This feature is used to control the reaction rate and limit the temperature rise across the catalyst. The Casale design also uses an ejector system for returning unreacted synthesis gas to the converter. Although use of the mechanical recycle compressor is eliminated, it is necessary to compress the fresh feed gas to a higher pressure to supply the energy required for the ejector. A typical design of the Casale-synthesis system is shown in Figure 5.3B.

The Kellogg-synthesis system for fresh feed synthesis gas containing inerts and water of saturation is shown in Figure 5.3C.[29] In the absence of these impurities, the flow sheet would be simpler and the converter for the same conversion would operate at lower pressure. A two-stage ammonia condensation system is necessary in the medium pressure range to condense the water of saturation and prevent it from reaching the catalyst. Steam can be generated in conjunction with the system, if the economic conditions are favorable.

The TVA[1], Chemico,[1, 9] and Uhde[8] synthesis loops are comparable to that of Kellogg in terms of pressure, temperature, hydrogen conversion, and ammonia concentration. They are also similar in equipment arrangement, the major exception being the detailed design of the converter. The Lummus conversion system[28] which is of a general TVA type is roughly equivalent. Fauser-Montecatini's system[1, 12, 18, 22] for a highly purified synthesis gas using an injector rather than a compressor for recirculation is shown in Figure 5.3D. It has been reported that steam can be generated in this system at the rate of 0.85 lb of steam per pound of ammonia.

Although there has been considerable interest stimulated in the pressure aspects of ammonia-synthesis processes, no attempt will be made here to suggest that a given pressure is the optimum for synthesis. There are particular advantages to each process and, certainly, such factors as plant size, cooling-water temperature, synthesis-feed-gas composition, vapor- and/or liquid-product requirements as well as the type of converter influence the choice of pressure level.

DESIGN CONSIDERATIONS

Pressure and Temperature

The framework upon which the design of an ammonia plant is based includes the following: plant size, nature and cost of the feedstock, utilities characteristics, availability, price structure, product specifications, and the degree of integration with other manufacturing facilities. The most economical process sequence for a given set of circumstances will be the one in which maximum advantage is taken of the operating variables. In the determination of the most economical process sequence, pressure and temperature are the most significant factors. Each plays an important role in establishing the plant investment and manufacturing cost and must be given careful study. In a qualitative fashion, the effects of pressure and temperature on ammonia plant performance are presented in Table 5.11. Synthesis-gas preparation, purification, and ammonia synthesis are included.

Economics

While it may seem obvious, it is still worth noting that the economics of ammonia production in dynamic markets depend as much on merchandising the ammonia product at a price which will exceed manufacturing costs as on manufacturing technology. This is mentioned because of the frequency of trade-paper and magazine reviews on what has been termed "ammonia's chronic over-capacity problem." Whether demand is stimulated by need and usefulness or by artificial means, there seems little doubt that world-wide plant capacity will grow at a rapid rate.

Ammonia plants can be located near product markets or close to a supply of raw materials. The economics can be calculated and projected for each alternate location. Over the years, the market-oriented plant has usually been chosen. Lately, with increased emphasis on lowered manufacturing costs and the development of facilities to ship ammonia at less expensive rates, several large plants have been proposed at low cost raw material locations. A trend toward the greater integration of nitrogen with other nutrients also can be observed so it remains to be seen which location strategy will become preferred.

In terms of plant economics, the cost of feedstock, fuel, and utilities in ammonia manufacture on a world-wide basis can vary from 20 to 70 per cent of the total manufacturing cost. The feedstock and plant size are key determining factors. For plants in the 20 per cent category, the investment is very high and, similarly, the reverse is true for the other bracket. In actual numbers, the investment cost for 300 ton per day complete plants can range from less than $85 per annual ton to as high as $220. Manufacturing costs can vary from under $30 to more than $85 a ton. High investment cost is connected usually with small plants using coal as the feed material, whereas low investment cost is normally associated with large, natural-gas-fed reforming plants.

TABLE 5.11. EFFECT OF TEMPERATURE AND PRESSURE ON PERFORMANCE

Process Section	Chemical Reactions	Increasing Temperature	Increasing Pressure
I. *Synthesis-gas preparation* A. Steam-hydrocarbon reforming or	$CH_4 + H_2O = CO + 3H_2$ $CO + H_2O = CO_2 + H_2$ $CH_4 + CO_2 = 2CO + 2H_2$ $CH_4 + 2H_2O = CO_2 + 4H_2$ $CH_4 = C + 2H_2$ $2CO = C + CO_2$ $C + H_2O = CO + H_2$	(a) Results in low residual CH_4 and more complete reforming. (b) Reduces reformer tube life. (c) Increases tube metal thickness. (d) Increases fuel consumption. (e) Increases CO content of effluent gas. (f) Tends to eliminate variation of CH_4 in effluent with minor changes in feed rate and composition. (g) Requires more oxygen if oxygen-enriched air used in secondary reforming step.	(a) For given residual CH_4 raises operating temperature. (b) For given residual CH_4 requires increase in reformer steam flow. (c) Increases chances for carbon deposition; must add steam to suppress carbon formation. (d) Reduces synthesis-gas-compressor horsepower. (e) Increases air-compression horsepower. (f) Increases feed-gas-compressor horsepower. (g) Raises residual CH_4 for given steam and fuel rate.
Noncatalytic partial oxidation	$CH_4 + \frac{1}{2}O_2 = CO + 2H_2$ $CH_4 + 2O_2 = CO_2 + 2H_2O$ $CH_4 + CO_2 = 2CO + 2H_2$ $CH_4 + H_2O = CO + 3H_2$ $CO + H_2O = CO_2 + H_2$ $CH_4 = C + 2H_2$ $2CO = C + CO_2$ $C + H_2O = CO + H_2$	Where applicable essentially the same as above.	
B. Co-shift conversion	$CO + H_2O = CO_2 + H_2$ $COS + H_2O = CO_2 + H_2S$	(a) Favors reaction rate (higher activity). (b) Increases CO leakage due to unfavorable equilibrium. (c) For given CO leakage requires more steam.	(a) Increases conversion efficiency or catalyst activity. (b) Increases allowable space velocity permitting a reduction in catalyst volume.
C. Waste heat recovery		(a) Increasing temperature increases heat recovery.	(a) Increasing pressure increases thermal efficiency because of greater recovery of unreacted steam as latent heat.
II. *Synthesis-gas purification* CO_2 removal A. Amine system	$HOCH_2CH_2NH_2 + H_2O + CO_2$ $= HOCH_2CH_2NH_3 + HCO_3^-$	(a) Reduces solubility of CO_2. (b) Raises pressure in solvent-regeneration system making stripped CO_2 product available at higher pressure. (c) Aids regeneration of solvent. (d) Increases chances of regenerator corrosion.	(a) Increases CO_2 driving force and reduces number of vapor-liquid contacts in CO_2 absorber. (b) Reduces solvent circulation. (c) Increases temperature of CO_2 regeneration system and reduces recovery of available heat in CO shift conversion effluent system (if direct exchange is used). (d) Reduces residual CO_2 in purified synthesis gas.

B. Carbonate systems	$K_2CO_3 + CO_2 + H_2O = 2KHCO_3$	Same as amine system
		(a) Increases absorption coefficient (K_{Ga}) but also increases equilibrium CO_2 pressure above solution.
		(b) Increasing stripping coefficient.
		(c) Increases equilibrium CO_2 pressure in regeneration system giving greater mean driving force for CO_2 stripping.
		(d) Raises pressure in solvent regeneration system and reduces recovery of available heat in CO shift conversion effluent system.
CO removal		
A. Catalytic methanation	$CO + 3H_2 = CH_4 + H_2O$ with residual CO_2 $CO_2 + 4H_2 = CH_4 + 2H_2O$	(a) Above normal temperature range of 500–750°F, the water gases shift reaction takes place to a small extent and results in production of carbon oxides; must operate in required temperature range for practically complete conversion of carbon oxides.
		(a) Increases allowable space velocity permitting reduction in catalyst volume.
		(b) For given catalyst volume improves methane conversion.
B. Copper liquor scrubbing (acetate system)	$Cu(NH_3)_2Ac + Co = Cu(NH_3)_2Ac \cdot CO$ $Cu_2(NH_3)_2CO_3 + CO = Cu(NH_3)_2CO_3 \cdot CO$ $NH_3 + H_2O = NH_4OH$ $2NH_4OH + CO_2 = (NH_4)_2CO_3 + H_2O$ $2Cu(NH_3)_4(Ae)_2 + CO + 2H_2O$ $= 2Cu(NH_3)_2Ac + 2(NH_4)Ac$ $+ (NH_4)_2CO_3$	(a) Decreases pick-up of CO (and residual CO_2).
		(b) Increases NH_3 losses in absorber and stripper.
		(c) Improves release of CO in regeneration system.
		(d) Increases chemical consumption.
		(e) Increases lean solution cooling requirements.
		(f) Decreases CO_2 content of regenerated solution.
		(a) Increases CO and (CO_2) partial pressure improving pick-up in absorber.
		(b) Increases high pressure pump costs.
		(c) Increases heat requirements for expelling CO_2 in regeneration system.
		(d) Promotes the reduction of Cu^{++} to Cu^+ (the active copper ion) since it allows CO to be retained in the solution long enough to effect the reduction of Cu^{++} to Cu^+.
III. *Ammonia syntheses*	$3H_2 + N_2 = 2NH_3$	(a) Favors reaction rate.
		(b) Decreases the equilibrium ammonia concentration.
		(c) Decreases catalyst life.
		(d) Promotes hydrogen and nitrogen attack of converter internals.
		(e) Increases cooling (or refrigeration) required for product condensation.
		(f) Requires increase in gas circulation.
		(a) Favors the equilibrium ammonia concentration.
		(b) Permits operating at high space velocity with reduction in catalyst volume.
		(c) Requires higher synthesis-gas-compressor horsepower.
		(d) Facilitates condensation of product ammonia in converter effluent circuit due to increased hydrogen conversion efficiency and reaction rate; if pressure is high enough, condensation of product accomplished with water cooling only.

At the present state of manufacturing technology and economics, natural gas available at a price equivalent to other fuels is the preferred raw material for ammonia production. Where natural gas it not obtainable, fuels derived from petroleum are used. Crude oil and residual fuel oil are processed via partial oxidation in many such installations. In recent years, processes have been developed for pressure reforming light naphtha. These processes have good economic prospects depending on the relative costs and availability of naphtha and heavier oils. Coal, the classic raw material for ammonia production, is used now mostly in particular circumstances.

Within the United States, the minimum economic plant size is about 100 tons per day. Even a plant of this capacity is installed only in special situations and, in the future, relatively few plants will be built at must less than 200 tons per day. The maximum plant size is fixed not so much by technology as by economic considerations, an important part of which is product marketing. Many authorities consider that a 1000 ton a day plant can be designed with a single train of equipment. Although the maximum commercial size for ammonia plants has been increasing in the past few years, a conducive economic environment for such plants has not yet materialized. Ten years ago, a 300-ton-per-day plant was considered maximum. Today, several 600-ton plants are under construction. It is very probable that 1000-ton-per-day plants will be erected within the next decade.

References

1. "Ammonia Production Technology," Wilson Dam, Alabama, Tennessee Valley Authority, 1951.
2. Anonymous, *Nitrogen*, **5,** 8 (1960).
3. Anonymous, *Nitrogen*, **16,** 35 (1962).
4. Ibid., p. 36.
5. Ibid., p. 40.
6. Ibid., p. 47.
7. Anonymous, *Nitrogen*, **17,** 23 (1962).
8. Anonymous, *Petrol. Refiner*, **38,** 216 (1959).
9. Anonymous, *Petrol. Refiner*, **40,** 218 (1961).
10. Ibid., p. 219.
11. Ibid., p. 220.
12. Ibid., p. 222.
13. Brown, C. O., *Chem. Eng. Prog.*, **50,** 556 (1954).
14. Curtis, H. A. (Ed.), "Fixed Nitrogen," pp. 229–239, New York, Reinhold Publishing Corp., 1932.
15. Ibid., p. 232.
16. Ibid., p. 239.
17. Eastman, du Bois, *Ind. Eng. Chem.*, **48,** 1118 (1956).
18. Fauser, Giacomo (to Montecatini), U. S. Patent 2,898,183 (March 9, 1955).
19. "1962 Fertilizer Trends (Including the Scope of TVA's Fertilizer Activities)," p. 9, Wilson Dam, Alabama, Tennessee Valley Authority, 1962.

20. Ibid., p. 49.
21. Fluor Corporation, Ltd. correspondence, dated 1962.
22. Hein, L. B., *Chem. Eng. Prog.*, **48**, 415 (1952).
23. Ibid., p. 416.
24. Kent, J. A., "Riegel's Industrial Chemistry," p. 86, New York, Reinhold Publishing Corp., 1962.
25. Ibid., p. 92.
26. Kirk, R. E., and Othmer, D. F., "Encyclopedia of Chemical Technology," vol. 1, p. 785, New York, Interscience Publishers, Inc., 1953.
27. Kohl, A. L., and Riesenfeld, F. C., "Gas Purification," New York, McGraw-Hill Book Company, Inc., 1960.
28. Lummus Company correspondence, dated 1962.
29. M. W. Kellogg Company design information.
30. Shreve, R. N., "The Chemical Process Industries," p. 401, New York, McGraw-Hill Book Company, Inc., 1945.
31. Ibid., p. 404.
32. Weyermuller, G., and Ogden, J. W., *Chem. Processing*, **36** (1962).

Bibliography

Books

"Ammonia Production Technology," Wilson Dam, Alabama, Tennessee Valley Authority, 1951.

Curtis, H. A. (Ed), "Fixed Nitrogen," New York, A.C.S. Monograph Series, Reinhold Publishing Corp., 1932.

"A Decade of Progress in the U.S. Fertilizer Industry—Present Trends and Future Prospects," p. 60–68, Association of Southern Feed, Fertilizer, and Pesticide Control Officials, 1961.

Faith, W. L., Keyes, D. B., and Clark, R. L., "Industrial Chemicals," p. 80, New York, John Wiley & Sons, Inc., 1957.

"Fertilizers—Production, Consumption, Prices and Trade—in Europe and U.S.A.," 9th Study 1957–1960, Paris, The Organization for European Co-operation, 1960.

"1962 Fertilizer Trends (Including the Scope of TVA's Fertilizer Activities)," Tennessee Valley Authority, Wilson Dam, Alabama, 1962.

Ignatieff, V. and Page, H. J., "Efficient Use of Fertilizers," No. 43, Rome, Food and Agriculture Organization of the United Nations, 1960.

Kent, J. A., "Riegel's Industrial Chemistry," p. 86, New York, Reinhold Publishing Corp., 1962.

Kirk, R. E. and Othmer, D. F., "Encyclopedia of Chemical Technology," vol. 1, p. 771 and vol. 6, p. 384, New York, Interscience Publishers, Inc., 1953.

Kohl, A. L. and Riesenfeld, F. C., "Gas Purification," New York, McGraw-Hill Book Company, 1960.

Lamer, M., "The World Fertilizer Economy," Stanford, Stanford University Press, 1957.

Markham, J. W., "The Fertilizer Industry," p. 96, Nashville, The Vanderbilt University Press, 1958.

The Monopolies Commission, "Report on the Supply of Chemical Fertilizers," London, Her Majesty's Stationery Office, 1959.

Monthly Bulletin of the British Coal Utilization Research Association, vol. 22, No. 2, 1958.

"Report on Progress in Applied Chemistry," vol. 45, p. 449, London, Society Chemical Industry, 1961.

Scholl, W. *et al.*, "Consumption of Commercial Fertilizers and Primary Plant Nutrients in the U.S.," A.R.S. Annual Reports, U.S. Department of Agriculture, Fiscal Year 1959.

Shreve, R. N., "The Chemical Process Industries," p. 387, New York, McGraw-Hill Book Company, Inc., 1945.

"1960 Statistical Yearbook," New York, Statistical Office of the United Nations, Department of Economic and Social Affairs, 1960.

"U.S. Plant Nutrient Consumption (Continental U.S., By States and Geographic Areas)" Tennessee Valley Authority, Wilson Dam, Alabama, 1962.

Woodward, H. F., Jr., "Advances in Petroleum Chemistry and Refining," vol. 5, p. 441, New York, Interscience Publishers, Inc., 1962.

"The World Food Budget 1962 and 1966," Foreign Agricultural Economic Report No. 4, United States Department of Agriculture, 1962.

Periodicals

Borgors, W. J., and Bridges, G. W., *Chem. & Ind. (London)*, p. 1426 (November 19, 1960).

Bozeman, H. C., *Oil and Gas Journal*, **58**, 148 (1960).

Chem. Eng. News, **39**, 23, 33 (1961); **40**, 41 (1962).

Chem. Eng. Prog., Brown, C. O., **50**, 556 (1954); Hein, L. B., **48**, 412 (1952); Agel, F. O., **56**, 41 (1960); Schramm, R. W., **58**, 86 (1962).

Chem. Week, **39**, 33 (1961); **40**, 41 (1962).

Chopey, N. P., *Chem. Eng.*, **68**, 180 (1961).

Foreign Commerce Weekly, **66**, 46 (1961).

Ind. Eng. Chem., Eastman, du Bois, **48**, 118 (1956); Anderson, R. B., **52**, 89 (1960).

Ind. Chem., **36**, 61 (1960); Hinrichs, H., **38**, 7 (1962).

J. Agr. Food Chem., Westerhoff, R. P., **6**, 576 (1958); **6**, 812 (1958).

Mills, A. K., and Bennett, C. O., *A.I.Ch.E. Journal*, **5**, 539 (1959).

Nitrogen, **5**, 8 (1960); **8**, 36 (1960); **10**, 36 (1961); **15**, 42 (1962); **16**, 35 (1962); **17**, 23 (1962); **19**, 8 (1962).

Oil, Paint, and Drug Reporter, **175**, 5 (1959); **176**, Sec. 2, 12 (1959); **179**, 7 (1961); **180**, 7 (1961); **181**, 7 (1962).

Petrol. Refiner, **38**, 212 (1959); **40**, 218 (1961).

Weyermuller, G., and Ogden, J. W., *Chem. Processing*, p. 36 (February, 1962).

6

Catalysts Used In Modern Synthetic Ammonia Processes

Hans J. Hansen

Haldor Topsoe, Chemical Engineers, Hellerup, Denmark

The different processes used today in the manufacture of synthetic ammonia involve a large number of steps, many of which consist in chemical reactions carried out over a catalyst. The processes are mainly determined by the raw material employed. As noted in Chapter 5, the processes used in the manufacture of ammonia can be divided into production of hydrogen and nitrogen, gas purification, and the actual synthesis process.

While the actual synthesis reaction, i.e., the combination of hydrogen and nitrogen to form ammonia, is a classic catalytic process which was first carried out on an industrial scale by BASF about fifty years ago, many of the other catalytic processes utilized today in connection with ammonia manufacture are of a later date. The ammonia synthesis catalysts now in use basically differ little from catalysts employed 40 to 50 years ago. Catalysts utilized in the production of hydrogen and in the purification of synthesis gas have undergone more developments in the course of the years. These developments were to a large extent promoted by changes in raw materials and advanced technologies. In this chapter a survey and a brief description are given of the catalysts used in modern manufacture of ammonia, with special emphasis on the ammonia catalyst.

AMMONIA-SYNTHESIS CATALYST

The synthesis of ammonia from a mixture of hydrogen and nitrogen is carried out at elevated temperature and pressure and can only be accomplished by means of a catalyst. As previously indicated, only one type of catalyst is of practical importance, and that is a promoted iron catalyst. The catalyst is obtained by reduction of iron oxide, often of a composition close to Fe_3O_4, promoted with various nonreducible oxides. The most important promoters are Al_2O_3, K_2O, and CaO. The catalyst is most frequently charged into the converter in the iron oxide form and reduced *in situ*.

A proper reduction procedure is necessary to obtain high catalyst activity. The reduction is carried out by passing hydrogen or more often a mixture of hydrogen and nitrogen over the catalyst at gradually increased temperatures. However, since water vapor has a poisonous effect on the reduced catalyst, the reduction should be carried out in such a way as to avoid high water vapor concentrations in the gas. In practice this means that the gas circulation rate should be as high as possible and the rate of temperature increase kept within certain limits. Moreover, to minimize poisoning of the already reduced catalyst by water vapor, it is important for the reduction to begin at the end of the catalyst bed at which the gas enters and to proceed through the catalyst bed in the direction of gas flow. Frequently, such a pattern can be favored by use of a special type of catalyst at the gas entrance to the bed (or in the first bed in converters with several beds). Such a catalyst should be one that starts to reduce at a lower temperature than the catalyst occupying the main part of the converter. Since such an easily reducible catalyst will become active at an early stage of the start-up, the beginning ammonia synthesis will produce heat, allowing a higher circulation rate and thus a faster reduction of the main part of the catalyst bed.

In order to function properly ammonia catalysts require gas of very high purity with respect to certain compounds. The most common catalyst poisons are oxygen compounds, sulfur compounds, chlorine compounds, and compounds of phosphorus and arsenic. The oxygen compounds which may reach the catalyst with the synthesis gas are primarily H_2O, CO, and CO_2, as well as O_2 itself. The effect of these compounds is *mainly* a temporary one, which means that a decrease in catalyst activity is noted whenever the concentration in the gas goes up, the activity being slowly restored when the concentration goes down again. However, the catalyst may fail to regain its full activity after temporary exposure to an elevated concentration of oxygen compounds (say 50 ppm). In other words, oxygen compounds also have a slight permanent effect.

Concerning the relative effect of the above-mentioned oxygen compounds, it should be noted that a certain volume concentration of O_2 or CO_2 is about as harmful as H_2O or CO in a concentration twice as high. This is because after reaching the catalyst bed one O_2 or CO_2 molecule will rapidly form two H_2O molecules and one CO molecule will be converted into one H_2O molecule (and CH_4). Moreover, oxygen compounds give rise to crystal growth in the catalyst material, the active catalyst being made up of crystallites of a size of a few hundred Ångström. This effect is the same as that resulting from exposure to high temperatures. Crystal growth goes on all the time the catalyst is at operating temperatures, but it is accelerated by high temperatures and high concentrations of oxygen compounds, and in particular by a combination of these two conditions.

The stability of a catalyst to high temperatures and in the presence of oxygen compounds can be affected by the promoter content. For instance, a quadruply promoted catalyst containing Al_2O_3, K_2O, CaO, and MgO has a higher stability than a triply promoted catalyst not containing MgO. However, a slightly lower activity of the catalyst is associated with the increased stability. This circumstance has served to advantage in the development of a series of ammonia catalysts, the choice between the various types within a series being governed by the actual operating conditions with respect to temperature and oxygen content of the synthesis gas. In certain cases it has even been advantageous to use two different types of catalyst in one converter. As mentioned above, this is sometimes also desirable to facilitate the reduction process. The requirement of good reduction characteristics and of an optimum composition with regard to catalyst activity and stability can very often be fulfilled simultaneously.

The most common source of sulfur compounds is oil used in the synthesis gas compressors and in the recirculators. The effect of sulfur on the catalyst is primarily a permanent one, a large part of the sulfur entering the converter being retained by the catalyst. It has been found that even in synthesis systems where the make-up gas coming from the main compressors and the gas coming from the recirculators pass through an ammonia-condensation system and where therefore a certain purification of the gas is effected, sulfur will reach the catalyst. To limit poisoning of the catalyst, one should employ oil with a sulfur content of not more than 0.1 to 0.2 per cent. In cases where no purification through ammonia condensation is obtained it is desirable to get down below 0.1 per cent. This of course assumes that there are no other circumstances which would lead to a very short catalyst life. Compounds of phosphorus, arsenic, and metals (for instance, lead) are likewise permanent catalyst poisons.

Chlorine and compounds of chlorine may be present in gas manufactured by electrolysis. Chlorine is a permanent poison having a detrimental effect on the catalyst even in extremely small concentrations. To avoid a substantial reduction in catalyst lifetime the chlorine concentration in the make-up gas has to be limited to an amount in the order of 0.1 ppm. Chlorine reacts with potassium oxide with formation of potassium chloride, which has a vapor pressure at normal operating temperatures high enough to cause it to migrate into the gas in appreciable quantities. Besides resulting in a considerable decrease in catalyst activity, the potassium chloride migration may lead to plugging of converter exchanger and converter outlet line.

Ammonia catalyst is normally manufactured in the form of irregular grains. It is used in sizes ranging from about 3 mm to about 25 mm. The activity of a catalyst varies with the particle size, the smallest size having the highest activity. There are two reasons for the lower activity of a large particle. Firstly, its intrinsic activity is lower because the unavoidable autopoisoning by reduction water during the catalyst reduction is more pronounced with the larger the particle. Secondly, the larger the particle size, the larger the role played by diffusion restriction. There is a lower limit on the particle size that can be used, and this is normally determined by the pressure drop that is permissible.

Two other considerations which sometimes affect the choice of particle size should be mentioned. In converters with cooling tubes in the catalyst bed the particle-size range of the catalyst should be small enough to ensure good packing between the tubes. The other consideration concerns converters in which the synthesis gas passes the catalyst bed in upflow. In this case it is important to choose a catalyst size large enough to exclude lifting or movement of the catalyst bed.

A current trend in the ammonia synthesis catalyst field is the increasing use of catalyst in a prereduced form. In the manufacture and use of prereduced catalyst, certain factors may be utilized advantageously. A reduced ammonia-synthesis catalyst, which is pyrophoric, may be made non-pyrophoric through a slight oxidation carried out at low temperature, and such a catalyst can very easily be brought back into the active state. With prereduced catalyst the start-up time for an ammonia converter charged with new catalyst can be reduced to a fraction of the time required with unreduced catalyst.

Ammonia catalyst is manufactured in the form of irregular grains. The next development in the ammonia catalyst field may well be catalyst manufactured in a regular form, more specifically as tableted cylinders. Besides giving a lower pressure drop, such tablets would have the advantage of having a system of relatively coarse pores. As mentioned previously, large catalyst particles of the ordinary type have a lower activity than smaller particles partly because of a certain poisoning by water vapor during the reduction and partly because of diffusion restriction. The system of coarse pores in addition to the system of very fine pores produced during the reduction may greatly reduce these two disadvantages of the large catalyst particle.

STEAM-REFORMING CATALYST

It is pertinent now to extend the definition of steam reforming given in Chapter 5 (page 70) to accommodate the present context. Steam reforming is the conversion of hydrocarbons into *hydrogen* and *carbon monoxide* through reaction with water vapor over a catalyst at suitable temperatures. This reaction is highly endothermic, and two basically different methods of supplying the required heat are used. In the tubular type of reformer the reaction is carried out over a catalyst placed in a number of tubes, and the heat is supplied through the tube wall from the outside. In the auto-thermal reformer, oxygen and/or air is fed to the reactor in addition to the hydrocarbon gas and the steam, and the required heat is produced by re-action between the oxygen and the hydrocarbons or hydrogen, if oxygen is present; the reaction with oxygen may take place before the gas mixture reaches the catalyst bed or, if the gas enters the reformer at a relatively low temperature, in the catalyst bed itself. Typical temperatures of reaction in tubular reformers are 500 to 800°C. In autothermal reformers, there may be temperatures as high as 1200°C, the highest catalyst temperatures being found, of course, in the inlet layer in the type of autothermal reformers where the reaction with oxygen takes place before the catalyst bed is reached. The pressure range of interest in reforming processes is 1 to 30 atm.

For steam reforming, nickel catalysts are used. The catalyst is normally in the form of nickel oxide when delivered and must be reduced *in situ* before it becomes active. The reduction is most easily carried out with a mixture of hydrogen and steam, but a mixture of hydrocarbon feed gas and steam may also be used.

Common forms of reforming catalyst are tableted or extruded rings or cylinders. Rings are most often employed in the size range 10 to 20 mm; tablets are sometimes used in smaller sizes. Several factors have to be taken into consideration when choosing the form and the size of the re-forming catalyst particles. The most important is pressure drop. In tubu-lar reformers pressure drop is a problem because of the relatively great height of the tubes, 10 meters not being unusual; high pressure drop means increased compression cost. In autothermal reformers pressure drop is much lower than in tubular reformers, but may still be a problem because of the possibility of gas by-passing the catalyst bed through the refractory lining when catalyst pressure drop is too high.

Besides giving a lower pressure drop, the ring form has the advantage of having a large external surface. This is advantageous because in the reforming process the effect of diffusion restriction is relatively great. Diffusion restriction is an important factor even at the moderate temperatures in a tubular reformer, and it becomes very pronounced at the high temperatures found in autothermal reformers.

It may here be mentioned that in tubular reformers the maximum possible heat transfer through the tube wall is often a more important factor for the capacity of the unit than catalyst activity and diffusion restriction. The requirement for good packing limits the size of the catalyst particles which may be used in tubular reformers, where the inner diameter of the tubes may be in the order of 100 mm. Finally it should be noted that in certain autothermal reformers the entering gas is preheated by backwards axial transfer of heat, and in these cases relatively small cylinders may be advantageous because they give relatively good heat transfer.

Sulfur compounds are serious poisons of a reforming catalyst, and to obtain satisfactory operation with a tubular reformer the sulfur level in the hydrocarbon feed gas should not exceed a few ppm. This means that quite often the feed gas will have to undergo a sulfur purification before it is sent to the reformer. In autothermal reformers where temperatures are higher than in tubular reformers larger amounts of sulfur compounds can be tolerated, although somewhat larger catalyst quantities will be required than in the case of a sulfur-free gas.

The most widely used, and also the most easily reformed, hydrocarbon feed stock is natural gas, i.e. methane. Recent efforts in the field of reforming catalysts have been directed towards the development of catalysts suited for the treatment of more difficult hydrocarbon feed stocks, i.e. feed stocks containing relatively large amounts of olefins as well as feed stocks consisting of heavier, saturated hydrocarbons, for instance distillates. Another aim has been the development of catalysts of high thermal stability.

When trying to develop a catalyst of high thermal resistance it is of foremost importance to obtain a carrier of high stability, i.e., a carrier which does not undergo changes in operation at high temperatures and moreover does not have a tendency to react with the catalytically active material (nickel). This has led to the development of carriers of oxides of high purity, such as MgO, Al_2O_3, and mixtures of oxides. Some of the merits of a catalyst based on a carrier of this type should be mentioned. It is very active and thus well suited for use in tubular reformers where temperatures are moderate. Moreover, its ability to maintain its activity is extraordinarily good even at the high temperatures found in autothermal reformers. This combination of high activity and good resistivity is related to the pore structure and its stability. The pore volume of the catalyst is to a large extent distributed on two types of pores, one relatively large size type and one fine size type. The large size pores diminish diffusion restriction; the small size pores provide the large active surface. Another important feature is the complete absence of silicon. A problem often encountered in autothermal reformers is migration of Si out of a silicon-containing catalyst, more specifically in the form of SiO. This may take place at high temperatures and in a reducing atmosphere. SiO removal may lead to mechanical breakdown of the catalyst, and SiO will be converted into SiO_2, which may be deposited for instance in the waste heat boiler and on the shift catalyst.

During the last decade it has become increasingly desirable to reform hydrocarbons with high molecular weight (up to distillate having a maximum boiling point of, say, 200°C) and hydrocarbon mixtures with considerable contents of olefins. While this can be done relatively easily in autothermal reformers, carbon formation is a problem when converting these feed stocks in tubular reformers. This is aggravated at the elevated pressure of operation desirable for reasons of economy, say 20 atm. Recent research has aimed at developing catalysts suitable for the above-mentioned difficult feed stocks, and this has led to the development of specially promoted catalysts.

CO-CONVERSION CATALYST

In the CO converter (or shift converter) carbon monoxide in the raw synthesis gas is reacted with water vapor, whereby hydrogen and carbon dioxide are formed. The classic catalyst used in this process is an iron oxide catalyst promoted with chromium oxide. The active state is Fe_3O_4; sometimes the catalyst is delivered in the Fe_2O_3 state and thus requires reduction after it has been charged into the converter. The catalyst is manufactured in the form of cylinders as well as in the form of particles of irregular shape.

A number of compounds act as poisons for the CO conversion catalyst. The most important of these are sulfur compounds and chlorine compounds. Other compounds are harmful because they clog the surface of the catalyst. One example is unsaturated hydrocarbons which may form gums on the catalyst, particularly through combination with nitric oxide; another example is soot which can form by various reactions during raw synthesis-gas manufacture.

The increased use of partial oxidation of heavy oil in the synthesis gas manufacture in recent years has called for the development of shift catalysts of high stability in the presence of sulfur compounds, and acceptable catalysts are now available for this duty.

The shift reaction is reversible, and the conversion obtained may be characterized by the thermodynamic equilibrium and the approach to equilibrium. The equilibrium is a function of gas composition and temperature. Common operating temperatures for a shift converter are 400 to 500°C, but they vary considerably from one plant to another and may be as high as 600°C and as low as 350°C; under special conditions even lower operating temperatures are used. The outlet CO concentration on dry gas basis is in the range 2 to 4 per cent. These concentrations by far exceed the amounts of carbon monoxide which can be tolerated in the synthesis gas for the ammonia catalyst; the carbon monoxide content must be brought down to the order of 10 ppm. Typical purification processes are liquid nitrogen wash and copper wash. Carbon monoxide may also be eliminated through catalytic conversion to methane (see below). However, with say 3 per cent CO in the gas, elimination by methanation would require relatively large quantities of valuable hydrogen and would furthermore lead to a methane concentration which ordinarily would be unacceptable, as methane accumulation in the synthesis loop would become excessive. To make the methanation process attractive for final purification of synthesis gas the CO concentration in the gas to be methanated should be in the order of $\frac{1}{2}$ per cent or less. Such low concentrations can for equilibrium reasons not be reached at ordinary operating temperatures; temperatures in the order of 300°C are called for. Operation at that low a temperature in turn requires catalysts of particularly high activity. Such catalysts have been developed and have in recent years found wide application. Ordinarily a primary shift converter converting the bulk of the carbon monoxide is followed by a secondary low temperature shift converter. After the secondary shift converter the carbon dioxide is removed from the gas; carbon dioxide removal sometimes also takes place between the two shift converters, which of course has a favorable effect on the reaction in the secondary converter.

CATALYSTS FOR HYDROGENATION OF OLEFINS AND ORGANIC SULFUR COMPOUNDS

Hydrocarbon feedstocks containing large amounts of olefins or more than a few ppm of sulfur compounds present problems in tubular reformers. The olefins may have to be hydrogenated ahead of the reformer, and the sulfur compounds must be removed. Hydrogen sulfide is easily removed by absorption on iron oxide, and activated carbon may be used for removal of organic sulfur compounds. However, in many cases it is preferable to convert organic sulfur to hydrogen sulfide for subsequent absorption on iron oxide. Hydrogenation of olefins and organic sulfur compounds may be carried out simultaneously over a cobalt molybdenum catalyst on an alumina support. The active catalyst is actually cobalt molybdenum sulfide, and the feed gas must contain a certain amount of sulfur compounds in order to keep the catalyst in the sulfide state. Thus it is very convenient to have sulfur compounds present in a gas containing olefins to be hydrogenated. Typical operating temperatures for cobalt moly catalyst are 250 to 450°C.

A zinc oxide catalyst is also often used for sulfur removal. Besides converting compounds like mercaptans, carbon disulfide, and carbonyl sulfide this agent absorbs the hydrogen sulfide formed by these hydrogenation reactions. The operating temperature for zinc oxide catalyst is about 400°C or slightly lower. The choice between the various processes for sulfur purification of the hydrocarbon feed stock depends on the type of compound to be removed, the concentration in which it may occur, and to some extent on the temperature level at which the purification is most practically carried out.

COS-CONVERSION CATALYST

In plants where raw synthesis gas is manufactured by gasification of heavy oil the removal of large amounts of carbonyl sulfide, say some hundred ppm, may be required. This is often accomplished through catalytic conversion to hydrogen sulfide, which may be removed through suitable processes. Carbonyl sulfide may be converted to hydrogen sulfide either by reaction with water vapor or by hydrogenation. While the hydrogenation reaction takes place over shift catalyst, the reaction with water vapor may be carried out over activated alumina at temperatures in the range 100 to 150°C.

METHANATION CATALYST

Methanation is the reaction between carbon monoxide or carbon dioxide and hydrogen. The process has been in use for many years for final purification of synthesis gas. As mentioned above, it has found wider application in recent years as a result of the extensive use of secondary low temperature CO conversion. Various types of catalysts are used—for example, noble metals (ruthenium) on activated alumina, nickel and promoted nickel catalysts on a carrier, and iron catalysts (e.g., spent ammonia catalyst). A typical operating temperature for noble metal and nickel catalysts is 300°C. Methanation over ammonia catalyst may be carried out at about the same temperature level without any ammonia synthesis taking place, or it may be carried out at 400 to 450°C and at the pressure used for ammonia synthesis under formation of a limited amount of ammonia, leading to the condensation of aqua ammonia in the cooler following the methanator. Sometimes a particularly rugged ammonia catalyst is used at temperatures approaching 600°C, in which case substantial amounts of ammonia are produced at the same time.

CATALYSTS FOR OXYGEN REMOVAL

The catalysts described in the section dealing with methanation will also purify the synthesis-gas mixture for oxygen with formation of water vapor. If only oxygen is to be removed, this may take place at ambient (or slightly higher) temperatures over a platinum metal catalyst on a carrier of activated alumina.

In some cases it is desirable to purify nitrogen from an air separation plant for oxygen. This may also be effected over the platinum metal catalyst; it requires, of course, the addition of a proper amount of hydrogen to combine with the oxygen.

7

Chemistry and Manufacture of Nitric Acid

H. A. Sorgenti

The Atlantic Refining Company

AND

G. F. Sachsel

Battelle Memorial Institute

Prior to the availability of a ready and inexpensive source of ammonia, nitric acid was primarily manufactured by reacting sulfuric acid with sodium nitrate. Ammonia oxidation with air has been available as a laboratory means of producing nitric acid since 1839. Commercialization of the process, however, did not take place in the United States until 1916.[56] For several years thereafter the use of ammonia oxidation for nitric acid production was directly tied to the growth and development of the synthetic ammonia industry. Currently, over 90 per cent of the world's nitric acid is produced by ammonia oxidation.

Today, nitric acid's primary outlet is in the manufacture of fertilizers rather than explosives. About 75 per cent of the acid produced is consumed in fertilizer manufacture, while only 15 per cent of its production goes into the manufacture of explosives.[54, 55] The remainder of the acid is used in a wide variety of outlets, the more important ones being synthetic fibers, dyes, and plastics. Red fuming nitric acid, nitrogen tetroxide, and other nitrogen-containing materials being used in rockets and missiles could prove to be another important area of future use. In addition, there is increased interest in nitrogen tetroxide as an oxidizing and nitrating agent in the production of a wide variety of organic chemicals. Nitric acid's future growth potential will, however, still be strongly dependent upon the needs of the agricultural industry.

Nitric acid is manufactured by oxidizing ammonia, converting the nitric

99

oxide produced to nitrogen dioxide, and then absorbing the nitrogen dioxide in water to form nitric acid. Each of these three fundamental steps will be considered in detail.

PROCESS CHEMISTRY

Ammonia Oxidation

The catalytic oxidation of ammonia to form nitric oxide is an extremely rapid heterogeneous reaction. Under favorable conditions nearly every collision between an ammonia molecule and the catalyst surface results in the formation of nitric oxide. When ammonia is oxidized with air the following reactions may take place:

$$NH_3 + \tfrac{3}{4}O_2 \rightarrow \tfrac{1}{2}N_2 + \tfrac{3}{2}H_2O(g) \tag{7.1}$$

$$NH_3 + O_2 \rightarrow \tfrac{1}{2}N_2O + \tfrac{3}{2}H_2O(g) \tag{7.2}$$

$$NH_3 + \tfrac{5}{4}O_2 \rightarrow NO + \tfrac{3}{2}H_2O(g) \tag{7.3}$$

$$NH_3 + \tfrac{7}{4}O_2 \rightarrow NO_2 + \tfrac{3}{2}H_2O(g) \tag{7.4}$$

$$NH_3 \rightarrow \tfrac{1}{2}N_2 + \tfrac{3}{2}H_2 \tag{7.5}$$

The equilibrium constants, as reported by Harrison and Kobe,[50] for these reactions are shown in Table 7.1. Selection of a suitable catalyst and the existence of proper operating conditions will promote the formation of nitric oxide (Eq. 7.3) and suppress side reactions which lead to the formation of elemental nitrogen or other nitrogen oxides. Commercially, ammonia oxidation is usually carried out on a 90 per cent platinum-10 per cent

TABLE 7.1. EQUILIBRIUM CONSTANTS FOR THE FORMATION OF CERTAIN ELEMENTS AND COMPOUNDS FROM ONE MOLE OF AMMONIA[50, 76]

Equilibrium Temperature °R	K_p, Atm, for Formation of Indicated Product				
	$N_2(g)$ Eq 7.1	N_2O (g) Eq 7.2	NO (g) Eq 7.3	NO_2 (g) Eq 7.4	H_2 (g) Eq 7.5
540	7.33×10^{56}	7.30×10^{47}	6.39×10^{41}	7.68×10^{47}	1.65×10^{-3}
900	7.07×10^{34}	4.44×10^{28}	1.13×10^{26}	1.43×10^{28}	3.33
1260	2.61×10^{25}	2.69×10^{20}	2.11×10^{19}	5.04×10^{19}	1.11×10^2
1620	1.49×10^{20}	7.36×10^{15}	3.80×10^{15}	9.94×10^{14}	8.48×10^2
1980	6.71×10^{16}	9.12×10^{12}	1.54×10^{13}	—	3.21×10^3
2320	3.18×10^{14}	8.85×10^{10}	3.36×10^{11}	—	8.14×10^3
2700	6.19×10^{12}	2.95×10^9	2.00×10^{10}	—	1.68×10^4

rhodium gauze catalyst, at 850 to 930°C and with a reaction time of 1×10^{-4} sec. Nitric oxide yields are in excess of 95 per cent. The conversion efficiency to nitric oxide is, however, a function of the catalyst composition and arrangement, temperature, pressure, gas flow rate, etc.[10, 70]

FACTORS AFFECTING NITRIC OXIDE YIELD

Figure 7.1 shows the effect of catalyst composition on nitric oxide yield. The addition of rhodium to platinum in all proportions up to at least 50 per cent is beneficial to catalyst performance. Most of the improvement is, however, associated with the addition of the first 10 per cent rhodium (Figure 7.1). Platinum-rhodium catalysts have been found to give low metal losses and high capacities under operating conditions. Other alloys and catalyst systems have also been investigated but have not been used commercially to any appreciable extent.[37, 49]

Nitric oxide yield increases as temperature is increased (Figure 7.2). The optimum temperature for any given catalyst is a function of gas flow rate. The greater the gas velocity the higher the temperature at which maximum yield is obtained (Figure 7.3).

Early data[43, 49] obtained with platinum catalysts indicated that increased pressures resulted in decreased nitric oxide yields. Laboratory scale data[10, 49] obtained with platinum-rhodium catalysts showed little or no effect of pressure. Atroshchenko[10] investigated the effect of pressure and the number of catalyst screens on nitric oxide yield. Over a 10 to 50 atm range, yield

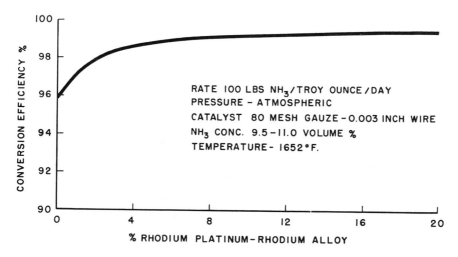

Figure 7.1. Effect of catalyst composition on ammonia conversion efficiency.

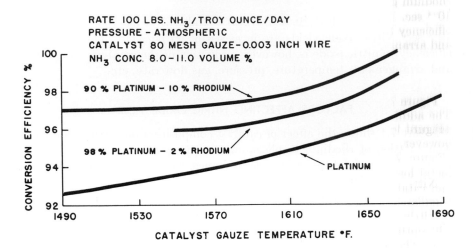

Figure 7.2. Effect of catalyst composition and temperature on ammonia conversion efficiency.

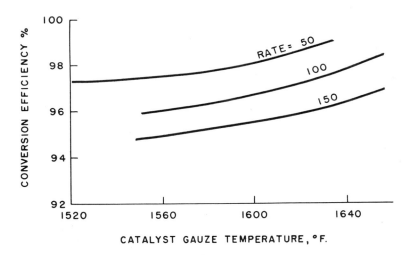

Figure 7.3. Effect of temperature and gas flow rate on ammonia conversion efficiency.

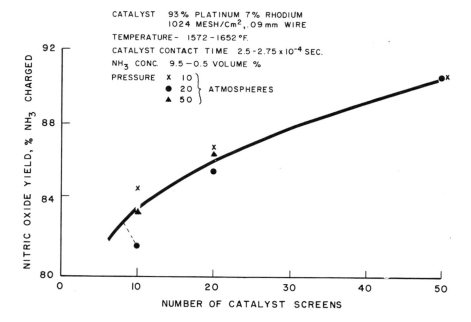

Figure 7.4. Effect of reactor pressure and number of catalyst screens on nitric oxide yield.

was practically independent of pressure, but increased somewhat as the number of catalyst screens was increased (Figure 7.4). Atroshchenko's low over-all yields were the result of preliminary decomposition of ammonia on the reaction vessel walls.

Although laboratory data indicate that the efficiency of ammonia oxidation should not be influenced by pressure, the maximum plant yield is known to decrease with increased pressure. However, under appropriate operating conditions and with improved burner designs pressure acid plants should operate at yields comparable to those obtained at atmospheric pressure.[78] Increased pressures while not significantly affecting nitric oxide yield almost proportionately increase the amount of ammonia that can be oxidized per unit of catalyst.

The effect of catalyst contact time and reactor residence time on nitric oxide yield is shown in Table 7.2. The reactor residence time was varied independently of the catalyst contact time by changing the number of catalyst screens. Since the reactor volume is practically independent of these changes a reduction in residence time corresponds to an increase in gas velocity. As shown in Table 7.2 nitric oxide yield increases with de-

Catalyst Contact Time, sec. $\times 10^4$	Reactor Residence Time, sec.	Ammonia Oxidized, lb/troy oz. pt/day	Nitric Oxide Yield, Per Cent NH₃* Oxidized
4.6	0.28	145	82.1
2.74	0.17	241	84.6
1.83	0.11	301	85.7
1.22	0.076	452	83.3
1.96	0.061	279	90.2
1.83	0.023	320	91.8

* Reactor Conditions: 860–900°C, 10 atm, 9.4 ± 0.5 volume per cent NH₃ in air and 93 pt-7Rh catalyst screens.

creased residence time but is not greatly affected by variations in catalyst contact time.

The improvement in nitric oxide yield noted with increasing gas flow rates can stem from several sources. Andrussow[4, 5] indicates that back diffusion of nitric oxide into the gas stream in front of the catalyst occurs at low flow rates and results in the formation of some nitrogen dioxide, which then reacts with ammonia to form nitrogen:

$$4NH_3 + 3NO_2 \rightarrow 7/2N_2 + 6H_2O \qquad (7.6)$$

Increased flow rates minimize the possibility of countercurrent diffusion of the reaction products which results in higher nitric oxide yields. The increase in yield with higher linear gas velocities could also be the result of the increased rate of transport of oxygen to the catalyst surface and the more rapid carry-off of the desorbed products.[8, 39, 65]

In addition to losses occurring during oxidation another source of possible yield loss is the reactions in which the final products take part. At high linear gas velocities about 10 to 15 per cent of the ammonia passes through the first catalyst gauze unreacted.[8, 11] Atroshchenko[11] studied the change in composition of the ammonia oxidation products between two widely separated gauzes. The nitric oxide content of the gas decreased between the screens, and the drop became more pronounced with increasing flow rate. No change was noted in nitric oxide content after the second screen. The decrease in nitric oxide content was attributed to the dissociation of nitric oxide to oxygen and nitrogen, or more likely the reaction of ammonia and nitric oxide to form nitrogen:

$$2NO \rightleftharpoons N_2 + O_2 \qquad (7.7)$$

$$4NH_3 + 6NO \rightleftharpoons 5N_2 + 6H_2O \qquad (7.8)$$

Data obtained by Dixon and Longfield[37] with less widely separated gauzes showed no effect on product yield. Under conditions where the residence time between catalyst screens is relatively short the reaction of nitric oxide with ammonia or the dissociation of nitric oxide should not have any significant effect on yield. Atroshchenko's data clearly indicates the nitric oxide is formed on the catalyst surface only.

REACTION MECHANISM

The catalytic oxidation of ammonia to yield nitric oxide is believed to require preliminary chemisorption of the oxygen by the catalyst.[39] Since the rate of ammonia oxidation is so extremely rapid, it requires that almost every collision between ammonia and the catalyst result in reactions which lead to the formation of nitric oxide. The absence of chemisorbed oxygen on the catalyst surface will lead to reactions that form nitrogen. Zawadzki[87] insisted that the chemisorbed oxygen involved in the reaction must be dissociated into atomic oxygen. Zawadzki reasons that the reaction with adsorbed molecular oxygen would be too endothermic to demonstrate such high efficiency.

Some investigators[81, 82, 83] have suggested that the reaction occurs by a heterogeneous-homogeneous mechanism. Others[12, 39] have concluded that the reaction is purely homogeneous. A number of reaction mechanisms have been postulated and all are based on the formation of some intermediate product.[53] Andrussow[6, 7] developed a reaction mechanism based on the formation of nitroxyl (HNO) as an intermediate product, while Zawadzki[87] and Raschig[72, 73] postulated that the reaction proceeds through the formation of an imide (NH). Epshtein[39] has suggested that ammonia and adsorbed oxygen react to form an activated complex which decomposed directly into nitric oxide and water. Bodenstein[17, 18] and Krauss[63, 64] formulated a mechanism based upon the formation of hydroxylamine (NH_2OH) as an intermediate. The reaction proceeding in the following manner:

$$NH_3 + O \rightarrow NH_2OH \tag{7.9}$$

$$NH_2OH + O_2 \rightarrow HNO_2 + H_2O \tag{7.10}$$

$$HNO_2 \rightarrow NO + OH \tag{7.11}$$

$$2OH \rightarrow H_2O + O \tag{7.12}$$

Regardless of which intermediate product is formed all of the proposed mechanisms include the reaction of chemisorbed oxygen with ammonia to form a product which then further reacts to yield nitric oxide and water.

In summary, the following conclusions may be drawn with regard to the oxidation of ammonia over a platinum-rhodium catalyst:

(1) Nitric oxide yield is improved by alloying the platinum catalyst with rhodium.

(2) Increased temperatures improve nitric oxide yields. The optimum temperature for a given catalyst increases with increasing gas flow rate.

(3) Increased reaction pressures increase almost proportionately the amount of ammonia that can be oxidized per unit mass of catalyst. Nitric oxide yield should not be significantly affected by increased pressures.

(4) Increased gas velocities result in increased nitric oxide yields.

(5) Ammonia and chemisorbed oxygen react on the catalyst surface to form an intermediate product which further reacts to yield nitric oxide and water.

(6) Under normal operating conditions the reaction of nitric oxide with ammonia or the dissociation of nitric oxide do not occur to any appreciable extent.

Nitric Oxide Oxidation

In nitric acid manufacture nitric oxide oxidation is of importance for two reasons: (1) The nitric oxide produced by ammonia oxidation must be completely converted to nitrogen dioxide before being fed to the absorption system and (2) the nitric oxide liberated during absorption by the reaction of nitrogen dioxide and water must be reoxidized.

Figures 7.5 and 7.6 show the relationship between the equilibrium constant, k_p, temperature, and the fraction of nitric oxide oxidized to nitrogen dioxide for the reaction:

$$NO + \tfrac{1}{2}O_2 \rightleftharpoons NO_2 \tag{7.13}$$

The relationships shown in Figures 7.5 and 7.6 were based on a total system pressure of 105 psig and a nonequilibrium gas mixture containing 9.5 mole per cent nitric oxide and 5.8 mole per cent oxygen, the remainder of the gas consisting of nitrogen and water vapor, which were assumed to act as diluents. Values of the equilibrium constant as a function of temperature are tabulated in Table 7.3.

The oxidation of nitric oxide has been of considerable interest for many years because of both its technical importance and unique characteristics. Kinetically, the reaction is third order and, in addition, its reaction rate constant decreases with increasing temperature. Bodenstein[16, 20] studied the kinetics of nitric oxide oxidation and found that the reaction was homogeneous and could be described by the following rate equation:

$$2NO + O_2 \xrightarrow[k_r]{k_f} 2NO_2$$

$$\frac{-d(NO)}{dt} = k_f(NO)^2(O_2) - k_r(NO_2)^2$$

(7.14)

Kornfield and Klinger[60] confirmed the values of the reaction rate constants obtained by Bodenstein while Hasche and Patrick[52] and Rao and Hougen[71] obtained somewhat higher values for the homogeneous reaction velocity constant. Figure 7.7 is a plot of the reaction rate constant as a function of temperature. The reaction being third order, pressure exerts a significant effect on the rate of reaction.[43, 71] The time required to achieve a given conversion decreases with the square of the pressure.

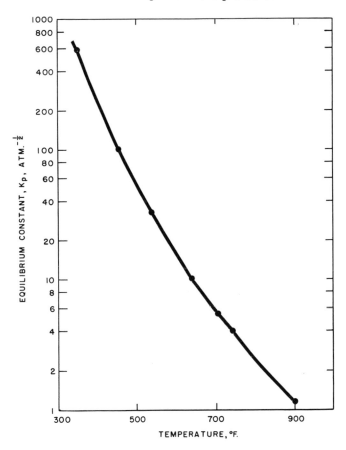

Figure 7.5. Equilibrium constant *vs* temperature.

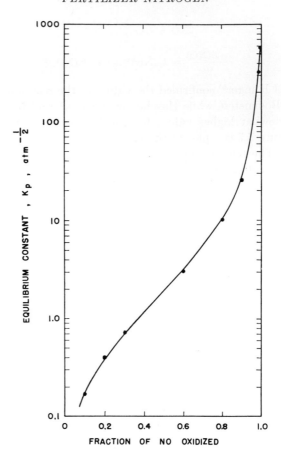

Figure 7.6. Equilibrium constant *vs* fraction of nitric oxide oxidized at equilibrium.

TABLE 7.3. EQUILIBRIUM CONSTANT FOR THE REACTION $NO + \frac{1}{2} O_2 \rightarrow NO_2$[16, 20, 48]

Temperature, °F	Equilibrium Constant, K_p, atm$^{-1/2}$
35	9.42×10^6
80	1.19×10^6
170	4.61×10^4
260	3.95×10^3
350	7.24×10^2
530	35.2
710	5.10
890	1.22

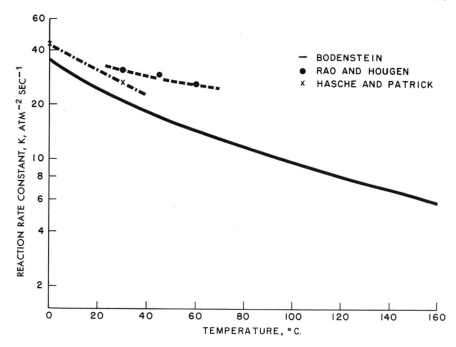

Figure 7.7. Rate constant for the reaction $2NO + O_2 \rightarrow 2NO_2$.

A number of theories have been advanced to explain the unusual nature of the reaction. Bodenstein,[16, 20] Tolman[79] and Kassel[58, 59] all attempted to account for the negative temperature coefficient of the reaction by the collision theory. Bodenstein suggested that the duration of collisions was shorter at higher temperatures and the possibility of third order collisions, therefore, less likely. The occurrence of consecutive bimolecular reactions has also been suggested as possible explanation for the peculiar characteristics of the reaction. Bodenstein,[15] on the basis of the work by Johnson and Weimer,[57] concluded that the reaction proceeded by means of two successive reactions which involved the formation of the temporary complex $(NO)_2$

$$2NO \rightleftharpoons (NO)_2 K_{eq} \text{ (rapid equilibrium)} \tag{7.15}$$

$$(NO)_2 + O_2 \rightarrow 2NO_2 k_r \text{ (rate determining)} \tag{7.16}$$

the following equation representing the rate of the over-all reaction:

$$\frac{-d(NO)}{dt} = k_r K_{eq}(NO)^2 (O_2) \tag{7.17}$$

The concentration of the complex was assumed to decrease with increasing temperature. The decrease in concentration of the complex results in a lower value of the equilibrium constant, K_{eq}, which more than offsets the increase in the reaction rate constant, k_r, with temperature, the over-all reaction thus having a negative temperature coefficient. Foerster[46] and more recently Treacy and Daniels[80] have suggested a similar mechanism but based on the formation of the temporary complex NO_3. From the standpoint of the various theories which have been postulated, the formation of some sort of an intermediate complex appears to provide the most plausible explanation for the third order nature and negative temperature coefficient of the reaction.

Considerable speculation has arisen as to whether the oxidation of nitric oxide is truly homogeneous. Several investigators[14, 52, 75] have maintained that the reaction rate is affected by the condition of the reactor surface in the presence of water vapor or other gases. The homogeneous or heterogeneous nature of the reaction is still a subject of considerable controversy.

Nitrogen Dioxide Absorption

The nitrogen compounds of major interest in absorption are nitric oxide, nitrogen dioxide, dinitrogen tetroxide, nitrogen trioxide (N_2O_3), nitric acid, and nitrous acid. The essential chemical reactions which occur during the absorption of nitrogen oxides from mixtures may be written as follows:

$$2NO_2 + H_2O \rightarrow HNO_3 + HNO_2 \tag{7.18}$$

$$2HNO_2 \rightarrow H_2O + NO + NO_2 \tag{7.19}$$

$$3NO_2 + H_2O(l) \rightleftharpoons 2HNO_3(aq) + NO \tag{7.20}$$

$$2NO + O_2 \rightarrow 2NO_2 \tag{7.21}$$

$$2NO_2 \rightleftharpoons N_2O_4 \tag{7.22}$$

Reaction 20 represents the over-all reaction when nitrogen dioxide is brought to equilibrium with liquid water and is obtained by the addition of reactions 18 and 19. The equilibrium constant for reaction 20 is given by:

$$K = \frac{P_{NO}\, P^2_{HNO_3}}{P^3_{NO_2}\, P_{H_2O}} = K_1 \times K_2 \tag{7.23}$$

where $K_1 = P_{NO}/P^3_{NO_2}$ and $K_2 = P^2_{HNO_3}/P_{H_2O}$. Values of K_1 have been determined by Abel Schmidt and Stein,[1] Burdick and Freed,[21] Chambers and Sherwood,[24] Epshtein,[38] and Denbigh and Prince.[36] Figure 7.8 shows

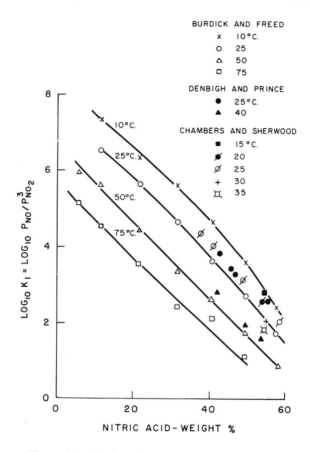

Figure 7.8. Nitric acid-NO-NO₂ equilibrium as a function of temperature.

the relationship between acid concentration and K_1 at various temperatures. Carberry[22] has correlated the equilibrium data in terms of dinitrogen tetroxide rather than nitrogen dioxide. The equilibrium data, when correlated in this manner, are temperature independent (Figure 7.9). The equilibrium constant for the dimerization or polymerization of nitrogen dioxide is tabulated in Table 7.4.

The over-all equilibrium constant, K, depends upon the partial pressures of nitric acid and water as well as the ratio $(P_{NO}/P^3_{NO_2})$. The nitric acid and water partial pressure have been measured a number of times; however, Forsythe and Giauque[47] indicate that they are unreliable. Table 7.5 is a tabulation of the equilibrium constant calculated by Forsythe and Giauque from thermodynamic data.

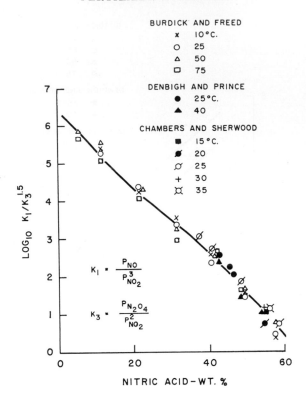

Figure 7.9. Nitric acid-NO-N$_2$O$_4$ equilibrium.

TABLE 7.4. EQUILIBRIUM CONSTANT FOR THE REACTION $2NO_2 \rightleftharpoons N_2O_4$[19, 34]

Temperature, °F	Equilibrium Constant, K_{atm}
48	26.80
84	5.13
116	1.39
175	0.414
230	0.204
266	0.168

Sherwood and Pigford,[74] Chilton,[34] and Wenner[86] have illustrated the calculations required in predicting the theoretical performance of a system for the absorption of nitrogen oxides in water. Ermenc[42] has put the required equilibrium data in graphical and nomographical form which greatly simplifies these calculations.

TABLE 7.5. EQUILIBRIUM CONSTANT FOR THE REACTION $3NO_2(g) + H_2O(g) \rightarrow$ $2HNO_3(g) + NO(g)$[47]

T °K	K_{atm}	T °K	K_{atm}
275	3.78×10^{-2}	350	1.01×10^{-3}
293.1	1.37×10^{-2}	400	1.87×10^{-4}
298.1	1.05×10^{-2}	450	4.36×10^{-5}
300	9.51×10^{-3}	500	1.65×10^{-5}

EFFECT OF TEMPERATURE AND PRESSURE

Low temperature operation benefits absorption. There are several reasons for this beneficial effect. The oxidation of nitric oxide has, as already noted, a negative temperature coefficient, and the reaction takes place more rapidly at low temperatures. At low temperatures the equilibrium in the gas phase shifts from nitrogen dioxide to dinitrogen tetroxide and the solubility of dinitrogen tetroxide in nitric acid is also increased. This results in a higher dinitrogen tetroxide concentration at the liquid-gas interface and more rapid transfer across the liquid film. In addition, Eq. 7.20 is reversible and increasing temperature favors nitric acid decomposition. Low temperatures retard the liquid phase reactions of Eqs. 7.18 and 7.19; however, these reactions are rapid in dilute solution. The net result is that low temperature operation is beneficial to absorber performance.

Increased pressures also result in improved absorber performance. The rate of nitric oxide oxidation increases with increased pressure. In addition, the rate of physical absorption increases with increased pressure and the chemical equilibrium also shifts, making higher acid strengths possible.

Atroshchenko[10] studied the effect of pressure, over a 10 to 50 atm range, on the rate of formation of nitric acid during the cooling of nitrous gases. As shown in Figure 7.10 the concentration of the nitric acid increases with increased total pressure and increased cooler residence time. Figure 7.11 relates the variation in the concentration of nitric acid in the condensate to the ammonia conversion efficiency and the per cent absorption of nitrogen dioxide. It is based on the assumption of complete condensation of water vapor from the gas stream, an assumption which is close to reality for systems operating under pressure. At higher pressures it is possible to produce an acid in excess of 70 per cent concentration; however, the gas stream will still contain a significant amount of nitrogen oxides (Figure 7.11). A system which produces nitric acid in a cooler-condenser would necessarily involve some additional means for recovery of the remaining nitrogen oxides. In the following equation:

$$NH_3 + 2O_2 \rightarrow NO + \tfrac{3}{2} H_2O + \tfrac{3}{4} O_2 \rightarrow HNO_3 + H_2O \quad (7.24)$$

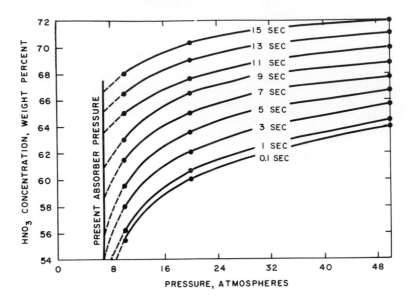

Figure 7.10. Nitric acid concentration *vs* pressure.

only one third of the water of reaction is required for the production of 100 per cent nitric acid. The bulk of the water is condensed on cooling of the nitrous gases, with the resulting formation of a dilute nitric acid. In this manner the partial pressure of the nitrogen oxides being fed to the absorber is decreased, resulting in poorer absorption efficiency. Atroshchenko and Yastrebenetskii evaluated the use of high speed condensers as a means of lowering the nitric acid concentration in the condensate and increasing the partial pressure of the nitrogen oxides in the absorber feed gas. Their work which was conducted at or near atmospheric pressure showed that the concentration, C, of the acid produced on condensation could be related to the cooler residence time, T, in seconds in the following manner:

$$C = 8.90\ T + 0.4 \qquad (7.25)$$

Figures 7.12 and 7.13 relate the percentage of the water condensed and the power required per ton of acid to the time of passage through the condenser.

REACTION MECHANISM

The problem of determining the mechanism by which nitrogen oxides are removed from gaseous mixtures by chemical reaction with water is not

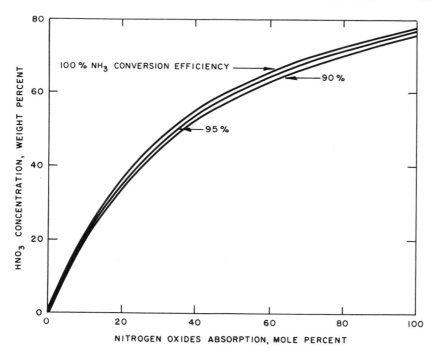

Figure 7.11. Nitric acid concentration in relation to ammonia conversion efficiency and nitrogen oxides absorption.

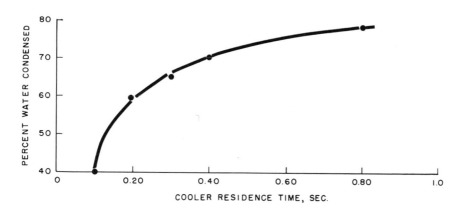

Figure 7.12. Per cent water condensed *vs* cooler residence time.

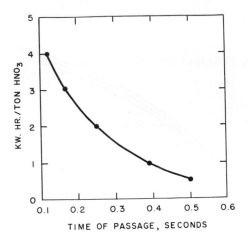

Figure 7.13. Power consumption *vs* time
of passage through condenser.

a simple one, as evidenced by the extensive literature on the subject. The
process has been studied in batch reactors,[25, 67] wetted-wall columns,[23, 25, 35,
36, 66, 85] bubble-cap towers,[68] sieve trays,[3] water jets,[62] and venturi atomizers.[2]
From the literature it is apparent that there has been disagreement on:
(1) what the rate controlling step is in the process, and (2) whether or not
a homogeneous vapor-phase reaction occurs between nitrogen dioxide and
water.

Chambers and Sherwood[25] used a batch absorption vessel and a wetted-
wall column to study the absorption of nitrogen dioxide from nitrogen-
nitrogen dioxide mixtures into caustic and acid solutions. Chambers and
Sherwood concluded that gas-film diffusion was the rate-controlling step
in the absorption process and that vapor-phase reaction occurred between
nitrogen dioxide and water.

Denbigh and Prince[36] and Caudle and Denbigh[23] used a wetted-wall
column to study the absorption of nitrogen dioxide-nitric oxide mixtures
from nitrogen using water, nitric acid, sodium hydroxide and calcium
chloride solutions as the absorbing media. They concluded that the rate
of absorption is controlled by the liquid-phase reaction between dinitrogen
tetroxide and water. The rate data were correlated by the following equation:

$$\frac{d(N_2O_4)}{dt} = k \left[(N_2O_4) - C(N_2O_4)^{1/4} (NO)^{1/2} \right] \tag{7.26}$$

where C is a constant evaluated from the equilibrium data for the reaction. In the absence of nitric oxide the rate of the reaction was directly proportional to the concentration of dinitrogen tetroxide in the bulk-gas stream, and decreased rapidly with increasing temperature and acid concentration. These investigators found no evidence of a gas-phase reaction.

Peters, Ross, and Klein[68] used a bubble-cap tower for absorbing nitrogen oxides from air and nitrogen into water and nitric acid solutions and concluded that the chemical reaction between dinitrogen tetroxide and water in the gas phase was rate controlling.

Peters and Holman[66] used a wetted-wall column to study the effect of temperature on the absorption of nitrogen oxides in water, sodium hydroxide, and sodium chloride solutions. They concluded that both liquid- and gas-phase reactions occur and that the rate of absorption is controlled by these reactions. The rate of absorption was proportional to the dinitrogen tetroxide concentration in the gas phase and decreased rapidly with increasing temperature.

Wendel and Pigford[85] studied the rate of absorption in a short wetted wall column and concluded that the controlling mechanism was the homogeneous liquid-phase reaction of dinitrogen tetroxide and water. The absorption rate was observed to decrease with increasing temperature and to be a linear function, from 77 to 104°F, of the concentration of dinitrogen tetroxide in the gas phase. Wendel and Pigford discussed at length the evidence indicating the existence of a gas-phase reaction and concluded that it was mostly indirect, and that a gas-phase reaction does not occur.

Peters and Koval[67] and Koval and Peters[61] studied the absorption of nitrogen dioxide in an agitated reactor and the absorption of nitrogen dioxide-nitric oxide mixtures in a wetted-wall column. They concluded that in an agitated reactor (due to increased gas-liquid contact area and time) nitrogen oxides are removed more efficiently than in typical bubble-cap or wetted-wall units. Because improvement in mass transfer conditions places more emphasis on chemical reaction rates as limiting factors, absorption efficiencies decrease as the NO_2 concentration in the entering gas decreases. They also concluded that N_2O_3 reactions play a major role in the controlling mechanism for aqueous removal of gaseous nitrogen oxides in this type of system. The wetted-wall studies confirmed the hypothesis that NO influences both mechanisms and kinetics of the absorption process. A fairly complex mechanism was suggested involving not only reaction of N_2O_4 with H_2O , but also forward and reverse reactions of N_2O_3 with H_2O.

Dekker, Snoeck, and Kramers[35] used a wetted-wall column to study the absorption of nitrogen dioxide from nitrogen into water. They concluded that diffusion of nitrogen dioxide-nitrogen tetroxide across the gas film, followed by solution of dinitrogen tetroxide in water accompanied by its rapid hydrolysis was the rate controlling mechanism.

Andrew and Hanson[3] studied the absorption of nitrous gases into water on a sieve plate and derived rate equations for the several possible important mechanisms. The controlling mechanism was found to be dependent upon the gas composition. At high nitrogen dioxide concentrations in the gas, the controlling mechanism is the solution of dinitrogen tetroxide in the liquid followed by its rapid hydrolysis. At low nitrogen dioxide gas concentrations the mechanism is dependent on the nitric oxide-nitrogen dioxide ratio in the gas phase. When this ratio is <0.5, the controlling mechanism is the liquid film limited solution of nitrogen dioxide; while when the nitric oxide-nitrogen dioxide ratio is >5, the controlling mechanism is the absorption of nitrous acid followed by its liquid-phase decomposition. At intermediate concentrations Andrew and Hanson concluded that more than one absorption mechanism was important.

From the wealth of data on the absorption process the following conclusions may be drawn:

(1) Low temperatures result in improved absorber operation and performance.

(2) The rate of physical absorption is increased by increasing pressures and the equilibrium is shifted favorably making higher acid strengths possible.

(3) The rate of absorption is controlled by chemical reaction rates and not by diffusional resistances.

(4) A homogeneous gas-phase reaction between nitrogen tetroxide and water does not occur to any appreciable extent.

(5) The controlling mechanism is a function of gas composition. In the absence of nitric oxide the rate of absorption is controlled by the concentration of nitrogen tetroxide in the bulk gas phase.

NITRIC ACID MANUFACTURE

Ammonia-Oxidation Processes

Several different processes are available for the production of nitric acid by ammonia oxidation. Initially, ammonia oxidation processes were operated essentially under atmospheric pressure. Today's ammonia oxidation processes are operated either under pressure or by a combination of atmospheric oxidation and pressure absorption. These three basic processes are described below.

Atmospheric Pressure Process.[56, 77, 78] Figure 7.14 is a schematic

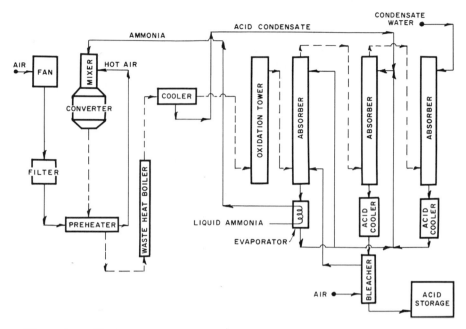

Figure 7.14. Nitric acid manufacture—atmospheric pressure ammonia oxidation process.

flowsheet of a typical atmospheric pressure plant. As shown in Figure 7.14 liquid ammonia is evaporated and mixed with air (9.5 to 11 volume per cent ammonia) before being fed to the converter. To maintain the proper temperature (1380 to 1470°F) in the catalyst zone the air is preheated, by combustion products, to between 300 and 390°F. The ammonia oxidation products flow from the air preheater through a waste-heat boiler and a series of cooler-condensers. The weak acid condensate formed in the coolers is fed to the appropriate absorption towers. The cooled nitrous gases pass through an oxidation tower and into a series of seven to ten absorbers. The gases flow through the absorbers countercurrently to increasingly dilute solutions of acid. In the final tower of the absorber train the gases are scrubbed with condensate water. Frequently, the final traces of nitrogen oxides are removed from the tail gases by alkali scrubbers to form sodium or calcium salts. Acid from the first tower is used to evaporate the ammonia after which it is returned to the top of the second tower. The product acid is removed from the second tower and fed to a bleaching tower. The acid leaving the bleaching tower is 45 to 52 per cent acid. The heat generated during absorption is removed by coolers after each absorption tower.

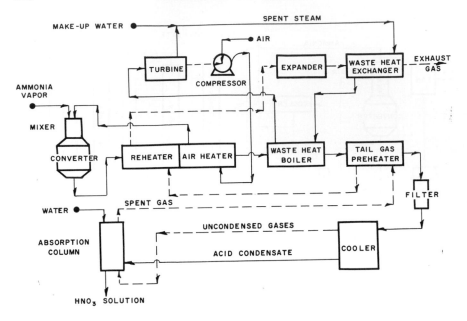

Figure **7.15**. Nitric acid manufacture-pressure ammonia oxidation.

Complete Pressure Process.[27, 69, 84] The DuPont pressure-ammonia-oxidation process is the process most widely used in the United States. Chilton[34] has reviewed the development of this process. Figure 7.15 is a flow diagram of one of the DuPont processes in current use. In this process air is compressed to 100 psig, preheated to 480 to 590°F and mixed with anhydrous ammonia which has been vaporized and superheated. The mixture is fed to a converter where it burns on a platinum-10 per cent rhodium gauze catalyst at about 1650°F. The combustion products leave the converter through a heat exchanger which heats both the waste gas from the absorption column and the incoming air. The partially cooled gases are then passed through a waste-heat boiler (which produces 150 psig steam), a tail-gas preheater, and a filter to remove traces of the platinum catalyst. The gases are then cooled and oxidized in a horizontal cascade cooler. The weak acid condensate from the cooler is fed to an appropriate section of the absorption column. The uncondensed gases are then fed to the base of the absorption column and flow upward countercurrently to water, the absorbing medium. Bleaching is accomplished in the body of the tower. The product acid withdrawn from the base of the tower has a strength of 57 to 60 per cent.

The spent gases leaving the absorber, consisting mostly of nitrogen, are recycled and heated by the combustion products in the tail-gas preheater

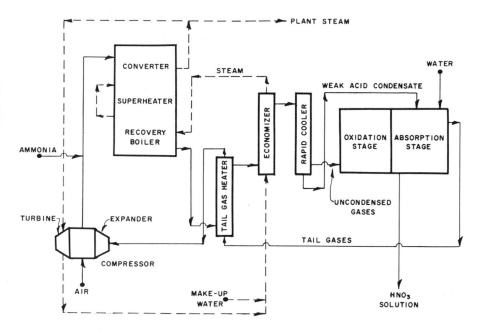

Figure 7.16. Nitric acid manufacture-intermediate pressure ammonia oxidation process.

and reheater. The heated gas drives an expander turbine and heats boiler feed water before being vented to the atmosphere. Catalytic combustion is used, when necessary, to eliminate toxic components from the tail gases.[30]

Recently, European chemical manufacturers have shifted their emphasis from atmospheric and combined atmospheric-pressure plants to systems operating at intermediate pressures. Figure 7.16 is a flow diagram of the Montecatini[29] process which operates a 40 psig and converter temperatures around 1500°F. In this process the combustion products are passed through a superheater and recovery boiler contained within the reactor shell. The lower reaction temperature eliminates the need for an air preheater. The gases flow from the reactor through a tail-gas heater, economizer, and a rapid cooler where most of the water vapor is removed. The weak acid condensate from the cooler is fed to the top of the absorption system. Absorption is carried out in a series of horizontal cascade absorbers with acid and gas flowing countercurrently. Recycling the hot tail gas through a recovery turbine enables the plant to operate at zero power input. Operation at intermediate pressures reportedly improves yield and decreases catalyst losses, as well as eliminating the need for an air preheater.

Atmospheric-Oxidation-Pressure Absorption.[43, 78] In this type of

TABLE 7.6. PROCESS REQUIREMENTS PER TON OF 100 PER CENT HNO₃[78]

Process	Ammonia, tons	Platinum (troy oz.)	Power, KW-hr	Steam Credit, tons	Cooling Water, gals	Acid Strength, % HNO₃
Atmospheric Pressure	0.290–0.300	0.0025	85–90	1.0	27,000	45–52
Complete Pressure	0.290–0.294	0.005–0.01	—*	0.8–1.25	30,000	57–60
Combined Atmospheric-Oxidation-Pressure Absorption	0.287–0.290	0.0025	—*	1.0	30,000	57–60

* Depends upon the power recovery scheme used.

plant the ammonia oxidation products leaving the converter at essentially atmospheric pressure are cooled and then compressed to pressures in the range of 30 to 105 psig. The compressed gases are passed through a condenser where a 55 to 62 per cent acid separates out. The condensate is pumped directly to a bleacher. The remaining nitrous gases are fed to a suitable absorption system. Condensate removed prior to compression is fed to the appropriate section of the absorption system. The tail gases leaving the absorption system are recycled, heated by the combustion products, and passed through an expander before being vented to the atmosphere.

Comparison of Ammonia-Oxidation Production Methods.[78] Table 7.6 compares the process requirements for the three basic ammonia oxidation schemes for nitric acid production. The number and variety of nitric acid processes available and in use indicates that there is no single optimum manufacturing method. Processes which operate at pressures greater than atmospheric pressure offer the advantages of decreased investment costs, higher absorption efficiency, and a higher strength product. Pressure systems have the disadvantages of somewhat lower oxidation yields, higher catalyst losses and greater power consumption. The newest pressure-ammonia-oxidation plants, however, operate with complete power recovery schemes.

Fauser Process

The nitric acid conventionally produced is too dilute for many industrial applications. It is generally concentrated by use of a dehydrating agent, usually sulfuric acid, to break the azeotropic mixture of water and 68 per cent nitric acid. A means of directly producing concentrated nitric acid would eliminate the requirement for dehydrating weak nitric acid and for reconcentration of the sulfuric acid used as a dehydrating agent. Some time ago, Fauser[44, 45] developed a process based on the pressure-temperature treatment of dilute nitric acid with oxygen and dinitrogen tetroxide in a high pressure autoclave to produce a 98 per cent acid. In the process, the reaction products from the atmospheric oxidation of ammonia with air are cooled and further oxidized. The water of reaction is removed as a weak acid condensate, and the remaining gas is compressed to a pressure of 8 atm and fed to a tower, refrigerated to 14°F, where the remaining nitrogen oxides are condensed as liquid dinitrogen tetroxide. Liquid dinitrogen tetroxide, oxygen, and dilute nitric acid are autoclaved for 4 hr at 158°F and 50 atm to produce a 98 per cent acid.

In recent years, Bamag-Meguin[26, 33] has extensively modified the Fauser process. These modifications permit the oxidation of ammonia either with air or oxygen, to produce 98 to 99 per cent nitric acid or low concentration acid by batch or continuous methods. Atroshchenko and Kargin[13] have recently published data on a batch autoclave operation which closely simulates the Fauser process.

Recent Developments in Nitric Acid Production

Wisconsin Process. The Wisconsin Process[40, 41] is based on heating air to a temperature where nitrogen fixation takes place. The process although proven to be technically feasible cannot economically compete with conventional processes. Figure 7.17 is a flow diagram for the process. Air is heated to reaction temperature, 4000°F, and then is rapidly cooled. The furnace effluent, which contains 1.8 to 1.9 per cent nitric oxide is heated and then fed into the regeneration section of the nitrogen dioxide absorber. Nitrogen dioxide which has been previously adsorbed is stripped by the hot gases from the silica gel. The hot gas stream then flows into drying towers where it strips the water from the downcoming silica gel. Water is removed from the gas stream in a cooler-condenser. The cooled gas is then fed back into the drying tower where the remainder of the water is removed by adsorption on silica gel. The weak acid condensate from the cooler is fed to the acid tower. The dried gas is filtered, passed through an oxidizer, which catalytically converts nitric oxide to nitrogen dioxide, cooled and fed to the nitrogen dioxide absorber where nitrogen dioxide is adsorbed on silica gel. The nitrogen dioxide removed from the lower section of the absorber may be condensed to form liquid dinitrogen tetroxide or blown to the acid tower to make 60 per cent acid.

Magnesium Nitrate Concentration Process.[32] A newly developed nitric acid concentrating process uses magnesium nitrate rather than sulfuric acid as the dehydrating agent. Figure 7.18 is a flow diagram for the process. An initial salt charge is made up by using magnesium carbonate

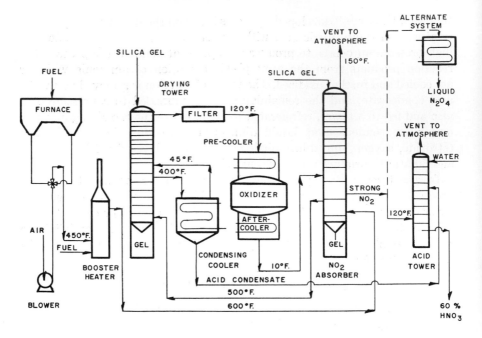

Figure 7.17. The Wisconsin Process for the production of nitric acid.

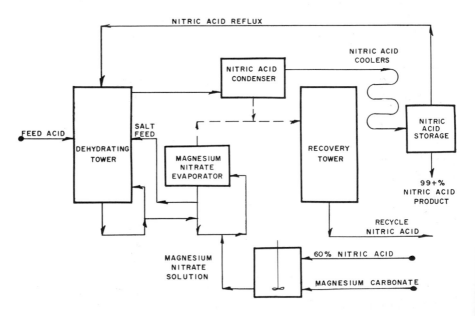

Figure 7.18. Magnesium nitrate nitric acid concentrating process.

and 60 per cent nitric acid. The charge is concentrated in an evaporator to about 72 per cent magnesium nitrate and is then fed to a tray distillation column. The salt solution which is at about a temperature of 212°F begins to pick up water from the acid which is fed to the column at about the same level. The acid solution is left at a concentration higher than the azeotrope and distills overhead. The 99 per cent acid is condensed, cooled, and some of the acid is returned to the column as reflux. Magnesium nitrate is withdrawn from the bottom of the tower at 338 to 356°F at a concentration of 55 to 70 per cent depending upon operating conditions. The salt solution is reconcentrated to 72 per cent magnesium nitrate. The Hercules Powder Company, developer of the process, claims that operating costs are about half those of sulfuric acid concentration processes, that investment is 30 to 40 per cent less, and that product yield and quality are slightly improved.

Nuclear Nitrogen Fixation.[28, 51] Yields of nitrogen oxides of 5 to 15 per cent have been reported by exposing compressed air to radiation from uranium-235. Nitrogen and oxygen molecules are ionized and decomposed by fission fragments as well as beta and gamma radiation. The preferred operating pressure is over 150 psi and the operating temperature is about 400°F. The uranium-235 is incorporated into a reactor-fuel matrix consisting of glass fibers.

The production cost for nitric acid by a process based upon nuclear nitrogen fixation would depend among other things on the efficiency of converting nuclear energy to chemical reaction energy.

REFERENCES

1. Abel, E., Schmidt, H., and Stein, M., *Z. Elektrochem.*, **36**, 692 (1930).
2. Anderson, L. B., and Johnstone, H. F., *A.I.Ch.E. Journal*, **1**, No. 2,135 (1955).
3. Andrew, S. P. S., and Hanson, D., *Chem. Eng. Sci.*, **14**, 105 (1961).
4. Andrussow, L., *Z. Angew. Chem.*, **39**, 321 (1926).
5. Andrussow, L., *Z. Angew. Chem.*, **40**, 166 (1927).
6. Andrussow, L., *Z. Angew. Chem.*, **63**, 21 (1951).
7. Andrussow, L., *Z. Angew. Chem.*, **41**, 205 (1928).
8. Applebaum, I. L., and Temkin, M. I., *J. Phys. Chem. (USSR)*, **22**, 179, 195 (1948).
9. Applebaum, I. L., and Temkin, M. I., *Doklady Akad. Nauk. (SSSR)*, **74**, 963 (1950).
10. Atroschenko, V. I., *J. Appl. Chem. (USSR)*, **19**, 1214 (1946).
11. Atroschenko, V. I., Zasorin, A. P., and Romanenko, E. E., *Trudy Kharkov Politech Inst. Im. V. I. Lenina* **26**, Ser. Khim. Tekhnol., No. 6, 63 (1959).
12. Atroschenko, V. I., and Yastrebenetskii, A. R., *J. Appl. Chem. (USSR)*, **26** (3), 251 (1953).
13. Atroschenko, V. I., and Kargin, S. I., "Nitric Acid Technology", 2nd Ed., Chap. 8, Moscow, State Scientific Publishing House, 1962.
14. Briner, E., Pfeiffer, W., and Malet, G., *J. Chem. Phys.*, **21**, 25 (1924).
15. Bodenstein, M., *Helv. Chim. Acta*, **18**, 743 (1935).
16. Bodenstein, M., *Z. Elektrochem.*, **24**, 183 (1918).
17. Bodenstein, M., *Z. Elektrochem.*, **41**, 466 (1935).
18. Bodenstein, M., *Z. Elektrochem.*, **47**, 501 (1941).
19. Bodenstein, M., and Lindner, P. Z., *Z. Physik-Chem.*, **100**, 68 (1922).

20. Bodenstein, M., and Lindner, P. Z., *Z. Physik-Chem.*, **100**, 105 (1922).
21. Burdick, C. L., and Freed, E. S., *J. Am. Chem. Soc.*, **43**, 518 (1921).
22. Carberry, J. J., *Chem. Eng. Sci.*, **9**, No. 4, 189 (1959).
23. Caudle, P. G., and Denbigh, K. G., *Trans. Faraday Soc.*, **49**, 39 (1953).
24. Chambers, F. S., and Sherwood, T. K., *J. Am. Chem. Soc.*, **59**, 316 (1937).
25. Chambers, F. S., and Sherwood, T. K., *Ind. Eng. Chem.*, **29**, 1415 (1937).
26. *Chem. Eng.*, **59**, 238 (1952).
27. *Chem. Eng.*, **63**, 274 (1956).
28. *Chem. Eng.*, **65**, 57 (1958).
29. *Chem. Eng.*, **65**, 56 (1958).
30. *Chem. Eng. News*, **34**, 4096 (1956).
31. *Chem. Eng. News*, **35**, 50 (1957).
32. *Chem. Eng. News*, **36**, 40 (1958).
33. *Chemical Week*, **83**, 67 (1958).
34. Chilton, T. H., *Chem. Eng. Prog. Monograph Series*, **56**, No. 3 (1960).
35. Dekker, W. A., Snoeck, E., and Kramers, H., *Chem. Eng. Sci.*, **11**, 61 (1959).
36. Denbigh, K. G., and Prince, A. J., *J. Chem. Soc. (London)*, 790 (1947).
37. Dixon, J. K., and Longfield, J. E., "Catalysis", Vol. 7, p. 281, New York, Reinhold, 1960.
38. Epshtein, D. A., *J. Gen. Chem. (USSR)*, **9**, 792 (1932).
39. Epshtein, D. A., *Doklady Akad. Nauk. (SSSR)*, **74**, 1101 (1950).
40. Ermenc, E. D., *Chem. Eng. Prog.*, **52**, 149 (1956).
41. Ermenc, E. D., *Chem. Eng. Prog.*, **52**, 488 (1956).
42. Ermenc, E. D., *Chem. Eng.*, **66**, 139 (1959).
43. Fauser, G., *Chem. and Met. Eng.*, **37**, 604 (1930).
44. Fauser, G., *Chem. and Met. Eng.*, **35**, 474 (1928).
45. Fauser, G., *Chem. and Met. Eng.*, **39**, 430 (1932).
46. Foerster, V. F., and Blich, J., *Z. Angew. Chem.*, **23**, 2017 (1910).
47. Forsythe, N. R., and Giauque, W. F., *J. Am. Chem. Soc.*, **64**, 48 (1942).
48. Giauque, W. F., and Kemp, J. D., *J. Chem. Phys.*, **6**, 40 (1938).
49. Handforth, S. L., and Tilley, J. N., *Ind. Eng. Chem.*, **26**, 1287 (1934).
50. Harrison, R. H., and Kobe, K. A., *Chem. Eng. Prog.*, **49**, 349 (1953).
51. Harteck, P., and Dondes, S., *Nucleonics*, **14**, 22 (1956).
52. Hasche, R. L., and Patrick, W. A., *J. Am. Chem. Soc.*, **47**, 1207 (1925).
53. Hoftijzer, P. J., *Chemische Weekbald*, **52**, 71 (1956).
54. Horner, K. C., Chemical and Rubber Ind. Rept. Chemical and Rubber Division, Business and Defense Services Adm., April 1957.
55. *Ind. Eng. Chem.*, **49**, 25A (1957).
56. Inskeep, G. C., and Henry, T. H., *Ind. Eng. Chem.*, **45**, 1386 (1953).
57. Johnson, H. L., and Weimer, H. R., *J. Am. Chem. Soc.*, **56**, 625 (1934).
58. Kassel, L. S., *J. Phys. Chem.*, **34**, 1777 (1930).
59. Kassel, L. S., "The Kinetics of Homogeneous Gas Reactions", p. 165, American Chemical Society Monograph 57, The Chemical Catalog Co., 1932.
60. Kornfeld, G., and Klinger, E., *Z. Physik. Chem.*, **4B**, 37 (1929).
61. Koval, E. J., and Peters, M. J., *Ind. Eng. Chem.*, **52**, 1011 (1960).
62. Kramers, H., Blind, M. P. F., and Snoeck, E., *Chem. Eng. Sci.*, **14**, 115 (1961).
63. Krauss, W., *Z. Physik Chem.*, **B39**, 83 (1938).
64. Krauss, W., and Neuhaus, A., *Z. Physik Chem.*, **B50**, 323 (1941).
65. Oele, A. P., "Chemical Reaction Engineering", p. 146, London, Pergamon Press, Ltd., 1957.
66. Peters, M. S., and Holman, J. L., *Ind. Eng. Chem.*, **47**, 2536 (1955).
67. Peters, M. S., and Koval, E. J., *Ind. Eng. Chem.*, **51**, 577 (1959).
68. Peters, M. S., Ross, C. P., and Klein, J. E., *A.I.Ch.E. Journal*, **1**, No. 1, 105 (1955).
69. *Petrol. Processing*, **12**, 117 (1957).

70. Polyakov, M. V., Urizko, V. I., and Galenko, N. P., *Zhur. Fiz. Khim.*, **25**, 1460 (1951).
71. Rao, M. N., and Hougen, O. A., *Chem. Eng. Prog. Symposium Series*, **48**, No. 4 (1952).
72. Raschig, F., *Z. Angew. Chem.*, **40**, 1183 (1927).
73. Raschig, F., *Z. Angew. Chem.*, **41**, 207 (1928).
74. Sherwood, T. K., and Pigford, R. L., "Absorption and Extraction", p. 369, New York, McGraw-Hill, 1952.
75. Smith, J. H., *J. Am. Chem. Soc.*, **65**, 74 (1943).
76. Sorgenti, H. A., and Sachsel, G. F., *Ind. Eng. Chem.*, **52**, 101 (1960).
77. Spratt, D. A., *The Fertiliser Society Proceedings*, No. 50 (1958).
78. Strelzoff, S., *Chem. Eng.*, **63**, 170 (1956).
79. Tolman, R. C., "Statistical Mechanics", New York Chemical Catalog Co. (1927).
80. Treacy, J. C., and Daniels, F. J., *J. Am. Chem. Soc.*, **77**, 2033 (1955).
81. Vainshtein, F. M., and Polyakov, M. V., *J. Phys. Chem. (USSR)*, **15**, 164 (1941).
82. Vladov, D., *Doklady Akad. Nauk. (SSSR)*, **109**, 561 (1956).
83. Vladov, D., *Fiz. Mat. Fak*, **53**, No. 3, 23 (1958–9).
84. Warner, F. E., *Ind. Chemist*, **17**, (1947).
85. Wendel, M. M., and Pigford, R. L., *A.I.Ch.E. Journal*, **4**, No. 3, 249 (1958).
86. Wenner, R. R., "Thermochemical Calculations", p. 277, New York, McGraw-Hill, 1941.
87. Zawadzki, J., *Discussions Faraday Soc.*, **8**, 140 (1950).

8

Chemistry and Production of Coke Oven Ammonium Sulfate

FRANK SEDLACK

United States Steel Corporation

Ammonium sulfate is formed by reacting ammonia with sulfuric acid according to the following reaction:

$$H_2SO_4 + 2NH_3 \rightarrow (NH_4)_2SO_4 \tag{8.1}$$

The pure salt is a white crystalline material containing 25.77 per cent ammonia. The commercial salt varies in color from white to grayish tan and contains 25.0 to 25.6 per cent ammonia.

RECOVERY OF AMMONIA

The ammonia formed during the high temperature carbonization of bituminous coal exists in both the liquor and gas that form part of the volatile products. The recovery of this ammonia can be accomplished by three different methods: (1) The direct process in which the fixed gases, after tar removal, are passed through a spray-type absorber containing a solution of sulfuric acid to fix the ammonia as ammonium sulfate; (2) the indirect process in which the ammonia is extracted from the gas by scrubbing with water and then removed from the extract by steam distillation and treatment with a calcium hydroxide solution (milk of lime), after which the vapor is passed through a spray-type ammonia absorber containing a solution of sulfuric acid, and (3) the semidirect process in which the ammonia in the liquor produced during the carbonizing process is removed by steam distillation and milk-of-lime treatment and introduced to the gas stream, the gas containing all of the ammonia then being passed through a spray-type absorber containing a solution of sulfuric acid.

128

SEMIDIRECT PROCESS

Of these processes, the semidirect is the most extensively used and therefore will be discussed in some detail. The ammonia present in the liquor produced during the carbonizing process is classified as "free" and "fixed". The free ammonia is in a form which is readily dissociated by heat, such as ammonium carbonate and ammonium sulfide and is usually present in approximately 1 to 1.5 grams per liter.

The fixed ammonia is in a form which requires the presence of an alkali such as milk of lime to effect the release of the ammonia from the compound in which it is present, such as ammonium chloride, ammonium sulfate, ammonium thiocyanate, and ammonium ferrocyanide. The ammonia in this form is usually present in approximately 3 to 4 grams per liter. The operation to recover this ammonia is carried out in an ammonia still.

AMMONIA STILL

In the processing of the ammonia liquor, a constant head tank supplies a uniform flow of liquor by gravity, to the top of the "free leg" of the ammonia still (Figure 8.1), and this liquor passes down the column over a series of plates equipped with bubble caps and overflow pipes. This liquor is heated to approximately 212°F by an upward flow of steam which dissociates the unstable ammonium salts according to the following reaction:

$$(NH_4)_2CO_3 + Heat = 2NH_3 + H_2O + CO_2 \qquad (8.2)$$

These vapors leave the top of the free leg at a temperature of 158°F to 167°F and pass into a dephlegmator to partially cool the vapors and remove excess water which is returned to the still.

The vapor leaving the dephlegmator consists of ammonia which varies between 10 to 25 per cent in concentration with the balance consisting of water, some acidic gases, and neutral oils.

The liquor leaving the base of the free leg passes into the "lime leg" where it is treated with milk of lime containing up to 40 grams per liter of lime, depending upon the fixed ammonia content. The lime reacts with the fixed ammonium salts, of which ammonium chloride is predominant, according to the following reaction:

$$2NH_4Cl + Ca(OH)_2 \rightarrow 2NH_3 + {}_2H_2O + CaCl_2 \qquad (8.3)$$

The liquor then flows into the "fixed leg" which consists of a series of plates equipped with bubble caps and overflow pipes to provide effective stripping of the ammonia by a countercurrent flow of steam. The vapors

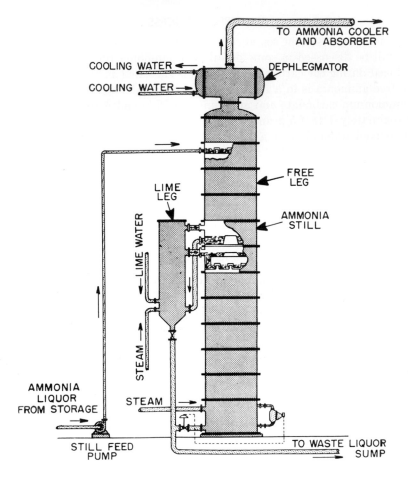

Figure 8.1. Ammonia still. (*Courtesy Koppers Company, Inc.*)

leaving the ammonia still are added to the gas stream, and the ammonia from both sources is recovered in the ammonia absorbers in a single operation.

REHEATER

The temperature of the coke-oven gas after leaving the tar precipitators, where residual tar is removed, is approximately 104°F to 108°F. The temperature is raised to approximately 130°F by passing the gas through a series of reheaters which are cylindrical holders containing steel tubes through which steam is circulated. This reheating is necessary to prevent condensation of the water vapor in the gas while passing through the ammonia-absorbing facilities.

AMMONIA ABSORBER

In the ammonia-absorbing facilities the ammonia-laden coke-oven gas enters the absorbers (Figure 8.2) near the bottom and is sprayed with a 3 to 6 per cent solution of sulfuric acid as it rises to the top of the absorber. The gas then flows through a pyridine absorber where it is sprayed again with a 10 to 12 per cent solution of sulfuric acid to convert the pyridine bases in the gas to pyridine sulfate according to the following reaction:

$$C_5H_5N + H_2SO_4 \rightarrow C_5H_5N \cdot H_2SO_4 \tag{8.4}$$

In some instances these absorber liquors are processed for the recovery of pyridine bases. The gas leaving the pyridine absorber is passed through an acid separator where entrained liquids are removed, after which the gas is prepared for light oil recovery.

As the dilute solution of sulfuric acid comes in contact with the counter-current flow of gas in the ammonia absorber, the ammonia in the gas chemically combines with the acid to form ammonium sulfate. The resulting solution drains to a crystallizer section from which it is recirculated to the absorber. A constant flow of 66° Baumé sulfuric acid is maintained to the absorber to replace the acid neutralized by the ammonia in the gas. After the solution becomes supersaturated, crystals of ammonium sulfate are precipitated in the crystallizer section and accumulated as a slurry in the bottom. A portion of the slurry is removed continuously from the crystallizer section and is pumped to a slurry tank where the salt settles and the liquor overflows to a liquor tank from which it is returned to the ammonia absorber.

The concentrated ammonium sulfate slurry is withdrawn from the bottom of the slurry tank and fed in batches or continuously to the centrifugal dryers. These dryers are arranged to perform the following sequence of operations automatically:

(1) rinse the dryer-basket screen with water,
(2) feed the slurry into the basket,
(3) centrifuge the slurry to free the crystals from the mother liquor,
(4) rinse the salt with water,
(5) neutralize the residual sulfuric acid with aqueous ammonia,
(6) remove the centrifuged salt from the basket, and
(7) discharge the salt onto a continuous conveyor.

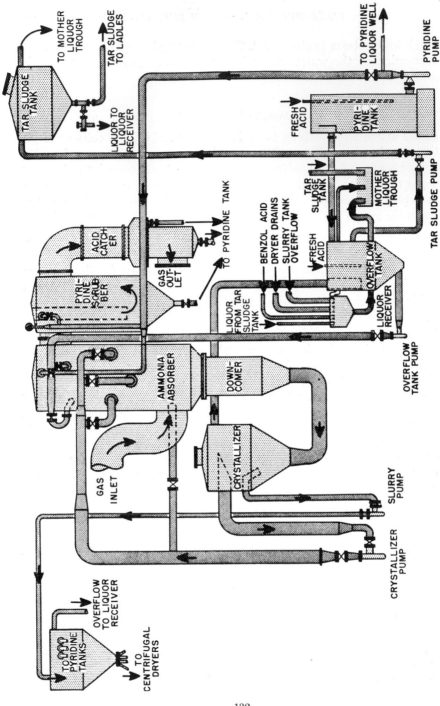

Figure 8.2. Ammonia absorber system. (Courtesy Otto Construction Corp.)

132

The mother liquor and the rinsings are returned to the liquor tank and recycled through the ammonia absorber. The centrifuged salt, containing 2 to 3 per cent moisture, is conveyed to a rotary-drum dryer where it comes in contact with a countercurrent flow of preheated air. This final drying reduces the moisture content of the ammonium sulfate to 0.1 per cent. The product directed to storage is neutral to a methyl orange indicator, free flowing, and noncaking.

The ammonium sulfate crystals produced in this manner are usually long and needle shaped in their original form, but break up into smaller particles during handling and transit. A typical chemical and screen analysis is shown in Table 8.1.

The size of the ammonium sulfate crystals can be increased by two different processes: (1) low differential controlled crystallization and (2) mechanical size enlargement by continuous compacting and granulation.

CRYSTAL CONTROL

In this process (Figure 8.3), the ammonia-laden gas is passed through a spray-type absorber over which is circulated a nearly saturated solution of ammonium sulfate containing about 6 per cent sulfuric acid. After leaving the absorber the solution is delivered to the solution circulating system of the crystallizer in which crystallization takes place by the combined cooling and concentration effects of evaporation under vacuum. By varying the circulating rate and the degree of concentration, the size range of the ammonium sulfate crystals can be controlled within narrow limits. As the crystals grow in size, they settle to the bottom of the suspension tank from which they are delivered to a slurry feed tank and from there to a centrifuge where the crystals are freed from the mother liquor, rinsed with water, and neutralized with aqueous ammonia. The product discharged from the

TABLE 8.1. TYPICAL ANALYSIS OF CONVENTIONAL AMMONIUM SULFATE

	% by Weight
Constituents	
Ammonia	25.53
Nitrogen	21.0
Moisture	0.1
Free Acid as H_2SO_4	nil
Screen Size (U.S. Standard)	
+6	0.0
−6 + 8	0.0
−8 + 30	22.0
−30	78.0

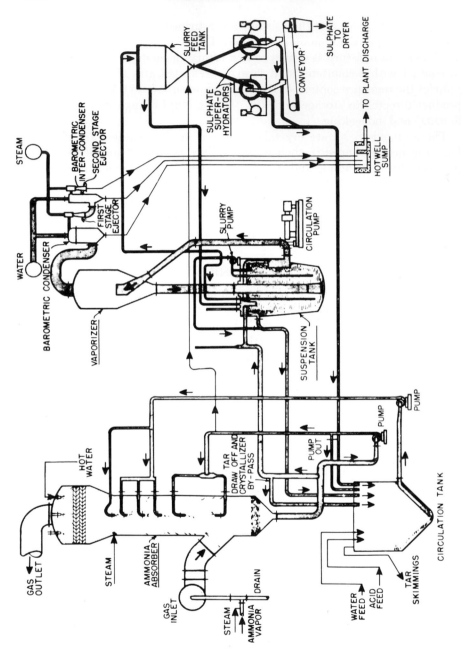

Figure 8.3. Ammonium sulfate crystallizer. (*Courtesy Wilputte Coke Oven Div. Allied Chemical Corp.*)

TABLE 8.2. TYPICAL ANALYSIS OF CRYSTAL CONTROLLED AMMONIUM SULFATE

	% by Weight
Constituents	
Ammonia..	25.53
Nitrogen..	21.0
Moisture..	0.1
Free Acid as H_2SO_4...........................	nil
Screen Size (U.S. Standard)	
+6...	0.0
−6 + 8...	1.0
−8 + 30..	97.0
−30..	2.0

centrifuge is delivered to a dryer where it is dried to a moisture content of 0.1 per cent. This product approximates the size and shape of rice, it is dust free, neutral to a methyl orange indicator, free flowing, and noncaking. A typical chemical and screen analysis is shown in Table 8.2.

GRANULATION

In the second process (Figure 8.4), fine ammonium sulfate is discharged from the centrifuge and delivered to a pair of compacting rolls which are horizontal steel rolls, 18 to 24 in. in diameter and 16 to 24 in. in effective length, rotating face to face and held together by hydraulically actuated pistons acting upon a set of high pressure bearings. The fine salt containing 2 to 3 per cent moisture is fed continuously, through a feed hopper, into the "nip" of the rolls from above. This material is drawn between the rotating rolls where the high pressure which is developed compacts and agglutinates the feed so that a continuous sheet of product about ⅛ in. thick is discharged from the bottom of the rolls. The compacted sheet is delivered by continuous conveyor to a dryer where the moisture is reduced to 0.1 per cent or less. The discharge from the dryer is conveyed to granulators which are serrated steel rolls about 10 in. in diameter and 42 in. long where the compacted product is reduced to a predetermined size. The discharge from the granulators is delivered to screens where the oversized and undersized material is removed. The oversized material is returned to the granulators for sizing and the undersized material is recycled through the compacting rolls. The screened product which is flat and irregular in shape, neutral to a methyl orange indicator, free flowing and noncaking, is sent to storage. A typical chemical and screen analysis is shown in Table 8.3.

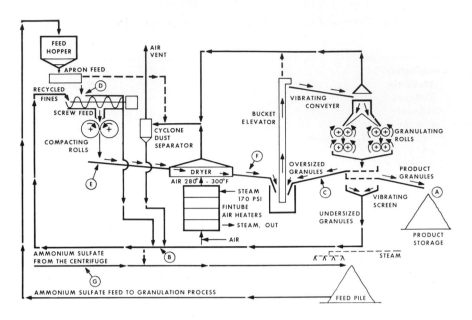

Figure 8.4. Process of granulation of ammonium sulfate.

TABLE 8.3. TYPICAL ANALYSIS OF GRANULATED AMMONIUM SULFATE

	% by Weight
Constituents	
Ammonia..	25.53
Nitrogen..	21.0
Moisture..	0.1
Free Acid as H_2SO_4..............................	nil
Screen Size (U.S. Standard)	
+6...	2.0
−6 + 8...	23.0
−8 + 30..	73.0
−30...	2.0

SATURATORS

The processes previously described for the production of coke-oven ammonium sulfate represent the more advanced methods for this type of recovery. Prior to the advent of the spray-type absorber, crystal control, and granulation, ammonia in coke-oven gas was and in some instances still is removed in an absorber referred to as a saturator (Figure 8.5). This fa-

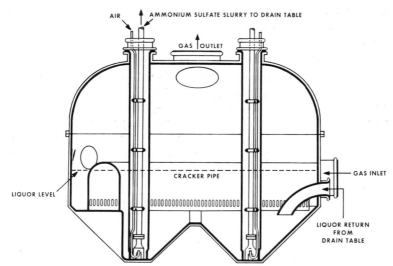

Figure 8.5. Saturator used prior to spray-type absorber.

cility is a large dome-shaped, cast-iron, lead-lined vessel. The ammonia-laden gas is admitted to the saturator through a distributor called a "cracker pipe," which in some designs runs completely around the inside circumference of the unit and has a cross section in the shape of a U. The bottom of the pipe is open, but the gas is discharged to H_2SO_4 through numerous vertical slots, located on each side of the pipe near the bottom. This arrangement is adopted to provide a large surface for direct contact between the ammonia and the dilute sulfuric acid. The salt precipitates and settles to the bottom of the unit when the saturator bath reaches a super-saturated condition. The salt is either siphoned from the bottom of the saturator or pumped to elevated drain tables from which it is charged to a centrifuge for removal of the mother liquor. The salt is rinsed with water, neutralized, and dried in rotary-type dryers. The liquor and rinsings are returned to the saturator. The acid concentration of the saturator bath is maintained at a constant level by periodic additions of 60° or 66° Baumé sulfuric acid.

CONCLUSION

Storage.   The dried ammonium sulfate made by these processes is conveyed to a well ventilated, weather-proof building where the temperature of the salt is allowed to come into equilibrium with the surrounding temperature prior to shipment in bulk or bags.

Yield. The yield of ammonium sulfate ranges from 15 to 27 lb per ton of coal, depending upon the type of coal carbonized and the carbonizing conditions.

Uses. The primary use of ammonium sulfate is as a nitrogen-supplying material for the manufacture of mixed fertilizers. Aside from economic considerations and the units of contained nitrogen, its main advantages for this purpose lie in its beneficial effect on the physical condition of the finished product. Ammonium sulfate is also used in the bulk blending of dry fertilizer materials, as well as for direct application to the soil before planting or side or top dressing to the growing crop. Small quantities of coke-oven ammonium sulfate are also used for industrial purposes, such as fireproofing, water treatment, fermentation, and synthetic fibers. Ammonium sulfate is discussed further in Chapter 11 along with other classic fertilizer salts.

9

Ammonium Phosphates and Ammonium Polyphosphates

CHRISTOPHER J. PRATT

International Fertilizer Development Corporation

Ammonium phosphates and fertilizers incorporating ammonium phosphate compounds are still exceeded in tonnage by salts such as ammonium sulfate and ammonium nitrate (see Chapter 10). However, ammonium phosphates and ammonium polyphosphates have been especially popular fertilizer materials in recent years and perhaps may eventually surpass most other ammonium salts in growth rate and tonnages utilized for fertilizer purposes.

Several reasons[49] account for their rapid acceptance. From an agricultural standpoint, ammonium phosphates contain both nitrogen and phosphorus in concentrated form. In fact, nitrogen and phosphorus content can approach 75 per cent of the total plant food in the case of crystalline diammonium phosphate. Furthermore, under many conditions, the assimilation of fertilizer phosphate is often increased by the presence of ammoniacal nitrogen, and vice versa.[23]

Another reason is that many ratios of N and P_2O_5 can be produced according to agronomic needs, and when required, complete compound fertilizers can be made by incorporating a potassium salt into the process stream. Most ammonium phosphate fertilizers can be manufactured in stable, crystalline or granular forms; in addition, they offer numerous advantages in cost of production, cost[40] of storage[40A] and transportation, ease of handling and application, plus almost total water solubility. These features make them particularly suitable for bulk blending.

According to a recent survey of the growth pattern of diammonium phosphate in USA made by Keim,[21] 32 ammonium phosphate plants were in operation or under construction during 1962, mostly for the production of

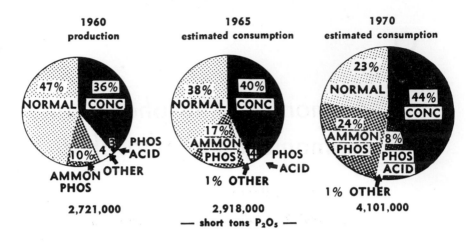

Figure 9.1. Phosphates, United States.

DAP in grades such as 21-53-0, 18-46-0, or 16-48-0. (Monoammonium phosphate was produced in a few plants only.) Wet-process phosphoric acid was used in all but six of the 32 plants reported. The rapid U. S. growth rate of ammonium phosphate fertilizers is indicated by an estimated increase from 285,000 short tons in 1960–61 to 325,000 tons in 1961–62, i.e., 14 per cent. During the 1959–1960 period the relative amounts of 18-46-0 and 16-48-0 used were about 27 and 73 per cent respectively. The estimated relative growth pattern of ammonium phosphate fertilizers according to Lockwood[25] is shown in Figure 9.1.

From a production viewpoint, ammonium phosphates and associated fertilizers offer considerable flexibility, since alternative sources of ammonia and phosphoric acid can be used, and in various combinations according to availability and cost. For example, in some plants synthetic anhydrous ammonia is reacted with relatively pure furnace-grade phosphoric acid to produce crystalline diammonium phosphate for use either alone or in mixtures containing potash and/or other materials. Alternatively, by-product ammonia from coke-oven plants and gas works can be used, when available.[37]

Similarly, either furnace-grade acid or wet-process phosphoric acid can be employed. However, wet-process acid contains impurities which make the production of crystalline ammonium phosphate difficult[17] and accordingly, methods for producing granular materials and which avoid the separation of precipitated impurities have been developed instead.[11, 24, 30, 54] Sulfuric acid is often added to the reaction system together with the phosphoric acid, and potash salts as well as other materials are frequently incorporated in the solid process stream prior to drying. In this way, an almost infinite combination of N-P and N-P-K compounds can be produced. More recently,[50] a method of adding urea slurry to the ammonium phosphate stream has been developed, which offers appreciable operating economies, as well as added flexibility and still higher plant food contents in the granulated product.

AMMONIUM PHOSPHATES

Principal Reactions

The ternary solubility diagram of the ammonia-water-phosphoric acid system indicates the existence of four possible anhydrous salts of ammonia and orthophosphoric acid, with mole ratios of $NH_3:H_3PO_4$ of 7:3, 2:1, 1:1 and 1:2. A trihydrated salt having a 3:1 ratio has also been reported. [4, 14, 30, 55] However, salts with a ratio greater than 2:1 are unstable and for fertilizer purposes only mono- and diammonium phosphates are of significance. These salts are produced in accordance with the following reactions:

$$H_3PO_4 \text{ (liq)} + NH_3 \text{ (g)} \rightarrow NH_4H_2PO_4 \text{ (c)} + 32.19 \text{ K cal} \quad (9.1)$$

$$H_3PO_4 \text{ (liq)} + 2NH_3 \text{ (g)} \rightarrow (NH_4)_2HPO_4 \text{ (c)} + 51.45 \text{ K cal} \quad (9.2)$$

Theoretically, when making monoammonium phosphate enough heat should be liberated by 1 lb of anhydrous ammonia in Eq. (9.1) to evaporate 3.24 lb of water under standard conditions. Similarly, when making diammonium phosphate by Eq. (9.2), 1 lb of anhydrous ammonia should correspond to 2.59 lb of water evaporated.[26] In practice, standard conditions are not achieved and the steam generated is somewhat less. Furthermore, when wet-process acid is used, side reactions due to impurities occur, e.g.,

$$CaSO_4 + H_3PO_4 + 2 NH_3 \rightarrow CaHPO_4 + (NH_4)_2SO_4 \quad (9.3)$$

$$H_2SO_4 + 2 NH_3 \rightarrow (NH_4)_2SO_4 \quad (9.4)$$

$$H_2SiF_6 + 6 NH_3 + 2 H_2O \rightarrow 6 NH_4F + SiO_2 \quad (9.5)$$

In addition, iron and alumina impurities in the wet-process acid are precipitated, principally as orthophosphates and contribute to the water-insoluble, citrate-soluble P_2O_5 in the fertilizer. The formation of citrate-insoluble phosphates is said to be reduced by maintaining a high pH value during ammoniation.[28]

TABLE 9.1

Property	Monoammonium Phosphate	Diammonium Phosphate
% N	12.17	21.19
% P_2O_5	51.71	53.76
Molecular weight	115.08	132.12
Specific gravity	1.803	1.619
pH (0.1 molar solution)	4.0	7.8
Crystal habit[46a]	tetragonal	monoclinic
Color	water-white	water-white
Partial pressure NH_3 (in mm Hg)		
75°C	—	0.9
100°C	—	5.6
125°C	0.05	28.8
Solubility in water (in grams per 100 grams H_2O)		
10°C	29	63
25°C	40	71
50°C	68	89
75°C	109	109
100°C	173	partial dissociation
110°C	215	partial dissociation

Properties

Pure mono- and diammonium phosphates[46] have the properties shown in Table 9.1.

Production Considerations

Vapor Pressures. In reactions between ammonia and phosphoric acid, a major consideration is the avoidance of excessive ammonia losses caused by conditions promoting dissociation of the product and the creation of high partial-pressures of ammonia over the reaction liquor. This applies principally to the production of diammonium phosphate and liquors having high mole ratios of NH_3 to H_3PO_4 as can be seen from Figure 9.2 which shows the rapid rise in the partial pressure of NH_3 over NH_3-H_3PO_4-H_2O systems caused by increases in temperature and mole ratios of NH_3 to H_3PO_4.[47] It can also be seen that the vapor pressure of ammonia over a saturated solution of diammonium phosphate is many times that for the dry salt at lower temperatures.

pH Values. For similar reasons, when making diammonium phosphate, reaction liquors are maintained at an appreciably lower pH value than

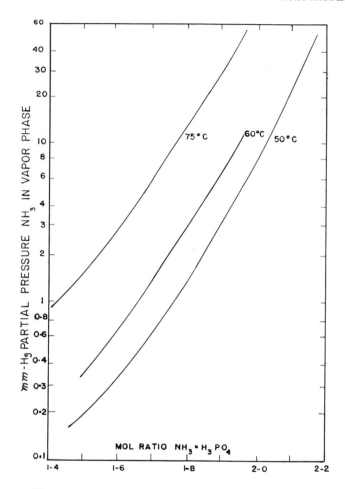

Figure 9.2. Partial pressure of NH_3 over NH_3-H_3PO_4-H_2O system.

the pH of the pure salt solution, in order to minimize ammonia losses. The pH figures for saturated solutions in NH_3-H_3PO_4-H_2O systems[47] are shown in Figure 9.3.

Solubilities. The solubility relationship for the NH_3-H_3PO_4-H_2O system shown in Figure 9.4 is an extremely important factor in the production of crystalline ammonium phosphates and ammonium phosphate-type fertilizers as well. It should be noted that in this system, the mole ratios of solutions and their resulting salts may be appreciably different, according to the controlling variables.

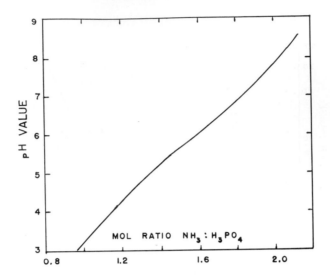

Figure 9.3. pH of saturated solutions in NH_3-H_3PO_4-H_2O system (60° to 75°C).

When producing diammonium phosphate from furnace-grade acid, ammonia losses can be minimized by operating at relatively low mole ratios of NH_3 to H_3PO_4, say in the 1.5 to 1.6 range. However, this corresponds to maximum solubility which, in turn, raises the specific gravity and viscosity of the slurry to values approaching the density of the diammonium salt.[47] Under these conditions, separation problems would arise; hence, higher mole ratios of NH_3 to H_3PO_4 are usually chosen, according to the design and characteristics of the crystallizer-separator unit.

Conversely, when making ammonium phosphate slurry from wet-process acid for subsequent granulation, it is important to reduce the free-water content of the slurry to as low a figure as possible in order to obtain good granulation control and to minimize subsequent drying needs. Consequently, operating conditions compatible with maximum solubility and minimum ammonia loss are chosen. In reference to Figure 9.4, at a slurry temperature of 75°C, this would be in the region of point X where mono- and diammonium phosphates would be present in about equal proportions and the NH_3 to H_3PO_4 mole ratio is about 1.45.

In theory, many N-P ratios are possible, ranging from the pure mono-salt at point Y to pure diammonium phosphate at point Z. In practice, the presence of impurities and the necessity to minimize ammonia losses restrict the maximum mole ratio of di- and monoammonium phosphates in the slurry and the final product to about 1.8 to 2.0, according to the

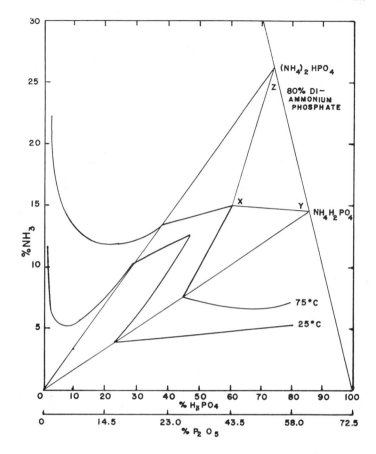

Figure 9.4. System NH₃-H₃PO₄-H₂O.

process and raw materials employed. It should be noted that (provided drying temperatures for products in this range do not exceed 90°C) ammonia losses are not excessive, as can be seen from Figure 9.5. Somewhat lower temperatures are generally preferred when drying crystalline diammonium phosphate.

Manufacturing Methods

Crystalline Ammonium Phosphates. First, the use of anhydrous ammonia will be considered. Mono- and diammonium phosphates can be produced in high purity, crystalline form from furnace-grade phosphoric acid and anhydrous ammonia (usually gaseous) according to Eq. (9.1) and Eq. (9.2) in units based on conventional vacuum crystallizers.[48] A typical process-flow diagram is shown in Figure 9.6, whereby acid of about

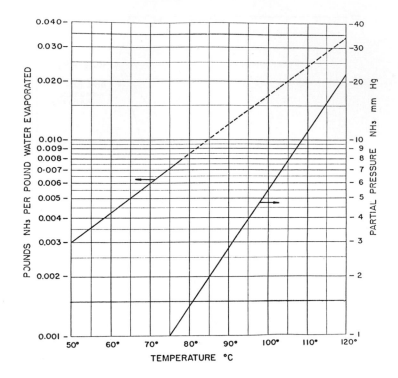

Figure 9.5. Approximate characteristics of system NH_3-H_3PO_4-H_2O (when $NH_4H_2PO_4$, $(NH_4)_2HPO_4$, and solution are all present).

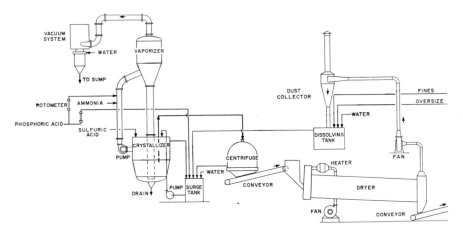

Figure 9.6. Diammonium phosphate production from furnace-grade acid. (*Courtesy TVA*) (Figure continued on opposite page.)

54 per cent P_2O_5 concentration and anhydrous ammonia enter the crystallizer via the recycle stream and are flash-cooled.[10] Ammonium phosphate nuclei are grown into crystals of appropriate size which are separated, dewatered on centrifuges, dried, screened (and sometimes cooled) prior to bagging and shipping.

The heat of reaction maintains the operation, which is controlled by balancing the make-up water and the vapor pressure in the flash chamber. Other operating variables which are usually monitored and controlled include pH, slurry density, and temperature. As with other crystallization processes, proper crystal growth is dependent on experienced plant design and skilled operation, otherwise excessive nucleation is likely to occur, leading to undersized, irregular cyrstals and excessive washing losses.[5, 36] Crystal habit can often be improved by the addition of a small amount of a modifier, such as sulfuric acid.[30]

For monoammonium phosphate production, the mole ratio of NH_3 to H_3PO_4 is generally maintained in the 1.0 to 1.1 range and the pH about 4.0 to 4.5, which gives minimum solubility, a good separation rate and a low ammonia loss, as well as a product with good storage properties. However, limited amounts of monoammonium phosphate are made for fertilizer purposes as compared to diammonium phosphate because of the lower nitrogen content of the monoammonium compound.

When making the diammonium salt by vacuum crystallization, the mole ratio of NH_3 to H_3PO_4 is generally raised to a value in the 1.7 to 1.8 range

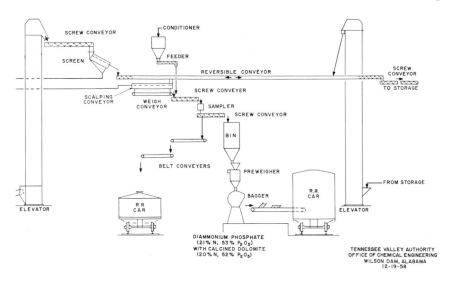

Figure 9.6—*cont'd*

and the pH to approximately 6.5. Drier temperature is usually not allowed to exceed 80°C in order to minimize dissociation and ammonia loss, in accordance with Figure 9.5, to give a product with moisture content in the 0.1 to 0.2 per cent range. The slurry solids content in the crystallizer is maintained about 27 to 30 per cent, in order to facilitate crystal separation.

Using By-Product Ammonia. During the last ten years, mono- and diammonium phosphates have also been made with by-product ammonia from coke ovens, in conjunction with furnace-grade phosphoric acid.[2, 30, 35] One of the major problems in using by-product gaseous ammonia from gas works and coke ovens for the production of ammonium salts such as ammonium thiocyanate, sulfate, or phosphate is the effective handling and scrubbing of huge volumes of gas having ammonia contents in the 0.5 to 1.0 per cent range only. Consequently, most by-product ammonium phosphate units are adaptions of ammonium sulfate scrubber-saturators, which are highly specialized in design and operation, as a result of many years of experience. Either one- or two-stage units can be used and two principal designs of saturator are employed.

In one of these, the Koppers type, the gas enters the saturator via a cracker or sparger ring submerged in the slurry and is scrubbed by acid sprays in the vapor head of the vessel, before passing to an acid trap and subsequent process units. In another major design of saturator, the Otto type,[29] incoming gas is scrubbed by a series of acid sprays in one or more gas-washing vessels, each washing stage being followed by an acid trap to reduce carry-over to a minimum. Single-shell units of this design can handle as much as 100 million cu ft of gas per day. A basic flow diagram of the Otto System is shown in Figure 9.7, which in some cases operates in conjunction with a vacuum-type crystallizer to ensure a closely controlled crystal size prior to centrifuging and drying.[37] A compactor-granulator unit can also be used to increase and control the size of the product, if desired.

In most instances, the production of the diammonium salt is preferred, since, compared to an equivalent amount of ammonia in the monoammonium phosphate form, about one-half of the corresponding phosphoric acid is needed. Inventory and storage costs are also less. Furthermore, the monoammonium salt can give rise to production difficulties, owing to the build-up of acicular crystals in vessels and process piping. This necessitates killing the process liquor at frequent intervals to dissolve accumulated salt and leads to additional production costs.

When making ammonium phosphates in by-product type saturators, ammonium recoveries are usually lower than when ammonium sulfate is

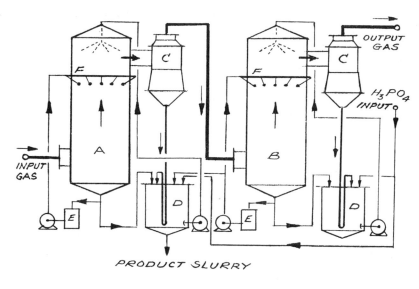

Legend:

A. Saturator
B. Scrubber
C. Acid traps

D. Recycle tanks
E. Pump tanks
F. Spray rings

Figure 9.7. Otto-type diammonium phosphate unit.

produced, unless two-stage operation is used. This is because phosphoric acid is a relatively weak acid and in addition, a balance has to be chosen between the optimum values of pH, slurry density, and NH_3 to H_3PO_4 mole ratio for practical reasons, as outlined earlier. With two-stage counter-current spray washing, recoveries in the 95 to 97 per cent range have been claimed. Since pyridine salts do not normally deposit at temperatures above 50°C, and pH values greater than 5.0, these compounds pass out with the scrubbed gas and do not seriously contaminate the crystalline ammonium phosphate product.

In some cases, by-product ammonia recovery units can be used to produce either ammonium sulfate or ammonium phosphate, or even a mixed salt such as 16-20-0, in accordance with prevailing price levels and market demand. No instance of using wet-process acid in conjunction with a coke oven by-product ammonia saturator is known, although a method for making crystalline ammonium phosphates from wet-process acid and anhydrous ammonia via a vacuum crystallizer of conventional design has been developed.[17]

Presumably, if circumstances warranted, by-product ammonia could be recovered from a gas stream or chemical process and converted to a strong aqueous solution which could be stripped with steam; the recovered ammonia could be used to produce crystalline ammonium phosphates or granular ammonium phosphate fertilizers from either furnace-grade or wet-process phosphoric acid, according to need.

Granular Fertilizers Based on Ammonium Phosphates. The difficulty of producing fertilizers based on crystalline ammonium phosphates from wet-process phosphoric acid (because of troublesome impurities) prompted a search for methods whereby the impurities were not separated from the ammonium phosphate crystals, but formed part of the product. The perfection of granulating techniques based on slurry nucleation or agglomeration,[11, 26] plus the results of investigations into the physical chemistry of ammonium phosphates led to several successful processes[6, 7, 11, 12, 16, 55] for making high analysis granular fertilizers based substantially on diammonium phosphates or mixtures of the mono- and diammonium salts.[24]

It was soon realized that, in addition to producing numerous grades of N-P compounds from reactions between ammonia and wet-process phosphoric acid, sulfuric acid could be added to the neutralizer to increase the relative nitrogen content by making ammonium sulfate *in situ*, or ground, solid ammonium sulfate could be added to the solid recycle stream. Similarly, solid potassium salts could be incorporated to produce an almost infinite number of N-P-K granular compounds. Lately, the addition of urea slurry to the process streams of some ammonium phosphate plants has been found practical,[50] which enables a new range of high nitrogen compounds to be produced, such as 30-30-0. When process liquor from a urea plant is used in this way prior to, or instead of, crystallizing or prilling, appreciable cost advantages can be gained.

Blunger Processes. In one widely used method of producing granular ammonium phosphate fertilizers, anhydrous, gaseous ammonia and wet-process phosphoric acid containing 30 to 50 per cent P_2O_5 are reacted in stainless steel vessels to produce a slurry of about 75 per cent solids content and the desired N-P ratio in accordance with the area XYZ in Figure 9.4. Frequently, some sulfuric acid is also added to the reaction system to increase the N content of the product.

The slurry overflows to a blunger—a twin shaft pugmill of special design—wherein it is mixed with a recycling stream of solid particles and is then passed to a rotary dryer and subsequent screening system for the separation of product-size granules. Oversized material is crushed and recycled to the blunger with undersized material and recovered dust for repeated mixing with fresh slurry.

The combination of slurry with undersized particles and granules takes place in two principal ways, termed nucleation or agglomeration, according to operating conditions and the type of product desired. With thin slurries, small recycled particles and high recycle ratios, dense, round granules with an onion-like, layered structure are formed. With thick slurries, large recycled particles cemented by slurry tend to be produced. This particularly applies to granules incorporating large amounts of solid salts such as ammonium sulfate or potash, which are usually added to the system via the stream of solid undersized particles returning to the blunger.[1, 11]

A typical flow diagram for this type of process[11] is shown in Figure 9.8, which also includes alternate porvisions for making triple superphosphate by the substitution of ground phosphate rock for ammonia. When making ammonium phosphate compounds, the ammonia is generally incorporated in two stages. Seventy-five to eighty per cent is added to the first vessel,

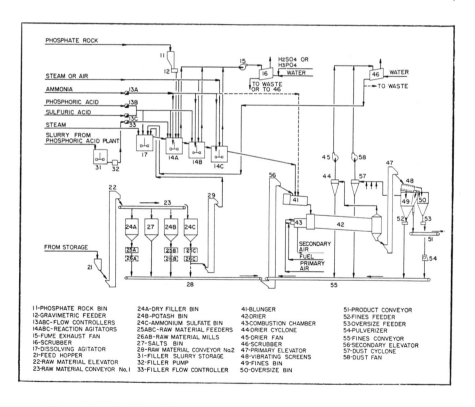

11-PHOSPHATE ROCK BIN	24A-DRY FILLER BIN	41-BLUNGER	51-PRODUCT CONVEYOR
12-GRAVIMETRIC FEEDER	24B-POTASH BIN	42-DRIER	52-FINES FEEDER
13ABC-FLOW CONTROLLERS	24C-AMMONIUM SULFATE BIN	43-COMBUSTION CHAMBER	53-OVERSIZE FEEDER
14ABC-REACTION AGITATORS	25ABC-RAW MATERIAL FEEDERS	44-DRIER CYCLONE	54-PULVERIZER
15-FUME EXHAUST FAN	26AB-RAW MATERIAL MILLS	45-DRIER FAN	55-FINES CONVEYOR
16-SCRUBBER	27-SALTS BIN	46-SCRUBBER	56-SECONDARY ELEVATOR
17-DISSOLVING AGITATOR	28-RAW MATERIAL CONVEYOR No.2	47-PRIMARY ELEVATOR	57-DUST CYCLONE
21-FEED HOPPER	31-FILLER SLURRY STORAGE	48-VIBRATING SCREENS	58-DUST FAN
22-RAW MATERIAL ELEVATOR	32-FILLER PUMP	49-FINES BIN	
23-RAW MATERIAL CONVEYOR No.1	33-FILLER FLOW CONTROLLER	50-OVERSIZE BIN	

Figure 9.8. The Dorr-Oliver granular fertilizer process typical flowsheet.

and the reaction is trimmed by adding the remainder to the second vessel. The heat of reaction evaporates much of the water in the slurry, and small amounts of ammonia present in the vapor from the reaction system are recovered in a scrubber by contacting with sulfuric or phosphoric acid. Scrubber liquor is returned to the reaction system. Gases from the dryer and other parts of the process are passed through dust-recovery cyclones, as well as a scrubber before venting to atmosphere. As a result, dust losses are kept to a minimum and ammonia utilization of at least 99 per cent can be achieved by good plant design and experienced operation.

Some of the grades made in this type of process include 14-14-14, 16-48-0, 12-36-12, 10-20-20 and 16-20-0, as well as 29-29-0 by adding urea in solid or slurry form to the blunger feed.[32]

TVA-Ammoniator Process. A limitation of blunger processes for making ammonium phosphate-type fertilizers is the difficulty of producing high nitrogen grades such as 18-46-0 and 16-48-0 from ammonia and wet-process acid, unless the acid is relatively pure. As can be seen from Figures 9.3 and 9.4, attempts to increase the mole ratio of NH_3 to H_3PO_4 in the slurry beyond certain limits will not result in a proportionate increase in the production of the diammonium salt. Instead, the pH will be increased and ammonia losses from the reactors and other units will be high.

One successful method of overcoming this difficulty is to undertake a further ammoniation step in the solid phase by using an ammoniator and process of the TVA type,[13, 55] as shown in Figure 9.9.

In the TVA method, the excess ammonia used as the driving force to

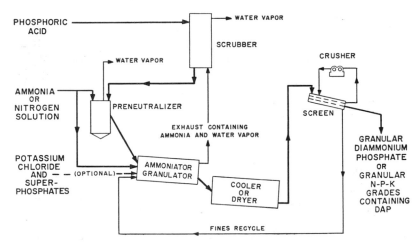

Figure 9.9. Flow sheet of TVA process for production of granular diammonium phosphate.

achieve a mole ratio of NH_3 to H_3PO_4 of 2:0 in the ammoniator-granulator drum is recovered by scrubbing the off-gas from the drum by the incoming phosphoric acid, prior to entering the preneutralizer. Granulation is controlled by adjusting the size and quantity of fines recycled to the ammoniator-granulator. This process enables a low recycle ratio to be used and also reduces drying needs, since nearly 90 per cent of the free moisture can be removed in the ammoniator-granulator by the heat of reaction.

The addition of a scrubber and neutralizer to a conventional TVA-type granulation unit[54] thus enables diammonium phosphate compounds to be made, such as 18-46-0, 15-15-15, 18-18-18, and 14-35-14, as well as 21-53-0, if electric furnace acid is employed. The TVA pilot plant is shown in Figure 9.10, in which the ammoniator-granulator drum and dryer can be seen. The process can be readily adapted to large-scale operation[7] for the production of 18-46-0, 16-48-0 and many N-P-K compounds.

The Spray-Tower Process.   An unusual method of producing ammonium phosphate compounds from wet-process phosphoric acid and anhydrous ammonia is the spray-tower process developed some thirty years ago by

Figure 9.10. Ammonium phosphate pilot plant. (*Courtesy TVA*)

Nissan Chemical Industries Limited of Japan and is currently used for producing grades such as 18-46-0, 19-42-0, 19-26-0, and 15-15-10.

In this method, the wet-process acid (plus sulfuric acid and/or a solution of potassium salt, as required) is sprayed into a short tower containing a rising stream of ammonia gas and forms prill-like beads containing substantial amounts of diammonium phosphate. The heat of reaction drives off the free water present and the dried product is extracted from the base of the tower via a seal box and conveyor. Excess ammonia in the vapor leaving the tower is recovered and recycled. As a result of the simplicity of this method, capital and operating costs are appreciably lower than corresponding costs for other processes of similar capacities. The process is shown schematically in Figure 9.11 and an illustration of a typical spray-tower is given in Figure 9.12.

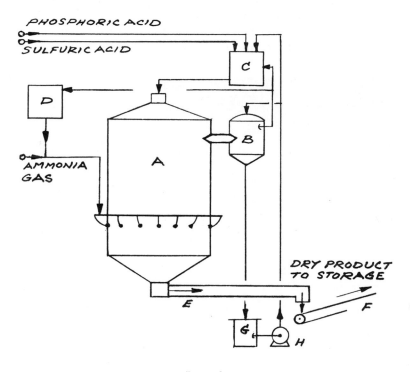

Legend:

A. Spray tower
B. Scrubber
C. Absorber
D. NH₃ recovery

E. Product conveyor
F. Storage conveyor
G. Recycle tank
H. Recycle pump

Figure 9.11. Nissan spray-tower process.

Figure 9.12. Nissan spray-tower for ammonium fertilizer production. (*Courtesy Nissan Chemical Industries Ltd.*)

In Japan, compounds produced in the spray-tower are applied directly to the soil and are also incorporated in granulated mixtures such as 15-15-15, 4-10-13, and 20-20-14. In the latter mixture, 60 per cent of the nitrogen is supplied by solid urea, the balance from ammonium phosphate.

Other Processes. Although the production of crystalline ammonium phosphates is at the present time virtually all based on furnace-grade phosphoric acid, several methods have been developed based on the use of wet-process acid. In one method[17a] (which is of TVA origin) the acid is partially ammoniated and precipitated impurities are removed by a continuous vacuum drum filter. The filtrate is concentrated by evaporation and further ammoniated in a vacuum crystallizer to produce diammonium phosphate crystals. These are separated by centrifuging and can either be dried, screened and bagged in pure form, or they may be combined with the repulped filter cake in a pugmill prior to drying and screening. In the latter case, about 80 per cent of the product is represented by water-soluble ammonium phosphate.

In a more recent process of European origin, wet-process phosphoric acid is first ammoniated in an agitated saturator to produce a slurry containing both crystalline diammonium phosphate and suspended impurities. Crystals deposited in the lower part of the saturator are continuously removed, separated and washed on a centrifuge, dried, screened and sent to storage. The slurry is concentrated by evaporation and spray-dried to yield a powdered product which can either be granulated alone or in conjunction with the crystalline diammonium phosphate. The weight ratio of powdered material to crystalline product is about 1:1.5. The former contains approximately 16 per cent nitrogen and 40 per cent total P_2O_5, while the latter averages 20.5 per cent nitrogen and 53 total per cent P_2O_5.

A new process for producing mono-ammonium phosphate has been the subject of recent patent applications.[3a] The product contains about 6 per cent of free moisture and is especially suitable for making granulated mixed fertilizer with higher N and P_2O_5 percentages than would be obtained by the use of single superphosphate or ammoniated superphosphate. Mono-ammonium phosphate made by this process becomes thixotropic when the moisture content is increased to about 15 per cent and so is ideal for granulation purposes. Below this moisture level no amount of physical handling will induce softening, thus permitting easy handling and storage. Subsequent granulation is readily accomplished by the addition of a little steam.[4a, 13a]

Ammonium Phosphate-Urea Compounds. Another process of interest and promise is a method developed by the TVA whereby process liquor from a urea unit is combined with the slurry stream in an ammonium phosphate-type plant to produce high nitrogen grades at relatively low cost levels, owing to the elimination of several urea finishing operations. A basic flow diagram of this method is shown in Figure 9.13, whereby granular two- or three-component products can be made having $N:P_2O_5$ ratios up to 2:1 and total NPK plant food contents up to 60 per cent.

In this process,[50] unconverted ammonia in a urea-NH_3-CO_2-H_2O stream from the synthesis reactor is neutralized with phosphoric acid in a TVA-type ammoniator and granulated in the normal way. A preneutralizer vessel can be used, if desired, to reduce the drying load and the recycle

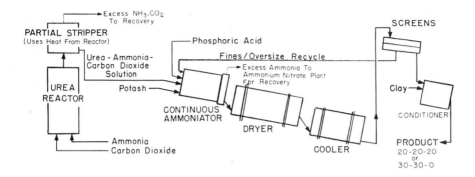

Figure 9.13. TVA urea-ammonium phosphate process.

ratio. The process reduces or eliminates the need for stripping, separating, and recycling unreacted ammonia in the urea plant. It also enables dry, solid fertilizers to be produced in relatively low cost equipment, compared to making crystals and/or prills in specially constructed evaporators and prilling towers. Furthermore, biuret formation[20] is virtually eliminated.[50]

AMMONIUM POLYPHOSPHATES

General

Superphosphoric Acid. The development of a range of superphosphoric acids[2, 3, 27, 33] from both furnace- and wet-process phosphoric acids[38, 41, 43, 44, 45] has led, in turn, to a new range of fertilizer materials having some unusual properties and great promise. These are the ammonium polyphosphates, which are made by reacting super-acids with anhydrous ammonia. Since these compounds inherit some of the properties of the acids used in their manufacture, a brief review of the latter will be of value.

Superphosphoric acid of electric furnace origin usually contains 76 to 77 per cent P_2O_5. When made by concentrating wet-process acid, corresponding super-acids normally have P_2O_5 contents from 68 to 76 per cent, according to the source of rock and type of evaporator used. Recent developments include the production of a wet-process super-acid having a P_2O_5 concentration of 83 per cent which, allowing for impurities, is equivalent to an almost anhydrous material, having a nonortho content of about 99 per cent.

Phosphoric acid solutions in the 32 to 54 per cent P_2O_5 range, as normally used for fertilizer production, contain most of the acid in the ortho form, but higher concentrations of P_2O_5 induce the formation of nonortho components, polymers, and condensation products.[18] Furnace-type super-acids of 76 per cent P_2O_5 concentration (equivalent to 105 per cent H_3PO_4) usually contain about 38 per cent of pyro-acid, plus a few per cent of meta- and polyphosphates. In typical super-acids of wet-process origin, non-ortho components are often higher still and may approach 55 per cent, or even more, according to the amount of impurities present and the method of concentration.

The general structural formulas of these acids are given below

Orthophosphoric

$$\text{HO—}\underset{\underset{\text{H}}{\overset{|}{\text{O}}}}{\overset{\overset{\text{O}}{\|}}{\text{P}}}\text{—OH}$$

Pyrophosphoric acid

$$\text{H—O—}\underset{\underset{\text{H}}{\overset{|}{\text{O}}}}{\overset{\overset{\text{O}}{\|}}{\text{P}}}\text{—O—}\underset{\underset{\text{H}}{\overset{|}{\text{O}}}}{\overset{\overset{\text{O}}{\|}}{\text{P}}}\text{—O—H}$$

Tripolyphosphoric acid

$$\text{H—O—}\underset{\underset{\text{H}}{\overset{|}{\text{O}}}}{\overset{\overset{\text{O}}{\|}}{\text{P}}}\text{—O—}\underset{\underset{\text{H}}{\overset{|}{\text{O}}}}{\overset{\overset{\text{O}}{\|}}{\text{P}}}\text{—O—}\underset{\underset{\text{H}}{\overset{|}{\text{O}}}}{\overset{\overset{\text{O}}{\|}}{\text{P}}}\text{—O—H}$$

and equilibrium compositions are given in Figure 9.14.

A unique feature of these super-acids, which is attributable to their nonortho contents, is their ability to suppress the precipitation of impurities present in the acids themselves and also in liquid fertilizers incorporating these acids. Another useful property is a much reduced corrosion rate for mild steel, compared to phosphoric acids of lower P_2O_5 concentration. In addition, when producing super-acid from wet-process phosphoric acid, most of the fluorine is removed during evaporation.[31, 38]

Ammonium Polyphosphates. Ammoniation of superphosphoric acids produces a range of water-soluble polyphosphates having correspondingly high N-P contents, plus the ability to sequester impurities present in liquid fertilizers.[9, 31, 42, 45] Furthermore, ammonium polyphosphates are relatively more soluble than ammonium ortho-phosphates, which enables higher grades of liquid fertilizers to be made without added risk of salting-out or freezing. For example, the addition of ammonium polyphosphate enables a 1:3 ratio in a fertilizer solution to be produced in terms of 10-30-0 instead of 8-24-0, without impairing stability at 32°F.

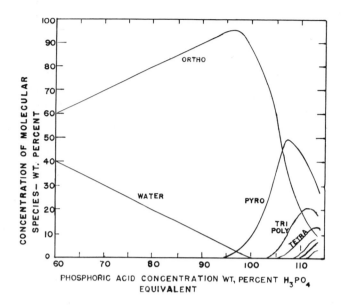

Figure 9.14. Equilibrium composition of concentrated phosphoric acid. (*Courtesy Monsanto Chemical Co.*)

Ammonium polyphosphates have been available in solution form for several years and have become widely accepted by liquid fertilizer producers. Some of the more popular solutions include 11-33-0, 10-34-0, and 8-27-0, which are used both as sequestrants and as bases for low freezing-point N-P and N-P-K liquid fertilizers. Solid ammonium phosphates are still under large-scale development and details are still lacking, but when commercially available they are likely to be widely used, not only as liquid fertilizer sequestrants but as components of high analysis liquid and granular fertilizers as well.

Recent work indicates that stable, granular water-soluble polyphosphates such as 21-53-0, 14-59-0, and 16-64-0 can be readily produced from both furnace- and wet-process acid. Such compounds are likely to prove very attractive, from the standpoint of savings in transportation costs and when ultra-high N-P and N-P-K formulations are desired.[40]

Production Methods

Ammonium Polyphosphate Solutions. Solutions of ammonium polyphosphate, such as 11-33-0 and 10-34-0, are made on a continuous production scale[39] by reacting anhydrous, liquid ammonia and super-acid in a mild steel vessel equipped with cooling-water coils and an agitator. The ammonia is introduced by a sparger, and provided the flow of reactants and the temperature are carefully controlled, ammonia losses and corrosion are negligible.

Liquid ammonia provides about 30 per cent greater plant capacity than gaseous ammonia, because of the additional latent cooling. Likewise, the use of aqua-ammonia, were it available, would increase plant capacity still further, by a similar figure. As can be expected, the neutralizer unit is sensitive to cooling water temperatures; an increase from 60° to 85°F reduces output by nearly 40 per cent. During neutralization, pH is maintained between 6.0 and 6.3, and specific gravity between 1.34 and 1.37.

In another method,[31] warm acid is transported to customers in insulated stainless steel trucks and ammoniated during unloading at a rate of about 10 tons per hour. Melting points for various ammonium polyphosphate solutions are shown in Figure 9.15.

Since the special properties of these polyphosphates are largely due to their nonortho contents, reaction temperatures must be controlled to prevent reversion to ortho-phosphates. Cooling-water coils can be used in conjunction with furnace-type acid, but this method has limitations when the super-acid is of wet-process origin, owing to scaling problems. One practical alternative is to blow air through a spray of hot ammoniated solution.[31] A maximum temperature of 190°F is usually recommended and is reported to give negligible ammonia loss when pH is maintained below 7.0. The relation between temperature and reversion rate is given in Figure 9.16.

Granular Ammonium Polyphosphates. A need for solid materials having the inherent properties of superphosphoric acid and ammonium polyphosphate solutions has led to the recent development of granular polyphosphates produced from electric furnace and wet-process acid, by the TVA and other producers. Representative products include 13-58-0, 16-61-0, 16-64-0, and 21-53-0.

In the pilot-scale TVA process,[50] shown in Figure 9.17, superphosphoric acid is continuously reacted with anhydrous ammonia in an agitated pressure vessel at approximately 400°F and 25 to 28 psig. The molten product flows to a twin-shaft pugmill wherein it is granulated with recycled fines at about 150°F or 240°F, depending whether furnace-acid or wet-process acid is used. Material discharged from the pugmill is cooled before screening to the desired size range. Optimum ammoniation is reported to be between 6.2 and 6.4 lb of ammonia per unit of P_2O_5 and a retention time of about 60 min is advocated. A recycle-to-product ratio of 2:1 appears satisfactory.

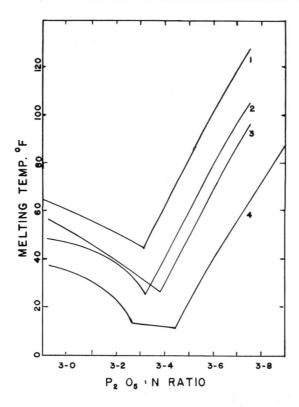

Figure 9.15. Melting points of ammonium polyphosphate solutions. (*Courtesy Western Phosphates
Inc.*)

No	% Conversion	%N
1	30	10
2	50	10
3	29	9
4	29	8

1 and 2—Ex Florida Rock.
3 and 4—Ex Western Rock.

The effect of major operating variables on the degree of ammoniation
is shown in Figure 9.18.

The nonortho content of these solid polyphosphates is said to be about
50 per cent. When made from wet-process super-acid, good storage prop-

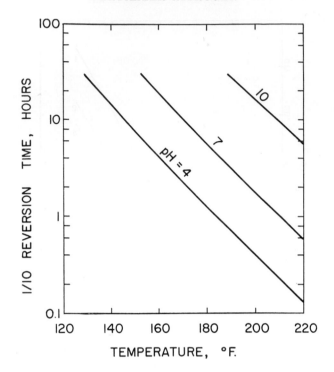

Figure 9.16. Reversion rates of pyrophosphates in ammonium polyphosphate solutions. (*Courtesy Western Phosphates Inc.*)

erties are exhibited, but when acid of electric-furnace origin is used, a tendency for the product to cake in storage arises. This can be largely overcome by the aid of a suitable coating agent, or by adding soluble sulfates of certain metals, such as iron or aluminum, to the acid prior to ammoniation, although this will increase the power required by the granulator.

If the polyphosphate is intended for subsequent use in mixtures containing ammonium nitrate, dolomite should not be used as a conditioner because of incompatibility between these two compounds.

Compared to polyphosphate solutions, granular forms offer savings in storage and transportation costs.[40] In addition, the slow reversion that occurs in polyphosphate solutions is avoided. It is of interest to mention that ammonium polyphosphates have negative heats of solution, hence some form of process heating is desirable when dissolving the solid material.

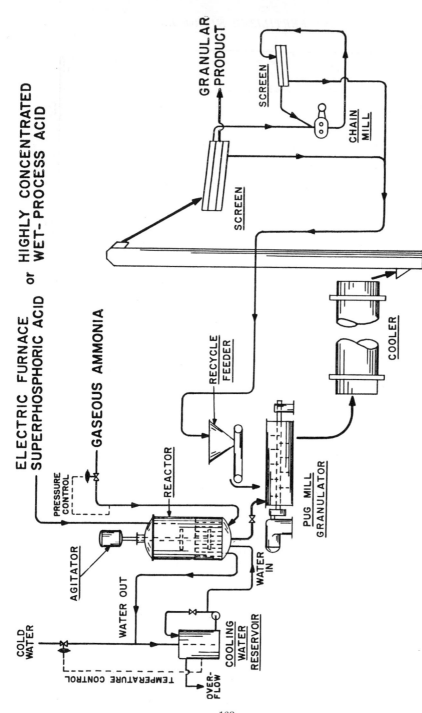

Figure 9.17. Flow diagram for solid ammonium polyphosphate production. (*Courtesy TVA*)

163

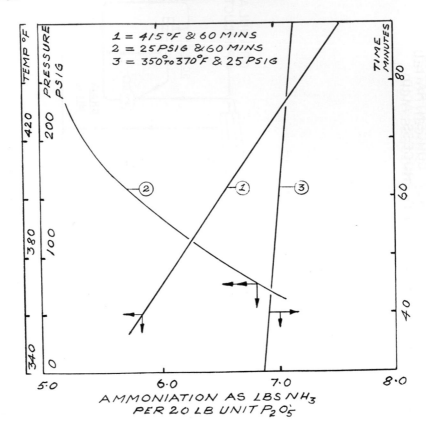

Figure 9.18. Operating variables *vs* degree of ammoniation for solid ammonium polyphosphates.

Applications

Sequestration. The amount of ammonium polyphosphate needed to suppress precipitation in liquid fertilizers depends on the impurities present and the subsequent ambient temperatures. As a general guide, the nonortho phosphate content of the treated solution should be in the 7 to 9 per cent range, and this can be added either as liquid or granulated polyphosphate. The fertilizer solution can be prepared on the batch or continuous basis, according to circumstances, and polyphosphates of electricfurnace or wet-process origin can be used; however, an allowance for the additional impurities contributed by wet-process acid must be made, the optimum amount being best determined by experiment. One formulation for 8-8-8, using solid polyphosphate of furnace origin is given overleaf.

Material	Per Cent
54% P₂O₅ wet-process acid	8.4
20% N ammonia solution	9.2
32% N urea-nitrate solution	17.1
62% K₂O potash	13.2
15-61-0 polyphosphate	6.1
Water	46.0
	100.0

A diagram of a typical solution-preparation unit is given in Figure 9.19.

High-Analysis Fertilizer Production. The nitrogen in ammonium polyphosphate has been shown by agronomic tests to be equivalent to the nitrogen in ammonium sulfate and the P_2O_5 to be as good as that from diammonium phosphate.[51] Consequently, ammonium polyphosphates are

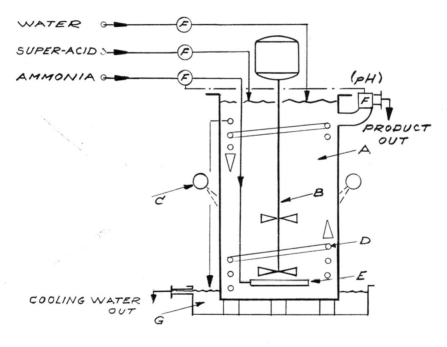

Legend:

A. Reaction vessel
B. Agitator
C. Cooling ring
D. Cooling coil

E. NH₃ sparger
F. Flow controls
G. Water sump

Figure 9.19. Continuous reactor for producing ammonium polyphosphate solutions.

extremely effective plant foods, either when applied directly to the soil in solid or liquid form alone, or in conjunction with other solids or liquids. Because of their very high plant food contents, care has to be used in application and placement.

The following are examples of high-analysis granular formulations based on solid ammonium polyphosphate:

15-30-15	Per Cent
33.5% N ammonium nitrate.	23.2
15-61-0 polyphosphate.	49.5
60% K$_2$O potash.	25.3
Inerts and coating agent.	2.0
	100.0

12-24-24	Per Cent
33.5% N ammonium nitrate.	18.7
15-61-0 polyphosphate.	39.7
62% K$_2$O potash.	39.0
Inerts and coating agent.	2.6
	100.0

High-analysis sequestered liquid polyphosphate fertilizers can be produced from a direct reaction between superphosphoric acid and anhydrous ammonia, as previously described, or they can be made by dissolving granular polyphosphates in water, with the addition of other materials, according to the grade desired. Typical examples are 10-34-0, 8-27-0, and 9-36-0.

Micronutrient Solvents. In many world areas, soils are deficient in plant micronutrients, such as boron, cobalt, manganese, and zinc. Continued application of all-synthetic fertilizers, such as ammonium sulfate or urea, plus heavy cropping may reduce the levels of these essential elements below the minimum requirements for healthy plant growth and lead to crop failures or even the death of foraging animals, unless these deficiencies are corrected.[15]

An increasing number of fertilizer producers now incorporate controlled amounts of micronutrient salts in their solid mixed and granulated products, as a successful way of treating deficient soils.[8, 19] However, the addition of micronutrients to fertilizer solutions has been more difficult,[33a, 49a] because many of the commercially available micronutrient salts are not readily soluble in liquid fertilizers, based on nitrate salts and ammonium orthophosphates.

More recently, it was found that the presence of nonortho-phosphates considerably increased the solubilities of some micronutrient salts in liquid fertilizers.[52] For instance, a 10-34-0 polyphosphate solution will dissolve 10 to 30 times the amount of copper, iron and zinc taken up by an 8-24-0 solution. Studies have also shown that superphosphoric acid can be used to prepare micronutrient solutions. The metallic oxides are first dissolved in the hot super-acid, which is then ammoniated to yield either the liquid or solid polyphosphate. In this way, solutions containing 0.5 to 2.0 per cent of various micronutrient elements can be prepared, and satisfactory stability under normal conditions is obtained.

REFERENCES

1. Anon., *Brit. Chem. Eng.* (Jan. 1959).
2. Anon., *Chem. Eng.* (Oct. 1, 1962).
3. Anon., *Chem. Eng.* (Nov. 13, 1962).
3a. Brit. Patent Applications, Nos. 3239/61; 11466/63; 16960/63.
4. Brosheer, J. C., and Anderson, J. F., *J. Am. Chem. Soc.*, **68**, 902 (1946).
4a. Brownlie, I. A., and Graham, R., *Int'l. Super. Mfc. Conf. Proc.* (Helsinki), Sept. 1963.
5. Buckley, H. E., "Crystal Growth", New York, John Wiley & Sons, 1951.
6. Burnet, G. J., *Agr. Food Chem.*, 258 (April, 1957).
7. Chopey, N. P., *Chem. Eng.*, 148 (March 19, 1962).
8. Doak, B. W., *International Superphosphate Manufacturers Conference (ISMA) Proceedings*, Avignon (1962).
9. Getsinger, J. G., *et al.*, *Agr. Food Chem.*, **10**, 341 (1962).
10. Getsinger, J. G., *et al.*, *Agr. Food Chem.*, **5**, 433 (1957).
11. Giorgini, M., and Weber, W., *ISMA Conference Proceedings*, Stockholm (1959).
12. Greek, B. F., *et al.*, *Ind. Eng. Chem.*, **11**, 81A, 638 (1960).
13. Haines, W., and Lange, F., *Ind. Eng. Chem.*, **6**, 966 (1956).
13a. Harris, F. J., *ISMA Conference Proc.* (Stockholm), 1959.
14. Harvey, E. W., and Frear, G. L., "Phosphoric Acid, Phosphates and Phosphate Fertilizers," Ed. by Waggaman, p. 308, New York, Reinhold Publishing Corp., 1952.
15. Hardesty, J. O., *et al.*, "Micronutrient Symposium," *Agr. Food Chem.*, (May/June 1962).
16. Horn, W. R., *Agr. Chem.* (Jan. 1957).
17. Houston, E. C., *et al.*, *Agr. Food Chem.*, **3**, 1, 43 (1955).
17a. Houston, E. C., *et al.*, *Agr. Food Chem.*, **3**, 43 (1952).
18. Huhti, A. L., and Gartaganis, P. A., *Can. J. Chem.*, **34**, (1956).
19. Jost, W., U.S. Patent 2,983,594 (May 9, 1961).
20. Kaasenbrood, *et al.*, *Agr. Food Chem.*, 93 (Jan./Feb. 1963) .
21. Keim, M. M., *ISMA Conference Proceedings*, Avignon (1962).
22. Kelso, T. M., *et al.*, 142nd Meeting, National Amer. Chem. Soc., Sept. 1962).
23. Lawton, K., "Phosphorus and its Compounds," Ed. Van Wazer, vol. 2, p. 1538 Interscience Publishers, Inc., New York, 1961.
24. Lutz, W., and Pratt, C. J., "Chemistry and Technology of Fertilizers," Ed. V. Sauchelli, p. 299, New York, Reinhold Publishing Corp., 1960.
25. Lockwood, M. H., *Commercial Fertilizer*, 24 (Feb. 1962).
26. Lutz, W., and Pratt, C. J., Ed. V. Sauchelli, *Ibid.*, p. 304.
27. McKnight, D., and Striplin, M. M., *Agr. Chem.* (Aug. 1958).
28. Miller, F. J. L., *Agr. Food Chem.*, **9**, 1, 2 (Jan./Feb. 1961).
29. Otto, C., U.S. Patent No. 2,599,067 (June 1952).
30. Payne, J. H., Van Wazer, *Ibid.*, p. 1127.
31. Petersen, A. W., *et al.*, 142nd National Meeting, Amer. Chem. Soc., Sept. 1962.
32. Phillips, A. B., *et al.*, *Agr. Food Chem.*, **5**, 834 (1957).

33. Phillips, A. B., *et al.*, *Agr. Food Chem.*, **8**, 310 (July/Aug. 1960).
33a. Potts, J. M., *Fertilizer Solutions* (Mar./April, 1963).
34. Pratt, C. J., *Brit. Chem. Eng.* (June 1958).
35. Rozian, I. W., Ed. V. Sauchelli, *Ibid.*, p. 251.
36. Schoen, H. M., and den Bogaerde, J. V., *Ind. Eng. Chem.*, **54**, 4, 57 (April 1962).
37. Schulze, W. G., *Proc. Amer. Inst. Min. Met. and Pet. Eng.*, **20** (1961).
38. Scott, W. C., *et al.*, *Ind. Eng. Chem.*, **53**, 713, (1961).
39. Scott, W. H., and Wilbanks, J. A., *Agr. Chem.* (May 1961).
40. Silverberg, J., *et al.*, *Commercial Fertilizer*, 28 (Nov. 1961).
40a. Silverberg, J., *Agr. Food Chem.* (June 1957).
41. Shetler, R. A., *ISMA Conference Proceedings*, Avignon, 1962.
42. Slack, A. V., *Farm Chemicals* (Nov. 1962).
43. Striplin, M. M., *et al.*, *Agr. Food Chem.*, **6**, 4, 298 (1958).
44. Striplin, M. M., *Chem. Eng.* (Sept. 18, 1961).
45. Striplin, M. M., *Agr. Food Chem.*, **7**, 9, 623 (Sept. 1959).
46. Smith, J. P., *et al.*, ex *Acta Crystallographica*, T. V. A., reprint 10 (Nov. 1957).
46a. ———, *Amer. Mineralogist*, **40**, 893 (1955).
47. Thompson, H. L., *et al.*, *Ind. Eng. Chem.*, **42**, 2176 (1950).
48. Thompson, H. L., *et al.*, *Ind. Eng. Chem.*, **41**, 485 (1949).
49. Terman, G. L., *Agr. Food Chem.*, **9**, 6, 166 (1961).
49a. Turner, J., *Fertilizer Solutions* (Mar/April 1963).
50. T. V. A., Proceedings of 4th Demonstration, Aug. 9162).
51. T. V. A., 4th Demonstration, Ibid., p. 64.
52. T. V. A., 4th Demonstration, Ibid., p. 50.
53. Van Wazer, "Phosphorus and its Compounds," vol. 1, New York, Interscience Publishers, Inc., 1960.
54. Yates, L. D., *et al.*, *Farm Chemicals* (July/Aug. 1954).
55. Young, R. D., *et al.*, *Agr. Food Chem.*, **10** (1962).

10

Ammoniated Phosphate-type Fertilizers

CHRISTOPHER J. PRATT

International Fertilizer Development Corporation

In addition to ammonium phosphate compounds, there are several other types of fertilizers which also contain nitrogen and phosphorus, plus potassium according to need. The best known of these are the ammoniated superphosphates and the nitrophosphates. Other materials of increasing interest include certain metallic salts of ammonia and phosphoric acid, such as magnesium ammonium phosphate which may eventually become available in commercial quantities from salt-water conversion plants.

A major difference between ammonium phosphates and ammoniated phosphate-type fertilizers is the degree of P_2O_5 water-solubility. In ammonium phosphates the P_2O_5 is almost totally water-soluble, whereas in ammoniated phosphate-type fertilizers the P_2O_5 is only partly water-soluble and may even approach total water-insolubility in some cases. A high citrate P_2O_5 solubility is, of course, an essential feature of both types, and suitable precautions must be taken to prevent reversion to tricalcium phosphate and other basic phosphates during manufacture and storage, since these are only very slowly available as plant food.

AMMONIATED SUPERPHOSPHATES

When phosphoric acid is not available, N-P (and N-P-K) fertilizers can be produced economically on a commercial scale by ammoniating single, enriched, or triple superphosphates with anhydrous or aqueous ammonia, or nitrogen solutions containing urea, ammonia, and various nitrogen salts. Such fertilizers have been made in great quantities in the US for many years and are still extremely popular.[48]

Chemical Reactions

Although the ammoniation of a superphosphate induces several complex reactions which vary according to operating conditions and materials used, the principal effect is to change part of the monocalcium phosphate in the superphosphate to dicalcium phosphate, and to produce a corresponding amount of monoammonium phosphate, as indicated below:

$$Ca(H_2PO_4)_2 + NH_3 \rightarrow CaHPO_4 + NH_4H_2PO_4 \qquad (10.1)$$

In practice, ammonia requirements may be greater than those indicated by the above reaction, since, apart from any losses, the presence of free sulfuric acid and phosphoric acid will lead to the formation of corresponding ammonium salts. Nevertheless, over-ammoniation of the phosphate component can be harmful as it may cause reversion of the water-insoluble, citrate-soluble dicalcium phosphate to more basic forms, such as tricalcium phosphate, i.e.,

$$3CaHPO_4 + NH_3 \rightarrow Ca_3(PO_4)_2 + NH_4H_2PO_4 \qquad (10.2)$$

The ammoniation of single and enriched superphosphates also gives rise to secondary reactions caused by the presence of calcium sulfate:

$$NH_4H_2PO_4 + CaSO_4 + NH_3 \rightarrow CaHPO_4 + (NH_4)_2SO_4 \quad (10.3)$$

$$2CaHPO_4 + CaSO_4 + 2NH_3 \rightarrow Ca_3(PO_4)_2 + (NH_4)_2SO_4 \quad (10.4)$$

The various changes induced by ammoniating single superphosphate are shown empirically in Figure 10.1. Similar reactions also occur when triple superphosphate is ammoniated, with the exception of those between calcium sulfate, ammonia, and ammonium phosphate.

A convenient way of expressing the degree of ammoniation is in terms of the pounds of NH_3 per unit of P_2O_5. For single superphosphate, a typical range is between 4 and 6 lb and for triple superphosphate the range is frequently 3 to 4 lb of ammonia, per 20 lb of P_2O_5, respectively.[12, 22] However, the relatively higher ammonia absorption properties of single superphosphate leads to a greater degree of P_2O_5 water insolubility,[62] as shown in Figure 10.2.

Commercial-scale trials with "high-analysis" triple superphosphate (made with the aid of superphosphoric acid and containing 52 to 54 per cent P_2O_5) indicate that this material does not ammoniate quite so readily as conventional triple superphosphate containing 46 to 48 per cent P_2O_5. For the high analysis product,[41] the optimum degree of ammoniation is of the order of 3.0 to 3.5 lb of ammonia per 20 lb of P_2O_5, and granular fertilizers which have been successfully made from ammoniated, high-analysis triple superphosphate include 13-13-13, 13-39-0, and 12-24-12.

Operating Variables

The rate and degree of ammoniation are effected by numerous variables, such as permeability and particle size[61] of the superphosphate, the moisture

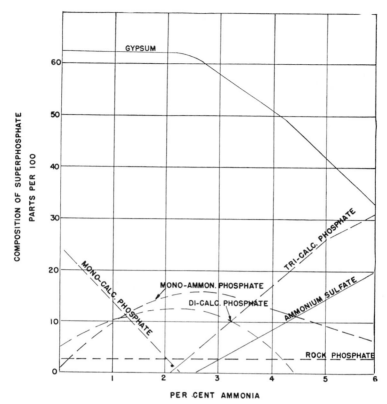

Figure 10.1. Chemical changes in components of normal superphosphate during ammoniation. (*Courtesy E. I. Du Pont deNemours*)

content and temperature, the form in which the ammonia is added, the reaction time allowed, and the design features of the ammoniating equipment. Figure 10.3 shows the effects of particle size, temperature, and moisture on the degree of ammoniation of triple superphosphate.[15] These variables also influence the ammoniation of single superphosphate in a similar way. Preferred particle sizes for both single and triple superphosphate are usually between 40 and 80 mesh and the material used should be porous. Hard, round superphosphate granules, particularly those produced in slurry-type, triple superphosphate plants, although admirable for other purposes, are often difficult to ammoniate and may have to be crushed first.

Concerning moisture content, a figure in the 6 per cent to 8 per cent range is favored by some producers, since this gives more freedom of operation in terms of higher temperatures. As can be seen in Figure 10.3, the degree of ammoniation diminishes very rapidly if the moisture content falls below 2 per cent.

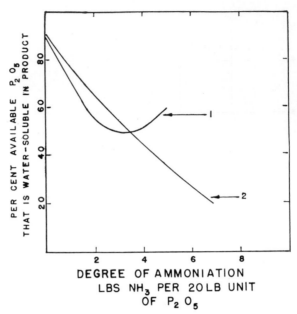

Figure 10.2. Effect of degree of ammoniation on water solubilities of superphosphates. 1—Triple superphosphate. 2—Single superphosphate.

Another important variable is reaction time,[32] a period of 3 to 4 min being found to be generally necessary prior to discharge from the ammoniator unit. This requirement not only determines the design and capacities of batch-type equipment, but has led to the development of continuous ammoniators, having retention times in the 3 to 4 min range. However, when granulation is also undertaken in drum ammoniators, larger volumes are needed and a better basis for design is the unit-drum surface area,[23] as described later.

Heats of Reaction

The absorption of anhydrous ammonia by superphosphates generates about 40 cal/100 g of product,[24] for each pound of ammonia absorbed per 20 lb of P_2O_5 , as shown in Figure 10.4. This value is substantially independent of the amount of P_2O_5 in the superphosphate and the source of phosphate rock. In plant design calculations, additional allowances must be made for reactions between ammonia and other components in the superphosphate, as well as for reactions between other materials which might be added to the ammoniator. The heat produced by ammoniating monocalcium phosphate, single superphosphate, or triple superphosphate is approximately the same in each case, for various degrees of ammoniation per unit of P_2O_5 , as indicated in Figure 10.4.

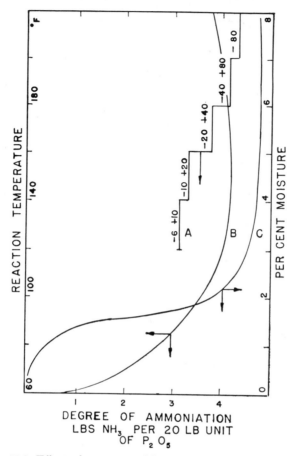

Figure 10.3. Effect of process variables on degree of ammoniation.
A—Particle size. B—Temperature. C—Moisture.

For convenience, typical degrees of ammoniation for various fertilizer materials, and the corresponding heats of ammoniation are given below,[60] in English units:

Material	Lbs NH₃ per 20 lbs P₂O₅	Btu's Evolved per lb of NH₃
Single superphosphate	5.8	1430
Triple superphosphate	3.8	1540
Phosphoric acid	7.2	1780
66° Be sulfuric acid	(0.324)	2940

It should be noted that in most cases the degree of ammoniation of phosphoric acid can be increased by the presence of single superphosphate, since each unit of P₂O₅ from phosphoric acid that can be paired with 2

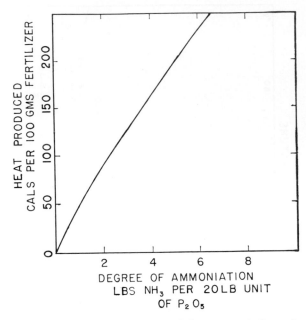

Figure 10.4. Heat developed by ammoniation of single superphosphate, triple superphosphate or monocalcium phosphate.

units of P_2O_5 from single superphosphate will react with an additional 2.4 lb of ammonia.

Higher temperatures tend to increase the amount of ammonia absorbed, but limitations are imposed by the need to maintain a minimum moisture content consistent with proper granulation and drying, as well as the minimum moisture requirements indicated in Figure 10.3. In addition, overheating is likely to promote excessive ammonia loss as well as the formation of troublesome fumes and may even lead to flash fires, particularly if ammonium nitrate is present. Operating temperatures in the ammoniator-granulator-dryer section of typical plants are generally in the 180° to 250°F range, the optimum value being found by experience in each case. One approximate guide to temperature rise during ammoniation[18] is given by:

$$\text{Increase in temperature} = 1.7 \times \text{pounds of ammonia}$$
$$\text{per ton of superphosphate}$$

Increases in temperature caused by additions of various ammoniating materials are shown in Figure 10.5.

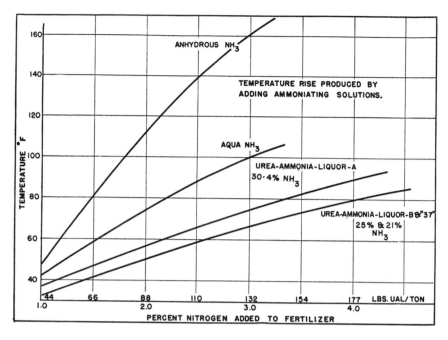

Figure 10.5. Temerature curves for various ammoniating materials. (*Courtesy E. I. du Pont deNemours*)

For some formulations, chemical reactions provide most or all of the heat required to evaporate the water in the process and to produce a cured fertilizer with satisfactory storage properties. In other instances, reaction heats must be supplemented by subsequent drying, since not only must the moisture content of the product be reduced to a minimum level, but the ammoniation reaction and various secondary reactions must be accelerated to completion, otherwise caking is likely to occur in the stored and bagged product. Adequate drying is also needed to arrest loss of P_2O_5 availability, as clearly shown[63] in Figure 10.6.

Cooling

The necessity for adequate cooling facilities is also evident from Figure 10.6, otherwise P_2O_5 reversion may take place in storage, even though the product be relatively dry. This especially applies to products containing substantial amounts of ammoniated, concentrated superphosphate. The loss of P_2O_5 availability due to higher storage temperatures is lessened by the presence of ammonium sulfate, which apparently exerts a beneficial tempering effect,[63] as indicated in Figure 10.7.

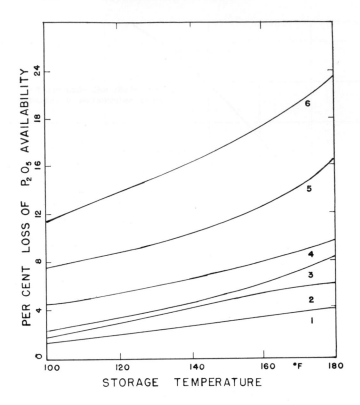

Figure 10.6. Effect of storage temperatures, time and moisture, on loss of P_2O_5 availability in 6-12-12 fertilizer.

Ref. Number	Moisture, Per Cent	Storage, Days
1	3 to 4	30
2	Do.	90
3	5 to 6	30
4	Do.	90
5	11	30
6	Do.	90

Ammonia Loss

Precautions must be taken during ammoniation (and also during drying and subsequent processing) to minimize loss of ammonia. The principal causes of high nitrogen losses include excessively high ammoniating and drying temperatures; inadequate times of reaction, drying, and cooling; and ineffective design and operation of the ammoniator, granulator, and dryer. The form in which ammonia is added can affect ammonia losses. In

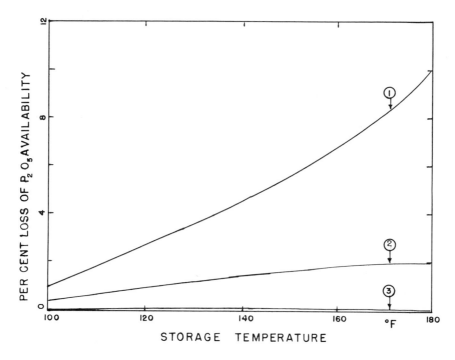

Figure 10.7. Tempering effect of ammonium sulfate on loss of P_2O_5 availability during storage for 60 days.

    Curve 1—8-43-0 Ex triple superphosphate (no $(NH_4)_2SO_4$ present).
    Curve 2—10-10-10 Ex single superphosphate.
    Curve 3—10-20-20 Ex triple superphosphate.

one reported case, changing from liquid to gaseous anhydrous ammonia increased ammonia losses by about 8 per cent. Hence, the addition of ammonia as an anhydrous liquid or in the form of nitrogen solutions helps to minimize plant nitrogen losses. Unduly high degrees of ammoniation will increase ammonia losses, although some producers prefer to operate at high ammoniation rates and peak output levels, at the expense of some additional nitrogen. The general relation between ammonia loss and degree of ammoniation[22] is indicated in Figure 10.8.

COMPOUND AMMONIATED FERTILIZERS

    Ammoniated superphosphates form ideal base materials for the production of powdered and granulated compound fertilizers, as well as fertilizer mixtures. However, the addition of salts, such as ammonium sulfate,

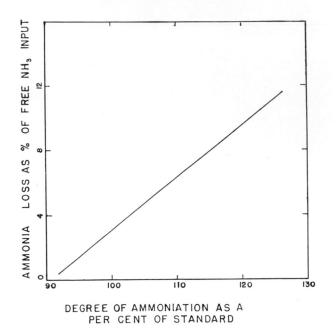

Figure 10.8. Degree of ammoniation and effect on ammonia loss.

Standard degrees of ammoniation

$= 7.2$ lb free NH_3 per unit
of P_2O_5 for phosphoric acid
$= 5.8$ lb ditto for single superphosphate
$= 3.8$ lb ditto for triple superphosphate

potassium chloride, ammonium nitrate, or urea, can give rise to storage and handling problems unless internal reactions are completed beforehand. Typical examples of these include the following:

$$(NH_4)_2SO_4 + Ca(H_2PO_4)_2 \rightarrow 2(NH_4)H_2PO_4 + CaSO_4 \qquad (10.5)$$

$$(NH_4)_2SO_4 + 2KCl \rightarrow 2NH_4Cl + K_2SO_4 \qquad (10.6)$$

$$(NH_4)NO_3 + KCl \rightarrow NH_4Cl + KNO_3 \qquad (10.7)$$

Under some conditions, diammonium phosphate can also react with superphosphates[25] to perform incipient ammoniation which is illustrated by the following reactions:

$$Ca(H_2PO_4)_2 \cdot H_2O + 2(NH_4)_2HPO_4 \rightarrow$$
$$Ca(NH_4)_2(HPO_4)_2 \cdot H_2O + 2NH_4H_2PO_4 \qquad (10.8)$$

$$Ca(H_2PO_4)_2 \cdot H_2O + (NH_4)_2HPO_4 \rightarrow$$

$$CaHPO_4 + 2NH_4H_2PO_4 + H_2O \tag{10.9}$$

Subsequent ammoniation of such mixtures by conventional methods usually results in a lower degree of absorption than would be obtained by ammoniating the superphosphate alone, which has led some producers to believe that DAP causes a nitrogen loss when used in conjunction with ammoniated superphosphate. However, this has been shown not to be the case, and under reasonable processing and storage conditions, such mixtures should be stable. The use of DAP together with ammoniated superphosphates enables relatively high nitrogen grades to be made, such as 15-30-0, 16-20-0, and 12-24-12.

The use of dolomite and certain other magnesium-containing materials in conjunction with ammoniated superphosphates (alone or in mixtures) either as a coating agent or as a source of magnesium for plant-nutrient purposes is limited because of the tendency to cause a reversion of some of the P_2O_5 to less available forms, as well as promoting the loss of some nitrogen, i.e.,

$$2Ca(H_2PO_4)_2 + CaCO_3 \cdot MgCO_3 \rightarrow$$

$$3CaHPO_4 + MgHPO_4 + 2H_2O + 2CO_2 \tag{10.10}$$

$$5NH_4H_2PO_4 + 3CaCO_3 \cdot MgCO_3 \rightarrow$$

$$Ca_3(PO_4)_2 + 3MgNH_4PO_4 + 2NH_3 + 6H_2O + 6CO_2 \tag{10.11}$$

These reactions are accelerated by increased storage times and temperatures. A high calcium content in the dolomite tends to cause reversion of some of the P_2O_5 to forms which are almost totally water-insoluble. Calcium sulfate present in single superphosphate also enters into some of these reactions and may reduce nitrogen losses on the following lines:

$$4NH_4H_2PO_4 + 2CaCO_3 \cdot MgCO_3 + CaSO_4 \rightarrow$$

$$Ca_3(PO_4)_2 + 2MgNH_4PO_4 + (NH_4)_2SO_4 + 4H_2O + 4CO_2 \tag{10.12}$$

When nitrogen solutions are used for ammoniating purposes, it is possible that additional reactions necessitating special consideration, will arise from this source. Many of these solutions contain urea, and complexes such as $CO(NH_2)_2NH_4Cl$ may form in conjunction with Eqs. (10.6) and (10.7). When ammonium nitrate is present, controlled cooling of the product is often necessary in addition to careful drying, because of the crystal transition temperatures at about 90°F and 184°F. Crystallization occurring in the stored and bagged product may also contribute to caking. The importance of proper drying and cooling in arresting the reversion of the phosphate component to less available forms has already been stressed.

An appreciation of these chemical and physical factors, plus the development of advanced processing equipment enables fertilizers to be made that, in terms of plant-food content and physical properties, would have been impossible a decade ago. The selection of the optimum particle-size ranges and the use of specific coating agents are other important considerations when producing stable, granular fertilizers based on ammoniated superphosphates.

Production Technology (Including Granulation)

Progress in ammoniated superphosphate manufacture[10] has been intimately associated with developments in granular fertilizer production, and it is difficult to refer to one without constant reference to the other. Therefore, in addition to a description of ammoniation techniques, a brief review of granular fertilizer technology will also be included. This will be applicable to the production of other types of fertilizers such as granular ammonium phosphates and N-PK- mixtures, as well as to ammoniated superphosphates.

Process Developments.   At first, ammoniation of superphosphates was undertaken on a simple batch basis, by sprinkling ammoniacal liquors or aqua-ammonia on powdered material and mixing either by hand, or in simple equipment of the pan or drum type, prior to slow curing and cooling in a storage pile. It soon became evident that the granular type of material produced by the rolling action in mechanical mixers gave many advantages to producers, distributors, and users. This led, in turn, to the development of highly specialized batch granulators, both with and without ammoniation, supplemented by screening equipment to give a product with a well-defined size range.

After the chemistry of ammoniation had been defined, the importance of proper cooling became apparent. Similarly, as other materials such as ammonium salts and potash were added to fertilizer mixtures, the need for adequate drying became evident to insure that products would be physically and chemically stable and would possess satisfactory storage and handling properties. In some plants, granulation was undertaken principally in the ammoniator and completed in the cooler and/or dryer. In other installations, separate granulators of the drum, pugmill, or pan type were used. A wide variety of processes thus came into being, which could be principally grouped into two categories, namely, plants using batch ammoniation and continuous cooling, drying, and screening; and installations in which ammoniation, as well as other unit operations were continuous.

Ammoniation. The foregoing developments were made possible to a large extent by refinements in the design of pugmill- and drum-type ammoniators, and to a lesser degree by the adaptation of pan granulators for ammoniating purposes. One of the most popular items in this category is the TVA rotary drum ammoniator-granulator,[62, 63] which is now used for producing ammonium phosphates on a large scale, as well as ammoniated superphosphates, and undoubtedly, also has future applications as a multiphase reactor in other industries. This machine is illustrated in Figure 10.9A and Figure 10.9B. The inventors advise that the spargers be located where the material is moving with the rotation of the drum, but not so close to the shell that lumps might lodge between sparger and shell. The center of the bed is relatively inactive and is not a suitable location for spargers. Holes in an ammonia sparger are oriented so that they face oncoming material. Holes in an acid sparger should be pointed upward.

Extensive literature is available on ammoniation and granulation practices, and typical examples of horizontal mixers, pug-mills[11, 17] and pan granulators[1, 21, 30] have been described. The TVA ammoniator-granulator has also been the subject of many investigations,[42, 62, 63] both on a pilot plant and a production scale. In one survey made during 1961 covering 77 plants,[2] the dimensions, construction details, and operating procedures pertaining to TVA ammoniators were examined and compared. Ammoniator volumes ranged more or less proportionately from about 100 cu ft for 10 tons/hr capacity to 500 cu ft for 27 tons/hr. However, more recent information indicates that larger unit volumes are preferable and also conducive to increased outputs and reduced nitrogen losses.

Latest information[24] demonstrates that a more reliable guide to optimum drum size than retention time is the cylindrical surface area and 20 to 30 sq ft/ton/hr is desirable; thus, an 8 ft diameter by 16 ft long ammoniator should be suitable for outputs up to 20 tons/hr. Appropriate drum speeds can be calculated on the following basis:

$$\text{rpm} = \frac{20 \text{ to } 27}{\sqrt{D}}$$

where D is the drum diameter in feet.

In some cases, horizontal mounting of the drum is used, while in others, a downward slope of $\frac{1}{4}$ in/ft has been adopted. Spargers should be submerged to a level corresponding to about 75 per cent of the bed depth, and are preferably made of Hastelloy C or stainless steel, when phosphoric and sulfuric acids are used. Some plants have installed reciprocating scrapers, and/or drum knockers to minimize internal build-up, and when large amounts of water vapor are removed in the ammoniator, it is advisa-

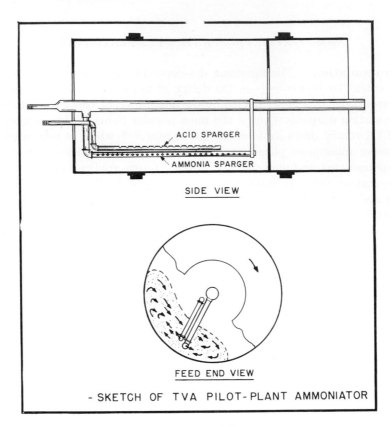

SIDE VIEW

ACID SPARGER

AMMONIA SPARGER

FEED END VIEW

- SKETCH OF TVA PILOT-PLANT AMMONIATOR

Figure 10.9A

Figure 10.9B. Rotary ammoniator-granulator. (*Courtesy A. J. Sackett & Sons Co.*)

ble to install a blower to assist evaporation; about 400 cu ft/min for each ton of output per hour has been advocated.

A schematic design of a pugmill ammoniator is given in Figure 10.10A and a pan granulator installation is shown diagrammatically in Figure 10.11. The latter is capable of producing excellent granules and is especially suitable for combining small amounts of liquids with solids on a continuous basis. It is possible to make some grades in a pan granulator without the use of a dryer, but as a rule, a dryer and cooler are advisable to provide flexibility.

As compared to other types of ammoniator-granulators, pan granulators tend to give higher nitrogen losses, largely because of the smaller bed depth and the shorter retention time. For this reason the addition of ammonia to superphosphates in a pan granulator is not favored by some operators. In general, it is considered that the pan machine should be regarded as a useful adjunct to a pugmill or rotary drum ammoniator, instead of a direct replacement.[21]

Preneutralization. A practical way to increase the output of most types of ammoniators is to undertake part of the liquid and gaseous-liquid reactions in a separate unit prior to mixing with solids in the ammoniator. Preneutralization, as this is called, has become an essential feature of many ammoniation-granulation plants[44, 45] and has been found to offer the following advantages: increased plant output for a relatively low additional capital cost; smaller recycle ratios; reduced production of fumes and less risk of flash fires; lower nitrogen loss; better granulation control; and ability to produce inverted, high nitrogen grades, such as 2-1-1(20-10-10) and 1-1-1 compounds such as (12-12-12).

In some cases, preneutralization is undertaken in a mild steel tank provided with adequate agitation and vapor removal facilities, as well as reliable flow and pH controls. In other instances, special equipment such as pipe-type reactors are used and the liquid is flashed into an ammoniator-granulator of the pugmill or drum type. Effective combination of preneutralized liquids and recycling solids in ammoniators at first presented problems, but these have largely been overcome by use of specially designed distributors, strategically located in the ammoniator. Figure 10.10 shows one recommended way of installing a block or slit-type sparger in a pugmill. Figure 10.12 illustrates a saw-tooth distributor which has been found to give uniform spreading of preneutralized slurry over the granule bed in a drum ammoniator, together with comparative freedom from blockages.

It is evident that ammoniation-granulation plants with large preneutralization units become closely similar to ammonium phosphate plants described in Chapter 9. In fact, granulated ammophos (16-20-0), mono-

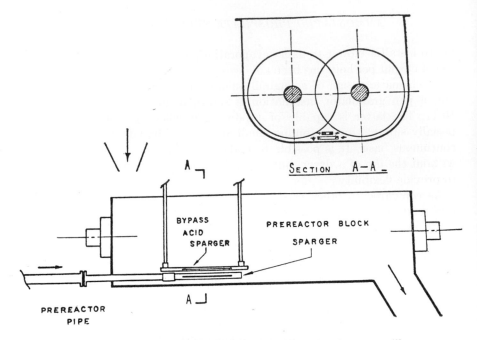

Figure 10.10A. Recommended location of spargers in a pugmill.

Figure 10.10B. Pugmill-ammoniator.
(*Courtesy Fertilizer Equipment & Engineering Co.*)

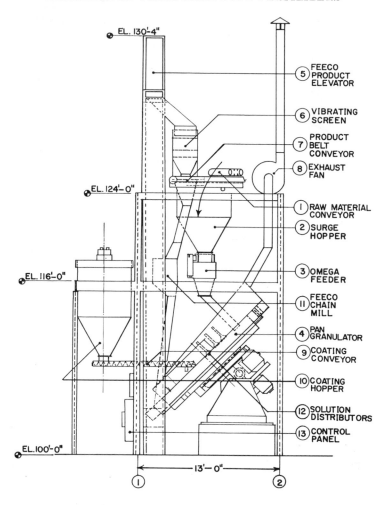

EL. 130'-4"

EL. 124'-0"

EL. 116'-0"

EL. 100'-0"

5 FEECO PRODUCT ELEVATOR

6 VIBRATING SCREEN

7 PRODUCT BELT CONVEYOR

8 EXHAUST FAN

1 RAW MATERIAL CONVEYOR

2 SURGE HOPPER

3 OMEGA FEEDER

11 FEECO CHAIN MILL

4 PAN GRANULATOR

9 COATING CONVEYOR

10 COATING HOPPER

12 SOLUTION DISTRIBUTORS

13 CONTROL PANEL

13'—0"

1   2

Figure 10.11. Pan ammoniation-granulation system (Ductag-type).
(*Courtesy Fertilizer Equipment and Engineering Co.*)

ammonium phosphate (11-48-0), and diammonium phosphate (16-48-0) can be made without difficulty by using suitable nitrogen solutions (or ammonia, phosphoric, and sulfuric acids) and establishing the requisite operating conditions. A typical flow diagram for a continuous granulated ammoniated phosphate plant is given in Figure 10.13. The interior of a plant and its equipment are shown in Figure 10.14A and 10.14B.

Granulation. Successful granulation is dependent on three principal factors; first, the preparation of a slurry that will granulate readily; sec-

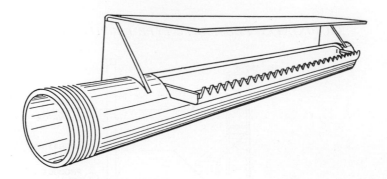

Figure 10.12. Saw-tooth slurry distributor for rotary drum, ammoniator-granulators. (*Courtesy TVA*)

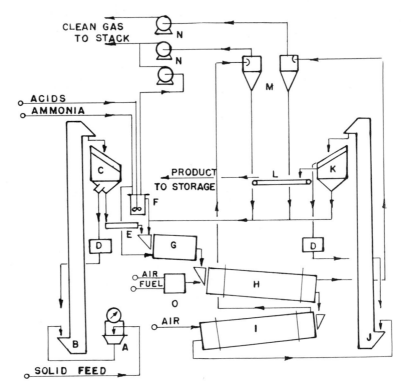

Legend:

A. Solids weigher
B. Primary elevator
C. Primary screens
D. Chain mills
E. Solids feeder
F. Preneutralizer
G. Ammoniator-granulator
H. Dryer

I. Cooler
J. Secondary elevator
K. Secondary screens
L. Product conveyor
M. Dust cyclones
N. Exhaust fans
O. Furnace

Figure 10.13. Typical ammoniated phosphate process flow diagram.

Figure 10.14A. General view of modern granulating plant showing Sackett Star Granulator, dryer combustion chamber and miscellaneous drying equipment. (*Courtesy A. J. Sackett & Sons Co.*)

Figure 10.14B. View showing location of equipment in medium-sized ammoniation/ granulation plant. (*Courtesy Longhorn Construction Co.*)

ond, the design of suitable equipment; and third, the selection and maintenance of proper plant conditions. In granular fertilizer production, it is thus important to ensure that the desired formulations and the corresponding wet mixes also contain the correct balance of water-soluble salts and free moisture.

With these provisions, and with well-designed equipment operated correctly, granulation will proceed readily. In fact, a survey of about one hundred U. S. plants showed that nearly 80 per cent employed no separate granulator at all.[26] About 10 per cent used a section of the ammoniator primarily for granulation purposes and another 10 per cent used part of the dryer as a granulator.

Control of granulation is maintained in several ways, principally according to the nitrogen content of the fertilizer produced. Low nitrogen grades tend to exhibit initial granulation difficulties and high nitrogen grades may granulate too rapidly. One review of US granulation control procedures, showed that the most favored methods for low N grades were based on adjusting the addition of water, granular potash, excess acid or steam, in that order. (Steam is a popular granulating aid in many plants outside the USA.) High N grades were mostly controlled by varying the ratio of liquid-to-solid nitrogen additions, or by adjusting the recycle ratio. A few plants used air-blowing or other means for controlling granulation and the appearance of the product.

Drying and Cooling. It is possible to produce some grades of fertilizers based on ammoniated superphosphates without the use of a dryer, by performing the required evaporation in the ammoniator and/or the cooler. However, the need to generate sufficient heat via chemical reactions calls for increased operating skill and may cause unavoidable fuming and nitrogen loss. Moreover, the absence of a dryer reduces the flexibility and scope of a plant; consequently, the majority of producers consider the additional capital and operating cost of a dryer to be justified.

In a survey of nearly eighty U. S. ammoniation-granulation plants, dryers were installed in over 90 per cent of these, and the large majority of units were of co-current, rotary drum type.[2, 20] Most were between 6 and 8 ft in diameter and 35 to 55 ft in length, although some plants having large continuous ammoniators reported using dryers of appreciably larger dimensions.

Many ammoniation-granulation plants employ rotary drum coolers for reasons already described. These are generally of the countercurrent air-flow type and are similar in size to the dryers preceding them. Hignett believes that larger coolers can frequently be used with advantage.[24] In one plant, a small fluidized bed cooler has been employed successfully for several years and, apart from considerable savings in size and cost, this unit offers excellent flexibility and simplicity of operation. It is possible that such a unit could also be utilized for ammoniation purposes, as well as for granulating and drying, as is done in other industries.

Screening, Dust, and Fume Control. Close fractionation of granule sizes is essential for two major reasons. First, the control of the size and quantity of the recycled fines affects the entire plant output, as well as determining the appearance and uniformity of the granular product. (This is especially true in the case of slurry-type plants whose operations are based on nucleation or agglomeration techniques.) Second, the product is almost always required to be within a well-defined and relatively narrow range of particle sizes. The rapid rise in the use of bulk-blended fertilizers has emphasized the importance of uniformity in particle size and shape, since these are critical factors in minimizing segregation after dry mixing. Many plants have adopted sloping, double-deck vibrating screens, followed by a chain mill or hammer mill to reduce oversize, which is recycled with the fines back to the ammoniator-granulator.

Suppression of dust and fumes is also a major consideration in the design and operation of compound granulated fertilizer plants,[47] as a means of minimizing plant losses as well as preventing air pollution. Generally, dust from units such as dryers, coolers, screens, and material transfer points, is collected by a dust system (designed in accordance with empirical factors[31] and experience) and is largely recovered in cyclones, before being vented to atmosphere via bag collectors or wet scrubbers. Fumes from neutralizers, ammoniating units, and dryers are likely to contain small quantities of ammonia which can be recovered in wet scrubbers and returned to the system, if this is found to be justified.

Plant Design and Materials of Construction. The layout and design of granulated fertilizer plants generally follow an established pattern, which is predetermined by the need to accommodate lengthy dryers and coolers and the necessity to provide simple flow-patterns for the in-process solid materials. Accordingly, the ammoniator-granulator is usually mounted above the dryer (if one is used) and the cooler is located below, or alongside, and parallel to the dryer. Raw materials are then fed to the granulator via a primary elevator, and after cooling, the granular material is transferred to the screens by a secondary elevator, although in some plants only the on-size product is cooled.

Preneutralizers or other types of liquid reactors are often positioned above the granulator feed point, to simplify the transfer of slurry. Duct work, cyclones, dust collectors, and scrubbers must be installed in a manner which reduces to a minimum the occurrence of blockages. Ample access to all equipment for cleaning and maintenance purposes must be provided, and the control center should preferably be located within direct sight of the ammoniator-granulator, which might be considered to be the heart of the plant, and thus is in need of frequent observation.

For process and storage buildings, steel sections protected with acid-resistant paint and covered in transite are popular construction materials. Translucent plastic panels, installed where needed, are more satisfactory than glazed windows, because of better corrosion resistance and easier cleaning. Regarding equipment, mild steel construction is suitable in most cases for handling solid materials, especially when dry. Stainless steel or rubber linings may be needed for the wetted parts of some equipment items, such as pumps, as well as for piping and fittings handling corrosive liquids such as phosphoric acid. Hastelloy C may be justified for certain critical applications, such as spargers and spray nozzles. Frequently, corrosion problems are specific to individual plants, and the optimum materials of construction are eventually found by practical experience.

Formulation Methods. As previously mentioned, when producing granular fertilizers, formulations must be undertaken with the two-fold aim of meeting product specifications regarding plant nutrient requirements and simultaneously providing a mix that will granulate properly. In addition, the free-water content of the feed should be kept as low as possible, in order to minimize drying needs.

Numerous theoretical formulations can be determined by trial and error, or by mathematical formulas,[38, 48, 53, 59] or can even be developed on the basis of appropriate computer programs,[40] which are also able to take into account heat-balance requirements and economic considerations.[38] On the basis of these guides, actual raw material needs and optimum operating conditions can then be finally established by trial in a pilot installation or a full scale plant.

One useful way of investigating possible raw material needs is to develop triangular diagrams[10, 38, 59] on the lines of Figures 10.15 and 10.16. These can be constructed in terms of either N, P_2O_5 and K_2O, or for one nutrient only, when it is desired to find the amount of a single plant food available from a mixture of three sources.[58] This approach can also be used to find corresponding degrees of ammoniation, solubility ratios, and appropriate cost data for composite materials.

The basic principle of these diagrams is shown in Figure 10.15, whereby any point in the triangle ABC represents the composition of a material in terms of N, P_2O_5, and K_2O according to the perpendicular distance between that point and the appropriate axis (each apex represents 100 per cent of

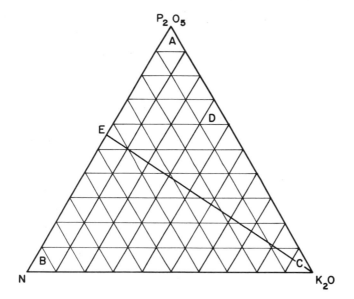

Figure 10.15. Basic triangular diagram for N-P-K fertilizers.

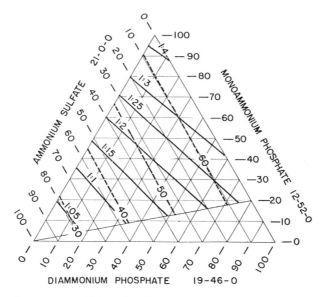

Figure 10.16. Triangular diagram for ammonium sulfate-phosphate formulations.

a single component). On this basis, point D corresponds to a product whose total plant food content contains 10 per cent N, 60 per cent P_2O_5, and 30 per cent K_2O. Similarly, a material such as 16-20-0 can be represented on the diagram by point E, since its total plant-food content is approximately 44 per cent N and 56 per cent P_2O_5.

Thus, triangle AEC represents the limits of formulation ratios that can be produced with 16-20-0 plus another phosphate-containing material and a potassium salt. Higher nitrogen ratios would necessitate the use or addition of a higher grade of nitrogen-containing fertilizer. Figure 10.16 represents a more complex diagram and is constructed in terms of N to P ratios and total N plus P_2O_5 nutrient contents which are indicated by the sloping dotted lines. Ratios of the corresponding salts needed can be determined in accordance with the nutrient contents desired, by finding the appropriate points of intersection.[16]

When undertaking raw material calculations, one must make adequate allowances for free moisture present and also for plant losses, otherwise the products will be below grade. One helpful method of calculating raw material requirements is given in Table 10.1.[52]

Within the limits imposed by cost and practicality, many grades can be formulated in several alternative ways by varying the types of ratios of raw materials. The ultimate choice is usually in accordance with minimum manufacturing costs and product suitability. This is illustrated in Table 10.2 as alternative successful methods of producing 20-10-10 reported by Young, and based on the use of a preneutralizer.[64] Inverse-ratio grades of this nature are normally difficult to produce and it is of added interest to

TABLE 10.1

Material	Lb	N	P_2O_5	K_2O	H_2O	NH₃ Added	NH₃ Absorbed
Nitrogen solution, 44% N (22-66-6)	386	169.8			23.2	84.9	
Muriate of potash, 61% K_2O	530			323.3			
Ordinary super, 19.5% APA, 6% H_2O	827		161.3		49.6		46.8
Triple super, 46% APA, 4% H_2O	237		109.0		9.5		19.1
Phosphoric acid, W.P. 75%, 54.5% APA, 16% H_2O	97		52.9		15.5		19.1
Total	2077	169.8	323.2	323.3	97.8	84.9	85.0
Water lost in drying	77				77.0		
Difference	2000				20.8		
Analysis at 1% end-product moisture and no ammonia loss			8.49	16.16	16.17		

TABLE 10.2

| | Per Ton | |
	Method A	Method B
Feed to preneutralizer:		
17-67-0 nitrogen solution.....	16 units N	18 units N
94 per cent sulfuric acid.....	461 lb	—
Phosphoric acid............	—	6.5 units P_2O_5
Water.....................	83 lb	50 lb
Ammonia as per cent of stoichiometric total..........	95	89
Ammonia loss, per cent......	0.5	2.7
Feed to ammoniator:		
17-67-0 nitrogen solution.....	2 units N	—
Diammonium phosphate.....	2 units N, 5 units P_2O_5	—
Triple superphosphate.......	5 units P_2O_5	3.5 units P_2O_5
Recycle ratio.................	1.0	1.9

note the drastic reduction in recycle requirements made possible by the use of a preneutralizer, without which a recycle ratio of 6 or 8 to 1 of product has generally been found necessary.

Process Control. In addition to the various methods previously outlined for control of granulation, measurement and control are necessary for other process variables such as the quantities and ratios of liquid and solid raw materials, the temperatures in the preneutralizer, the ammoniator-granulator, the dryer and cooler, and the gas velocities at various points in the system. Ammeters on main drives are also useful guides to plant performance.

In all but the smallest installations, it is preferable that instruments and controllers be mounted on a panel board in a suitable control room to minimize damage from dust and fume and to provide centralized operation. In some recent fertilizer plants, promising steps have been taken to improve operator scrutiny by means of closed circuit television cameras, mounted in strategic places, such as the interior of granulators and dryers. Attempts to close control loops with the aim of establishing fully automated plants have also been under consideration for some time. However, to a considerable extent, successful granular fertilizer production is an art and will thus continue to be largely dependent on operating skill.

NITROPHOSPHATES

Although nitrophosphate compounds are fundamentally based on reactions between phosphate rock and nitric acid,[33, 49] ammonia is also used in their manufacture to improve quality and grade by inducing the formation of associated ammonium salts *in situ*. Accordingly, a description of nitrophosphate fertilizers will be included in this section.

The use of nitric acid instead of sulfuric acid to produce phosphate fertilizers from phosphate rock received a stimulus in Europe shortly after World War II, when a prolonged sulfur shortage appeared likely. The shortage was of limited duration, but the advantages of making compound fertilizers without the aid of sulfuric acid and/or phosphoric acid has since appealed to producers in various parts of the world. This particularly applies to countries importing sulfur, such as India, and also where feedstocks for ammonia production are available at reasonable cost, since part of the ammonia can be employed to make nitric acid and part used in the nitrophosphate process. Although produced in great quantities in Europe, nitrophosphates are made to a limited extent at the present time in the USA, where a general preference exists for mixed goods, ammoniated superphosphates, ammonium phosphates, and liquid fertilizers.

The chemistry of nitrophosphate fertilizer production is complex and numerous reactions and inter-reactions can take place according to the types and ratios of raw materials used, as well as the operating conditions established. An example of one reaction between phosphate rock and nitric acid, in the presence of some phosphoric acid either added as a raw material or produced indigenously, can be shown as:

$$Ca_{10}F_2(PO_4)_6 + 20HNO_3 + 4H_3PO_4 \rightarrow$$
$$10Ca(NO_3)_2 + 10H_3PO_4 + 2HF \tag{10.13}$$

Part of the HF is evolved as gaseous derivatives and the remainder, which may amount to 0.3 to 0.5 moles of F, will react with some calcium nitrate, i.e.,

$$Ca(NO_3)_2 + 2HF \rightarrow CaF_2 + 2HNO_3 \tag{10.14}$$

The CaF_2 is precipitated during a later ammoniation stage and reduces to some extent the nutrient value of the product.

Based on the ratio of tricalcium phosphate to nitric acid present, the following empirical reactions can take place:

$$Ca_3(PO_4)_2 + 6HNO_3 \rightarrow 3Ca(NO_3)_2 + 2H_3PO_4 \tag{10.15}$$

$$Ca_3(PO_4)_2 + 4HNO_3 \rightarrow 2Ca(NO_3)_2 + Ca(H_2PO_4)_2 \tag{10.16}$$

$$Ca_3(PO_4)_2 + 2HNO_3 \rightarrow Ca(NO_3)_2 + 2CaHPO_4 \tag{10.17}$$

In some processes and for certain grades, material balances correspond approximately with Eq. (10.16). Although Eq. (10.17) is probably over-simplified and difficult to control, some processes can be made to yield dicalcium phosphate in accordance with the mole ratios shown, probably via an intermediate series of reactions. One example[36] of the relation between P_2O_5 availability and the degree of acidulation is given in Figure 10.17.

In most cases, the end products of reactions between phosphate rock and nitric acid cannot be directly used for fertilizer purposes because of the hygroscopic and corrosive nature of the calcium nitrate formed. Therefore, further processing is usually undertaken to overcome this limitation, either to remove the calcium nitrate or to convert it *in situ* to less hygroscopic materials. Accordingly, most nitrophosphate processes fall into one or the other of these categories.

An exception is the Swiss Lonza process in which a trihydrate form of calcium nitrate is produced instead of the customary tetrahydrate, since the former is less hygroscopic and thereby avoids the need for separation

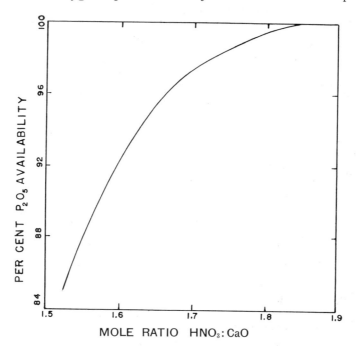

Figure 10.17. Degree of acidulation and effect on P_2O_5 availability in product.

Florida rock: 49.4% CaO, 34.6% P_2O_5
Nitric acid: 39–42% HNO_3
Retention: 45–60 min.

from the nitrophosphate. The product is said to have good storage properties in average European climates, and in addition, up to 80 per cent of the P_2O_5 can be produced in a water-soluble form.

Processes Based on Calcium Nitrate Separation

Numerous European nitrophosphate processes based on the removal of the calcium nitrate have been developed, and the majority of these are variations of the earlier "Odda" Norwegian process. In 1962 about two million metric tons of "complex" nitrophosphate fertilizers were said to be produced by these processes. The principal ones, in addition to the Odda method, are those of BASF, Hoechst and Chemische Fabrik Kalk in Germany, and the FAS process of the Dutch State Mines.[43]

In the more recent versions of the Odda process,[57] phosphate rock having a fineness of about 95 per cent through 30 mesh (Tyler) is digested in 1.3 to 1.5 parts of nitric acid per part of rock. This reaction yields about 70 m cal per metric ton of rock, which helps to maintain a temperature of 55° to 70°C in the reactors. The liquor is next crystallized either batchwise or continuously in agitated vessels fitted with brine-cooled coils, to separate the calcium nitrate. In some plants, instead of producing calcium nitrate tetrahydrate, a little ammonium nitrate is added prior to crystallization, which yields the double salt $5Ca(NO_3)_2 \cdot NH_4NO_3 \cdot 10H_2O$ and which also reduces cooling requirements by raising the crystallization temperature from about 10°C to 25°C.

An economic separation limit exists, beyond which it is preferable to leave some of the calcium nitrate in the liquor, because of increasing energy requirements for refrigeration. In some plants, the cooling provided by the evaporation of the anhydrous liquid ammonia needed for producing the requisite nitric acid and for subsequent ammoniation of the nitrophosphate slurry is usually sufficient to crystallize 60 to 70 per cent of the total calcium nitrate, which after separation results in a product containing about 40 to 50 per cent of the total P_2O_5 in a water-soluble form.

When batch crystallization is undertaken, a rotary drum vacuum filter is used for separation purposes. With continuous crystallization, two centrifuges in series, plus an intermediate nitric acid wash, are favored by some producers. In most cases, after separation the $CaO:P_2O_5$ ratio in the mother liquor is 2 to 1 or lower. The separated crystals are melted at about 42°C, clarified, neutralized with ammonia gas prior to evaporation and prilling, and are then cooled in a fluid-bed heat exchanger before screening and bagging.

In the Dutch process, the calcium nitrate (kalksalpeter or KS) is produced in the form of flakes, either as the decahydrate of calcium ammonium nitrate containing 15.5 per cent N, or as anhydrous calcium nitrate containing 16.7 per cent N. The former tends to be hygroscopic and will deliquesce when the ambient relative humidity exceeds 50 per cent. The latter, although still more hygroscopic, can absorb some 40 per cent of its own weight of water before deliquescing. If the amount of water absorbed is less, the product is normally satisfactory. KS material in either form is packed in moisture-proof bags to reduce subsequent caking tendencies as much as possible.

Mother liquor from the calcium nitrate separation section is neutralized step-wise in two to four successive, agitated vessels, the heat evolved being about 1250 m cal per metric ton of ammonia consumed. Considerable evaporation occurs, which may cause the formation of a pasty slurry, when producing certain formulations.

If the $CaO:P_2O_5$ ratio is less than 2 after calcium nitrate removal, subsequent ammoniation will first convert all of the remaining calcium to dicalcium phosphate, and will then result in the formation of mono- and diammonium phosphates, according to the amount of P_2O_5 in solution and the pH of the liquor, in the following general way:

$$a\mathrm{Ca(NO_3)_2} + b\mathrm{HNO_3} + c\mathrm{H_3PO_4} + d\mathrm{NH_3} \rightarrow$$
$$e\mathrm{CaHPO_4} + f\mathrm{Ca(NO_3)_2} + g\mathrm{NH_4H_2PO_4} + h\mathrm{NH_4NO_3} \tag{10.18}$$

Increasing the degree of ammoniation results in the formation of additional diammonium phosphate, up to the limit imposed by prohibitive ammonia losses.

In the Odda process, the pH is raised from 1.5 to 3.5 in the first ammoniation section and subsequently to about 5.5 or 6.0 in the final vessel. The neutralized slurry contains about 10 to 15 per cent of water and has a specific gravity of approximately 1.6. A final evaporation prior to granulation to about 5 per cent of free water is frequently undertaken, usually in vertical-tube evaporators.

In some plants, the product is granulated in a double-screw machine after the addition of the desired potassium and/or magnesium salts, and is dried to about 1 per cent free moisture in a rotary dryer, prior to cooling and coating with kieselguher or other suitable agent. The product is packed in moisture-proof bags and a popular grade is 20-20-0, which contains about 50 per cent of the total P_2O_5 in a water-soluble form. A flow diagram of a separation-type nitrophosphate process is given in Figure 10.18 and views of a commercial installation of this type are shown in Figures 10.18A and 10.18B.

For the Dutch process, the proportions in which the various products

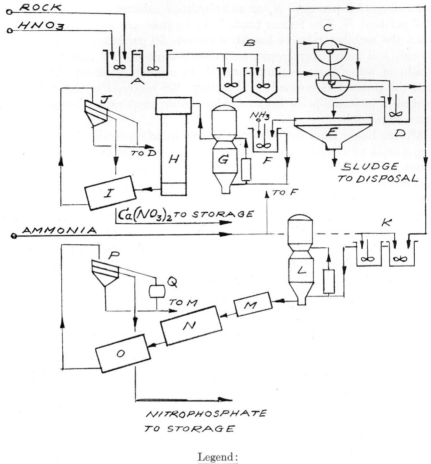

ROCK
HNO₃

AMMONIA

$Ca(NO_3)_2$ TO STORAGE

SLUDGE TO DISPOSAL

NITROPHOSPHATE TO STORAGE

Legend:

A. Digesters

B. Crystallizers

C. Filters

D. Melter

E. Clarifier

F. Neutralizer

G. Evaporator

H. Prilling tower

I. Cooler

J. Screens

K. Ammoniators

L. Evaporators

M. Granulator

N. Dryer

O. Cooler

P. Screens

Q. Oversize mill

Figure 10.18. Flow diagram for separation-type nitrophosphate process.

Figure 10.18A. Nitrophosphate process reaction vessel. (*Courtesy Staatsmijnen in Limburg*)

Figure 10.18B. Brine coolers and crystallizer vessels. (*Courtesy Staatsmijnen in Limburg*)

are obtained in a typical plant per day have been reported as 300 tons of 20-20-0 (FAS.) and 100 tons of calcium ammonium nitrate or 130 tons of granulated anhydrous calcium nitrate (KS) Raw material requirements per ton of product are approximately:

Kg	FAS	Double Salt	Anhydrous Calcium Nitrate
Phosphate rock	600	—	—
Nitric acid	472	660	772
Ammonia	130	14	—

(Nitric acid requirements include those for the ammonium nitrate present. The amount needed to dissolve 600 kg of rock is slightly less.)

A novel method for treatment of calcium nitrate separated from nitrophosphate slurries has been proposed by Nossen,[37] whereby the calcium nitrate solution is concentrated and sprayed onto a bed of calcium oxide heated to about 650°C in a fluidized roaster or rotary kiln. The solution decomposes to lime and nitric oxide, and the latter is absorbed in water to form nitric acid. The chemically pure lime can be made available for sale, and the nitric acid can be recycled to the rock digestion system. A small ammonia burner is proposed for supplying make-up nitric acid needs, which are about 2 to 3 per cent by weight of the rock used. The calcium nitrate decomposition cycle can be shown as

$$Ca(NO_3)_2 \rightarrow CaO + N_2O_5 \text{ , where } N_2O_5 = 2NO_2 + \tfrac{1}{2}O_2 \quad (10.19)$$

$$N_2O_5 + 7H_2O \rightarrow 2(HNO_3 \cdot 3H_2O), \text{ where } NO_2 = NO + \tfrac{1}{2}O_2 \quad (10.20)$$

On a pilot-plant scale, less than 2 per cent of the nitric acid is said to be lost by these reactions.

Processes Based on Chemical Conversion of Calcium Nitrate

As an alternative to the removal of calcium nitrate from nitrophosphate slurry, or leaving it in the product, conversion to less hygroscopic compounds is frequently undertaken. Several interesting proprietary processes based on this principle have been developed, which permit the use of different raw materials, according to cost and availability. In most cases, the calcium nitrate content is first reduced by ammoniation on the following lines:

$$Ca(H_2PO_4)_2 + 2Ca(NO_3)_2 + 2NH_3 \rightarrow$$
$$2CaHPO_4 + 2NH_4NO_3 + Ca(NO_3)_2 \quad (10.21)$$

The remaining calcium nitrate can then be converted to less hygroscopic

material by treatment with various acids according to availability, plus
additional ammonia and/or potassium salts, i.e.,

$$Ca(NO_3)_2 + H_2SO_4 + 2NH_3 \rightarrow CaSO_4 + 2NH_4NO_3 \quad (10.22)$$

$$Ca(NO_3)_2 + 2H_3PO_4 + 2NH_3 \rightarrow Ca(H_2PO_4)_2 + 2NH_4NO_3 \quad (10.23)$$

$$2Ca(NO_3)_2 + 2H_3PO_4 + 4NH_3 \rightarrow 2CaHPO_4 + 4NH_4NO_3 \quad (10.24)$$

$$Ca(NO_3)_2 + (NH_4)_2SO_4 \rightarrow CaSO_4 + 2NH_4NO_3 \quad (10.25)$$

$$Ca(NO_3)_2 + 2KCl \rightarrow CaCl_2 + 2KNO_3 \quad (10.26)$$

$$Ca(NO_3)_2 + K_2SO_4 \rightarrow CaSO_4 + 2KNO_3 \quad (10.27)$$

In practice, acidulation of the rock and the subsequent addition of
ammonia and other reactants must be undertaken under very carefully
controlled conditions; otherwise nitrogen losses will become excessive and
reversion of the P_2O_5 to water-insoluble forms will occur. These reversion
reactions are promoted by the presence of trivalent iron and aluminum
salts, as well as fluorine. Accordingly, the Fe or Al content should not exceed 0.9 per cent. However, reversion is fortunately minimized and stabilized by the addition of magnesium sulfate or potassium sulfate[36] (and
to some extent, aluminum sulfate) as shown in Figure 10.19.

The addition of only 6 to 10 lb of stabilizer salt per ton of product is

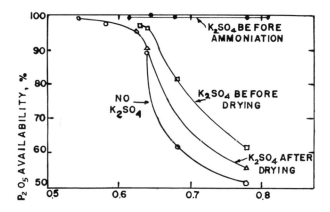

Figure 10.19. Effect of potassium sulfate and its time of addition on P_2O_5 availability in product.

Acidulate HNO_3/CaO Mole Ratio = 1.86
K_2O/P_2O_5 WT. Ratio = 1.0

said to enable a pH of 10 to be reached, without giving rise to excessive reversion, compared to a limiting figure of pH3 when the stabilizer is not present. On a commercial scale, even when every precaution is taken, some 2 to 3 per cent of the P_2O_5 usually reverts to tricalcium phosphate (or an associated hydroxy or fluoride complex) on the following lines:

$$3CaHPO_4 \rightarrow Ca_3(PO_4)_2 + H_3PO_4 \qquad (10.28)$$

Commercial Processes

In addition to processes involving the separation of calcium nitrate, such as the Odda method and variants previously described, several large-scale processes based on treatment with acids and salts on the lines of the foregoing reactions are widely used in Europe and some of these will be briefly outlined. In certain cases, provision can be made for the plant to use alternative raw materials depending on cost and availability, and the various reactions may proceed simultaneously or in succession, according to the operating conditions established and the products desired. Over-all reactions are indicated for each type of process and a general flow diagram is shown in Figure 10.20.

Nitric-Sulfuric Processes. The PEC and Saint-Gobain Processes are well-known examples of this type, in which phosphate rock is digested with a mixture of nitric acid (and sometimes sulfuric acid, when available) and the calcium nitrate formed is converted to less hygroscopic salts by ammoniation. The simplified over-all reaction can be empirically expressed as:

$$Ca_3(PO_4)_2 + H_2SO_4 + 2HNO_3 + NH_3 \rightarrow$$
$$2CaHPO_4 + 2NH_4NO_3 + CaSO_4 \qquad (10.29)$$

In one U. S. plant based on the PEC Process,[3, 9] the reaction system comprises sixteen U-shaped vessels placed in a horseshoe pattern and connected in series. Each vessel is about $2\frac{1}{2}$ ft in diameter and is fitted with a water jacket. A powerful impeller in one arm of each vessel forces slurry downwards, and another impeller in the other arm pulls the slurry upwards and into the next reactor. 316L stainless steel is used for the vessel and impellers.

Phosphate rock is digested with nitric acid in the first three vessels and anhydrous gaseous ammonia is fed via spargers to the following twelve vessels in carefully controlled quantities. Adequate venting of the reaction system is installed to remove nitrite fumes which might otherwise cause a fire hazard. When formulations containing potassium are made, potash is added to the last reactor. Sulfuric and phosphoric acids can also be used

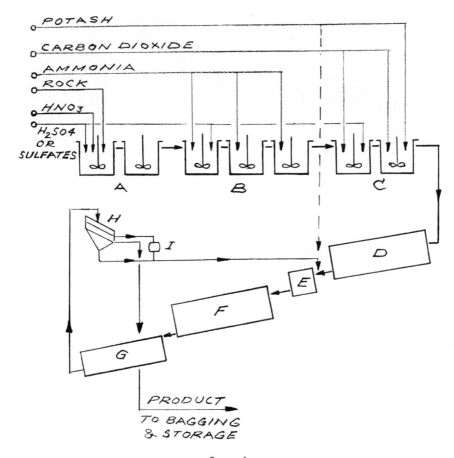

Figure 10.20. General flow diagram for non separation-type nitrophosphate processes.

Legend:

A. Digesters
B. Ammoniators
C. Carbonators
D. N° 1 dryer
E. Granulator

F. N° 2 dryer
G. Cooler
H. Screens
I. Oversize mill

in the process, according to availability and the end product desired. A view of the reactor room in a PEC plant is shown in Figure 10.21.

Slurry from the last reactor contains 30 to 40 per cent water, which is removed in a Spherodizer.[3] This is a specially designed rotary pelletizer-dryer, in which slurry is sprayed against a falling curtain of dried, recycled

Figure 10.21. View of a PEC nitrophosphate plant reactor room. (*Courtesy Chemical & Industrial Corp.*)

fines. Drying is accomplished by hot gas at 400° to 500°F which is blown into the drum at about 25,000 scfm. The drum is 12 ft in diameter and 30 ft long, and is made of mild steel. Recycle ratios used are of the order of only 1.5 to 1 of product. The Spherodizer is illustrated in Figure 10.22.

The product containing less than 1 per cent moisture is cooled in a 12 ft diameter by 30 ft long countercurrent cooler and is coated in an 8 ft diameter by 32 ft long conditioning drum. The plant produces some 600 tons per day of pelletized fertilizer in the 6 to 12 mesh range, and product moisture is between 0.5 and 1.5 per cent, according to grade. Numerous formulations can be made, and although in many grades the P_2O_5 component is largely water-insoluble, citrate solubilities in the region of 95 per cent are obtained. If higher water solubilities are required, the usual 1:1 ratio of ammoniacal nitrogen to nitrate nitrogen can be increased by producing ammonium phosphate *in situ* with the nitrophosphate.

In the Saint-Gobain Process, a series of reaction vessels is also used in which digestion, neutralization and ammoniation are carefully undertaken. Slurry from the last reactor is sent to a specially designed tempering mill, followed by a granulator for combining with recycled fines, before drying,

Figure 10.22. "Spherodizer" granulator-dryer. (*Courtesy Chemical & Industrial Corp.*)

screening, cooling and coating. The simultaneous production of ammonium phosphate is said to enable grades to be made having P_2O_5 water solubilities as high as 70 per cent, when required. A popular grade is 14-14-0, in which the nitrogen is present in half-ammoniacal, half-nitrate form, and the P_2O_5 is mostly present as dicalcium phosphate.

In another Saint-Gobain process, a nonammoniated nitrophosphate can be made by digesting phosphate rock with nitric and sulfuric acids to form a paste containing 19 per cent P_2O_5, 16 per cent being present as water-soluble, monocalcium phosphate and 3 per cent as water- and citrate-insoluble phosphates. The product contains at least 4 per cent calcium nitrate and is hygroscopic; special attention to packing and storage is therefore essential.

A possible future application of the nitric-sulfuric type of process is the recovery of P_2O_5 from the leached-zone deposits in Florida which have not proved amenable to extraction by older established techniques.[38] The simultaneous production of uranium oxide has also been proposed.

Nitric-Phosphoric Processes. When available, phosphoric acid can also be used in conjunction with nitric acid to produce a series of nitrophosphate compounds, which can then be ammoniated in accordance with the following general reaction:

$$2Ca_3(PO_4)_2 + 6HNO_3 + 2H_3PO_4 + 6NH_3 \rightarrow$$
$$6CaHPO_4 + 6NH_4NO_3 \tag{10.30}$$

Several processes, such as the PEC, Saint-Gobain, and Societe des Phosphates Tunisiens, can be modified to operate on this principle, to make nitrophosphates in the 15-22-0 range. Additional phosphoric acid enables $N:P_2O_5$ ratios as high as 1:3 to be attained and by careful ammoniation the ammoniacal nitrogen: nitrate nitrogen ratio can be increased to 1.5 or even to 2.0.

Nitric-Carbon Dioxide Processes. Some nitrophosphate plants, such as the PEC type, can also be adapted to use carbon dioxide in conjunction with nitric acid, according to the empirical reaction:

$$Ca_3(PO_4)_2 + 2HNO_3 + CO_2 + H_2O + 2NH_3 \rightarrow$$
$$2CaHPO_4 + 2NH_4NO_3 + CaCO_3 \tag{10.31}$$

The reaction slurry, which is largely phosphoric acid, monocalcium phosphate, and calcium nitrate, is stabilized, ammoniated, and carbonated, before it is granulated with returned fines, dried, screened, and cooled. The P_2O_5 in the product is mostly water-insoluble, but soluble in citric acid solution, and a P_2O_5:nitrogen ratio approaching 3:1 can be attained when desired. Typical operating requirements for a PEC plant per ton of 13-11-12 and based on 500 short tons per day output are given in Table 10.3.

Nitric-Sulfate Processes. The addition of a sulfate salt, such as ammonium or potassium sulfate, simultaneously with nitric acid in the digester step, enables the decomposition of calcium nitrate to be made before neutralization and ammoniation, instead of afterwards, as is the case when mixed acids are used. (The addition of potassium chloride in the digestion stage would add to corrosion difficulties because of the aqua-regia that would be formed.) The over-all empirical reaction when using potassium sulfate can be represented as:

$$Ca_3(PO_4)_2 + 4HNO_3 + K_2SO_4 + 2NH_3 \rightarrow$$
$$CaSO_4 + 2CaHPO_4 + 2KNO_3 + 2NH_4NO_3 \tag{10.32}$$

In the proprietary Auby Process, basic slag has been used in place of ammonia, to provide smoother control of neutralization with the simultaneous addition of extra P_2O_5.

Although the aforementioned processes are primarily of European origin, in America the TVA has undertaken considerable development and pilot-

TABLE 10.3

	Operating Requirements Per Short Ton Product
Materials:	
Nitric acid (100% basis)	612 lb
Anhydrous ammonia	166 lb
Phosphate rock (34% P_2O_5)	660 lb
Potassium chloride (60% K_2O)	410 lb
Carbon dioxide	130 lb
Stabilizer	70 lb
Bags	20–100 lb bags
Utilities:	
Electricity	49 KWH
Fuel oil	0.29 bbl
Cooling water	1000 gal
Other Operating Needs:	
Operating labor	5 operators/shift
Bagging and shipping labor	5 operators/shift

plant work on most of these[27, 28, 36, 54, 56] in order to determine the most suitable ways by which they might be adapted for use under typical U.S. circumstances. One interesting modification is the use of the TVA drum ammoniator-granulator in place of the customary multi-stage ammoniation section,[27, 58a] in order to reduce capital investment and simultaneously to increase the possible range of nitrophosphate grades that can be made. Cost comparisons between 12-12-12 made by conventional ammoniation-granulation and by the nitrophosphate route in TVA pilot plants indicated that the latter offered savings of nearly 10 per cent in delivered cost per ton of product, under certain conditions.[3]

Summary

Typical 1:1:1 nitrophosphate raw material requirements (excluding a few per cent of stabilizer) based on the various alternative methods described previously are compared below.

	Approximate Composition, Per Cent			
Formulation:	11-11-11	14-14-14	12-12-12	12-12-12
34.5% P_2O_5 phosphate rock	34.2	23.7	34.7	35.3
42% nitric acid	25.5	32.8	26.1	35.7
98% sulfuric acid	13.8	—	6.8	—
38% P_2O_5 phosphoric acid	—	9.7	—	—
100% carbon dioxide	—	—	5.7	—
100% ammonia	7.3	9.4	7.2	5.3
60% K_2O potash	19.2	24.6	19.5	—
50% K_2O potassium sulfate	—	—	—	23.7

Agronomic Value of Nitrophosphates

Considerable differences of opinion have existed in many countries regarding the efficacy of nitrophosphate fertilizers, compared to conventional mixtures and compounds, based on water-soluble P_2O_5 materials. Recent work indicates that the nitrophosphates tend to be very suitable for specific soils and crops, but perhaps less suitable on an all-round basis, compared to water-soluble phosphate fertilizers. When adequate P_2O_5 build-up exists in the soil and harvesting is not of a short-term nature, satisfactory results have been reported. For soils high in alkalinity and low in residual P_2O_5 , results in many cases with short-term crops have been less satisfactory than those obtained with fertilizers based on the superphosphates.[14, 35]

OTHER SALTS

Ammonium Metaphosphate

Several processes have been proposed or piloted for the manufacture of ammonium metaphosphate and related compounds[29] by reacting P_2O_5 , ammonia, and water in the vapor phase, i.e.,

$$P_2O_5 + 2NH_3 + 3H_2O \rightarrow 2NH_4H_2PO_4 \tag{10.33}$$

ammonium
orthophosphate

$$P_2O_5 + 2NH_3 + 2H_2O \rightarrow (NH_4)_2H_2P_2O_7 \tag{10.34}$$

ammonium
pyrophosphate

$$P_2O_5 + 2NH_3 + H_2O \rightarrow 2NH_4PO_3 \tag{10.35}$$

ammonium
metaphosphate

Investigations showed that rapid cooling of the vapor-phase product followed by hydration with steam was essential in order to yield a material with reasonable storage properties. If hydration was not undertaken, an extremely hygroscopic product resulted. In most cases, the metaphosphate usually included appreciable quantities of phosphoronitridic acid and derivatives, which analysed approximately 17-73-0.

More recent work has resulted in improved metaphosphate-type compounds produced via vapor phase reactions. However, the development of superphosphoric acid and associated ammonium polyphosphates has so far provided a more practical approach to high analysis, solid and liquid fertilizers.

Magnesium Ammonium Phosphate

One interesting ammonium salt is magnesium ammonium phosphate, $MgNH_4PO_4$, which is formed by interaction between dolomite coating agents and ammonium phosphate fertilizers under humid conditions, thus leading to caking problems. It is more advantageously found as a major constituent of Peruvian bird guano and recently has been proposed as an additive to fertilizers where it is desired to incorporate magnesium without diluting N and P_2O_5 values. A production method based on the use of olivine and phosphate rock has been outlined.[34]

In the suggested method, olivine and phosphate rock are dissolved simultaneously or successively in sulfuric acid and the leachate is carefully ammoniated to produce dicalcium phosphate and magnesium phosphate. The dicalcium phosphate is removed by filtration and the filtrate is again carefully ammoniated to yield magnesium ammonium phosphate and ammonium phosphate:

$$CaH_4(PO_4)_2 + NH_3 \rightarrow CaHPO_4 + NH_4H_2PO_4 \qquad (10.36)$$

$$MgH_4(PO_4)_2 + 2NH_3 \rightarrow MgNH_4PO_4 + NH_4H_2PO_4 \qquad (10.37)$$

The Mg can be recovered as $MgNH_4PO_4$ containing about 29 per cent MgO, 10 per cent N, and 52 per cent P_2O_5, or as the hydrated salt, $MgNH_4 \cdot PO_4 \cdot 6H_2O$.

Magnesium ammonium phosphate has also been developed on a semi-commercial scale for use as a direct fertilizer,[4, 18] having a general formula 8-42-0, plus an MgO content of 24 per cent. A special feature of this material is its slow solubility in water and soils, which enables it to be used in direct conjunction with seedlings, ornamental plants, and vegetables without damage to roots or foliage. Latest production methods have not yet been disclosed.

One recently piloted method, which may have a considerable future potential, is associated with the production of fresh water from raw sea water and so offers a dual advantage.[5, 7, 47a] Raw water fed to an evaporator-type conversion plant is first treated with wet-process phosphoric acid and ammonia to precipitate scale-forming elements such as calcium, magnesium, and iron in the form of metal ammonium phosphates. These are settled, dewatered, and heated to 90°C to convert the hexahydrates to monohydrates. The slurry is then filtered, washed, mixed with recycled fines, and granulated in the usual way. Water of crystallization cannot be removed by heating the dry hexahydrate without loss of ammonia. This process yields a product containing about 7 per cent nitrogen, 44 per cent P_2O_5, 21 per cent MgO, and 5 per cent CaO, plus many valuable micronutrients in the form of metal phosphates of iron, zinc, manganese, and cobalt. It is estimated that a sea-water-conversion plant of one million gallons per day capacity would produce about 11,000 tons of fertilizer per year at a cost somewhat higher than that of producing a similar grade by conventional means. However, this cost would be subject, in most cases, to a credit based on the increased value of the treated water. The process is shown diagrammatically in Figure 10.23.

Other metal ammonium phosphates likely to be of commercial interest in the future[12a, 32a] include ferrous ammonium phosphate (7-35-0) and zinc ammonium phosphate, as well as others based on iron, copper, and manganese, having a general formula $MeNH_4PO_4 \cdot H_2O$.

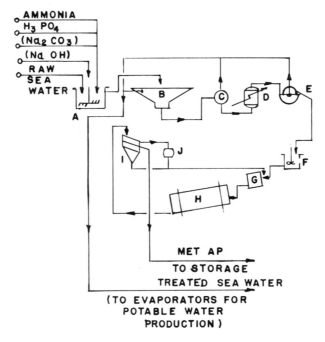

Figure 10.23. Schematic flow diagram for metal ammonium phosphate/seawater process.

Legend:

A. Treatment tank
B. Thickener
C. Centrifuges
D. Heater
E. Filters

F. Surge tank
G. Granulator
H. Dryer
I. Screens
J. Oversize mill

Miscellaneous Ammonia-Containing Materials

Several miscellaneous ammonia-containing materials are in limited use, or have been proposed for fertilizer purposes in addition to conventional mixtures and compounds. Some of these, such as ammonium bisulfite, are made by ammoniating sulfurous or waste plant-liquors or stack gas[6, 20] prior to disposal. The addition of ammonia to solid organic wastes from processing plants, from garbage-treatment units, and from sewage plants is also occasionally undertaken to yield soil conditioners having useful fertilizer properties. One recent development of interest[17a] is the production of synthetic humus by the simultaneous oxidation and ammoniation of coal to give ammonium humates having nitrogen contents as high as 22 per cent. This might enable low cost, effective nitrogen fertilizers to be made in the future from waste material such as washery rejects, gas-works liquors, and low-grade solid fuels such as brown coal and peat.

REFERENCES

1. Anon., *Comm. Fertilizer* (June 1959).
2. Anon., *Crop Life* (March 1961).
3. Anon., *Chem. Processing* (March 25, 1963).
4. Anon., *Chem. Eng. News*, **83,** (Sept. 1961).
5. Anon., *Chem. Eng. News*, **52,** (Jan. 1962).
6. Anon., *Nitrogen*, **34,** (Dec. 1959).
7. Anon., *Chem. Eng.* (April 1962).
8. Anon., *Chem. Eng.* (July 1962).
9. Anon., *Chem. Eng.* (Aug. 22, 1960).
10. Anon., *Chem. Eng.* (May 15, 1961).
11. Alfrey, N. K., *Proc. Fert. Ind. Round Table*, 108 (1960).
12. Bridger, G. L., *Proc. Fert. Ind. Round Table*, 69 (1957).
12a. Bridger, G. L., *et al.*, *J. Agr. Food Chem.* 10, 3, 181, (May/June 1962).
13. Brown, *et al.*, *J. Physical Chemistry*, **62,** 366 (March 1958).
14. Burg, van, P. F. J., *Proc. Fert. Soc., London* (1963).
15. Franklin, C. E., *Proc. Fert. Ind. Round Table*, 27 (1960).
16. Giorgini, M. & Weber, W., ISMA Conference Proceedings, Stockholm (1959).
17. Hansen, A., *Proc. Fert. Ind. Round Table*, 96 (1959).
18. Hardesty, J. O., *Proc. Am. Inst. Chem. Eng.*, Colo. (1954).
19. Hein, L. B., *et al.*, *Journ. Agr. Food Chem.*, **4,** 318 (April, 1958).
20. Heil, F. G., *J. Agr. Food Chem.*, **9,** 457 (June 1961).
21. Henderson, *et al.*, Proc. Fert. Round Table (1962).
22. Hignett, T. P., *Farm Chemicals*, **34,** (April 1963).
23. Hignett, T. P., *Farm Chemicals*, 30 (March 1963).
24. Hignett, T. P., *Farm Chemicals*, 32 (April 1963).
25. Hignett, T. P., *Proc. Fert. Ind. Round Table*, 85 (1961).
26. Hignett, T. P., and Slack, A. V., *J. Agr. Food Chem.*, 5 (Nov. 1957).
27. Hignett, T. P., *et al.*, *J. Agr. Food Chem.*, 6 (Nov. 1958).
27a. Hokkaido Colliery Co., Brit. Pat. 895,437.
28. Houston, E. C., *et al.*, *Ind. Eng. Chem.*, 43 (Oct. 1951).

29. Houston, E. C., "Chemistry and Technology of Fertilizers," Ed. V. Sauchelli, p. 345, New York, Reinhold Pub. Corp., 1960.
30. Huang, T. H., and Cheng, L. T., *Agr. Chem.*, 52 (Dec. 1962).
31. "Industrial Ventilation" (Publ.) Committee on Industrial Ventilation, P. O. Box 453, Lansing, Michigan.
32. Kumagi, *et al.*, *J. Agr. Food Chem.*, **2**, 25 (1954).
32a. Lunt, O. R., *et al.*, *California Agriculture*, Univ. Calif. 16(2), 6, 7 (1962).
33. Lutz, W. A. and Pratt, C. J., "Chemistry & Technology of Fertilizers," Ed. V. Sauchelli, p. 322, New York, Reinhold Pub. Corp. 1960.
34. MacIntire, W. H. and Marshall, H. L., *J. Agr. Food Chem.*, 7 (Aug. 1959).
35. Mattingley, G. E. G., *Proc. Fert. Soc.*, *London* (1963).
36. Nielsson, F. T. and Yates, L. D., *J. Agr. Food Chem.* 1, 672 (Aug. 1953).
37. Nossen, E., *J. Agr. Food Chem.*, **7**, 752 (Nov. 1959).
38. Payne, J. H., "Phosphorus and its Compounds," Ed. Van Wazer, New York, Interscience Pub. Inc., p. 1071, 1961.
39. Payne, J. H., *Ibid.*, p. 1133.
40. Payne, J. H. and Daniels, S. D., *J. Agr. Food Chem.*, **4**, 925 (Dec. 1956).
41. Phillips, A. B., *et al.*, *J. Agr. Food Chem.*, **8**, 4, 310 (July/Aug. 1960).
42. Phillips, A., *et al.*, *J. Agr. Food Chem.*, **6**, 442 (June 1958).
43. Plusje, M., *Proc. Fert. Soc.*, *London*, 12 (1950).
44. Preneutralization Symposium, *Proc. Fert. Ind. Round Table* (1960).
44. Preneutralization Symposium, *Proc. Fert. Ind. Round Table* (1959).
46. *Proc. Fert. Round Table* (1961).
47. Rose, G. W., "Chemistry and Technology of Fertilizers," Ed. V. Sauchelli, p. 633, New York, Reinhold Pub. Corp., 1960.
47a. Salutsky, M. L., *et al.*, Nat'l Acad. Science, Nat. Res. Council Pub. No 942.
48. Sauchelli, V. "Manual on Fertilizer Manufacture," 2nd ed., p. 34, Baltimore, Davison Chemical Co., 1954.
49. Sauchelli, V., "Manual on Fertilizer Manufacture," *Ibid.*, p. 77.
50. Sauchelli, V., "Manual on Fertilizer Manufacture," *Ibid.* (1954).
51. Schneider, G. L., *Proc. Fert. Ind. Round Rable*, 54 (1961).
52. Schmalz, T. R., *Proc. Fert. Ind. Round Table*, 32 (1959).
53. Smith, R. C., "Chemistry and Technology of Fertilizers," Ed. V. Sauchelli, p. 424, New York, Reinhold Pub. Corp., 1960.
54. Stanfield, Z. A., *J. Agr. Food Chem.*, 1 (Nov. 1953).
55. Stewart, R., *Proc. Fert. Soc.*, *London*, 34 (1955).
56. Striplin, M. M., *et al.*, *Ind. Eng. Chem.*, 44 (Jan. 1952).
57. Torvund, L., *Chem. Trade J.*, London, 508 (March 29, 1963).
58. Tucker, W. J., *Proc. Fert. Ind. Round Table*, 30 (1959).
58a. Versteegh, P. M. R., and Lugt, W. *J. Agr. Food Chem.*, **10**, 6, 434 (Nov./Dec. 1962).
59. Waggaman, W. H., "Phosphorus, Phosphoric Acid and Phosphate Fertilizers," p. 420, New York, Reinhold Pub. Corp., 1952.
60. Walstead, D., *Proc. Fert. Ind. Round Table*, 29 (1960).
61. Waters, *et al.*, *J. Agr. Food Chem.*, **9**, 272 (Nov./Dec. 1961).
62. Yates, L. D., *et al.*, *Farm Chemicals*, 117 (July 1954).
63. Yates, *et al.*, *Farm Chemicals*, 117 (August 1954).
64. Young, R. D., *Proc. Fert. Ind. Round Table*, 102 (1960).
65. Young, R. D., *J. Agr. Food Chem.*, **9**, 4 (Jan./Feb. 1961).

11

Ammonium Sulfate, Nitrate, and Chloride Fertilizers

CHRISTOPHER J. PRATT

International Fertilizer Development Corporation

Although the newer fertilizers (such as the ammonium phosphates and the nitrophosphates as well as urea and nitrogen solutions) are made in ever-increasing quantities throughout the world, the classic fertilizers[58] —ammonium sulfate, ammonium nitrate, ammonium chloride, and calcium nitrate—continue to be produced and consumed on a huge and unabated scale, as Table 11.1[24] shows.

Appreciable tonnages of ammonium chloride are made for fertilizer purposes and are principally used in India and the Far East. For example, in Japan at the present time, annual output of ammonium chloride is of the order of 360,000 tons and the available production capacity is believed to be about double this figure.

Production methods for such fertilizers vary widely, according to prevailing conditions. Hence, a process which is justified in one case might be quite unfeasible under different circumstances. For many years, the basic production route for the ammonium salts of strong acids was via neutralization of the acid, followed by crystallization and drying, usually on a batch basis. Modern processes use a variety of raw materials and by-products; reactions in the solid, liquid, and vapor phases, and combinations of these; as well as several alternative finishing methods in addition to crystallization (such as granulating, prilling, and compacting).

Complete coverage of the chemistry and production of the major ammonium salts is not possible in one chapter, for the technology of each is both a science and an art, and sufficient to justify a separate volume. Accordingly, this chapter will be confined to basic features and more recent

TABLE 11.1. WORLD PRODUCTION AND CONSUMPTION OF FIXED NITROGEN
(THOUSANDS OF METRIC TONS. 1 METRIC TON = 0.9842 LONG TON)

	1959/60	1960/61	1961/62
Production:			
Sulfate of Ammonia	3087	3134	3084
Calcium Cyanamide	313	302	290
Nitrate of Soda	227	186	214
Nitrate of Lime	424	462	467
Ammonium Nitrate as such for use as fertilizer	1419	1669	2124
Lime Ammonium Nitrate types	1684	1816	1885
Ammonia and solutions as direct/indirect fertilizer	1596	1686	1760
Urea for fertilizer use	578	779	979
Other Forms of Nitrogen	2984	3388	3722
	12,312	13,422	14,525
Increase p.c. on prior year	9.1	9.0	8.2
Consumption:			
World Total all forms	12,269	13,089	14,395
Increase p.c. on prior year	10.1	6.7	10.0
Use in Agriculture by:			
Europe (inc. USSR)	4764	5045	5303
America	2861	3115	3569
Asia	2269	2336	2664
Africa	325	337	401
Oceania (inc. Hawaii)	48	60	63

developments, with specific references to the production of types and grades suitable for fertilizer purposes.

RAW MATERIALS

The principal raw materials used to produce ammonium fertilizer salts in this group are:

synthetic or by-product ammonia,

corresponding virgin or by-product acids,

associated double salts such as ammonium carbonate and calcium sulfate, and

waste streams from other processes.

When by-product or waste materials are employed in conjunction with vapor-liquid phase reactions and crystallization, minor impurities present may affect the physical nature of the product, either adversely or beneficially, according to circumstances. Sometimes, controlled amounts of other materials are incorporated as "modifiers" to improve the size and shape of the product, as for example, the addition of trivalent ions to ammonium sulfate liquor to induce a better crystal formation by changing the habit from an orthorhombic to a hexagonal system.[27] Similarly, the use of wet-process phosphoric acid when making granular ammonium sulfate-phosphate or nitrate-phosphate fertilizers will, as a rule, fortuitously assist granulation and storage properties.

AMMONIUM SULFATE

General

According to circumstances and the availability of raw materials,[11] ammonium sulfate is produced in several different ways, the more important being based on:

combining ammonia and sulfuric acid in vacuum- or atmospheric-type reactor-evaporators;

scrubbing ammonia-containing gas from coke ovens and other carbonization units with sulfuric acid in specially-designed washer-saturators;

evaporating waste streams containing ammonium sulfate and separating the relatively pure salt by crystallization;

reacting ammonium carbonate and calcium sulfate, filtering off the calcium carbonate, evaporating and crystallizing the ammonium sulfate produced;

reacting ammonia and sulfuric acid in a spray tower to yield a dry, powdered product; and

simultaneous production with other ammonium salts (such as phosphate and nitrate) in ammoniation-granulation and other granular fertilizer processes.

The reaction between ammonia and sulfuric acid is represented by the equation:

$$2NH_3(g) + H_2SO_4(l) \rightarrow (NH_4)_2SO_4(c) - 67{,}710 \text{ cal/gram mole} \quad (11.1)$$

The heat generated by this exothermic reaction is approximately equivalent to 4232 Btu's/lb of N.

The system $(NH_4)_2SO_4 \cdot H_2O$ is shown in Figure 11.1 and the more important properties of ammonium sulfate are given in Table 11.2.

Crystallization

Except for spray-tower and granulation processes, crystallization is a major unit operation in all of the methods listed above. Accordingly, a brief

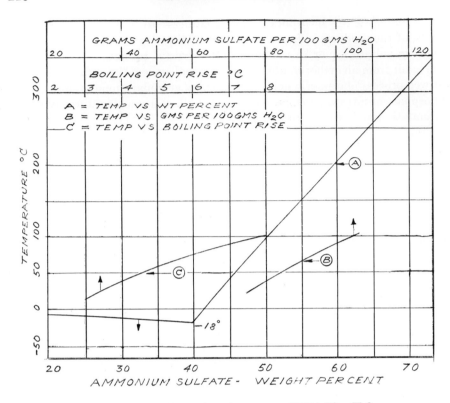

Figure 11.1. Solubility data for system $(NH_4)_2SO_4$—H_2O.

consideration of the more important factors influencing plant design, operating conditions, and product quality relative to crystal formation will be of use. Fundamental data can be obtained in the appropriate literature.[23, 57]

Crystallization develops in two stages; nuclei are first formed in a supersaturated solution and are subsequently grown to the size required. In both stages, the controlling force is the degree of supersaturation in the mother liquor.[57] A solution is said to be metastable when it is supercooled to the point just prior to the spontaneous generation of fine solid particles. After precipitation the solution is termed unstable, or labile, and each particle will act as a nucleus which will grow into a single crystal, provided a constant supply of metastable solution is maintained.

The rate of nucleation is small when the degree of supersaturation is low, but it can become violent if supersaturation is allowed to rise appreciably. The rate of crystal growth is usually a linear function of supersaturation.

The design and operation of industrial crystallization equipment is

TABLE 11.2. PROPERTIES OF PURE AMMONIUM SULFATE

Color	white
Molecular weight	132.14
Density 20°/4°C—solid	1.769
Specific gravity—sat. solns	1.2414 at 20°C
	1.2502 at 93
Specific heat—solid	0.345 cal/g/°C
Specific heat—sat. soln	0.67 at 20°C
	0.63 at 100°C
Heat of crystallization	11.6 cal/kg in 42% solution
Heat of dilution	6.35 cal/kg from 42% to 1.8% solution
Melting point	512.2°C (954°F)
Thermal stability	Decomposes above 536°F
pH	5.0
Loose bulk density	60 lb/cu ft
Angle of repose	28°
Stoichiometric requirements (tons per ton of product):	
NH_3	0.2578
H_2SO_4	0.7422

therefore directed largely towards controlling metastable conditions, which are affected by many process factors, such as temperature, pH, agitation, impurities, crystal area, and even the surface nature of the crystallizing vessel. In continuously operating equipment, equilibrium operating conditions are said to be reached when the number of grown crystals equals the number of stable nuclei produced. Thus, by controlling the number of nuclei formed and the number of crystals removed, uniformly sized crystals will be produced when a constant feed is supplied, i.e.,

$$\text{average crystal size} = \frac{(k) \text{ production rate}}{\text{nucleation rate}}$$

In continuous processes, the production rate is usually held at a constant figure; thus, crystal size becomes a function of nucleation rate. Since one gram of typical nuclei in the 0.01 mm size range represents about 10^9 potential small crystals, the process unit must offer means of controlling the amount of fines produced by precipitation and attrition. Furthermore, some way of classifying the crystals before withdrawal from the system must be provided; otherwise a wide range of particle sizes would result in the product, which would probably lead to washing and processing difficulties, as well as caking in storage.

Crystal Recovery

Ammonium sulfate crystals are recovered from reaction slurries in several ways. One method is to recycle a side-stream of slurry through batch or continuous centrifuges. Another way is to install a salt catch-pot at the base of the crystallizer and tap off the crystals, either batchwise or continuously, prior to removal of mother liquor in a centrifuge.

The crystals are usually washed in the centrifuge with ammonia and/or water, dried in a rotary drum dryer, screened if necessary, and sent to storage. In some plants, the use of high efficiency batch or continuous centrifuges in conjunction with large, high purity crystals enables drying to be eliminated. In other cases where crystal size is small and where unavoidable impurities are present, both drying and cooling may be necessary to avoid subsequent caking during storage. Some smaller plants use top feed rotary, vacuum filter-dryers to dewater, wash, and dry the crystals in one operation. Compactors are also used to produce a fragmented type of material from dried, fine crystals, as well as from undried centrifuged salt containing 0.8 to 1.5 per cent free moisture. In a few cases, ammonium sulfate slurries of by-product origin are successfully granulated in pugmill or drum systems. Occasionally, ammonium thiocyanate is also produced by fractional crystallization from coke-oven gas, and is separated and dried by similar means.

Crystal Size and Purity

Specifications for ammonium sulfate crystal sizes vary according to individual producers and users, as well as between countries of origin. In USA, a general preference has been for a product which shows a cumulative retention of about 70 per cent on a 30-mesh Tyler screen. More recently, larger rice-shaped crystals have been in demand, and a 90 per cent retention on a 20-mesh (Tyler) screen is favored by some users, particularly for spreading by air and bulk-blending purposes. A typical size-analysis for the larger material is shown in Table 11.3.

Some manufacturers have found it difficult to meet the larger-size specifications, especially when using by-product ammonia or acid, because of crystal-size limitations imposed by the presence of impurities. In some instances, the use of additives has helped to increase crystal size,[27] and in several plants, compacting equipment has been installed for this purpose.

Crystal purity of ammonium sulfate is usually specified by producers or purchasers in terms of nitrogen content and free acidity, plus limitations on specific impurities in certain cases, when raw materials are of by-product origin. For example, a minimum of 20.6 per cent N, a maximum of 0.02 per cent free H_2SO_4 and 0.2 per cent moisture, and limiting values on

TABLE 11.3. TYPICAL SIZE ANALYSIS FOR AMMONIUM SULFATE

Tyler Mesh	Cumulative Per Cent Retained
On 10	10
On 16	40
On 20	90
On 28	98

stated organic or inorganic impurities might be stipulated in a purchasing specification.

Alternative Production Methods

Anhydrous Ammonia and Sulfuric Acid. Realization of the need for controlled supersaturation, nucleation, and classification led to the development of present-day large, continuous reactor-evaporator-crystallizers and reactor-crystallizers in which exothermic or endothermic reactions can also take place. A typical example is the production of ammonium sulfate from anhydrous ammonia and concentrated sulfuric acid, for which considerable cooling must be provided to remove the heat of reaction.

Reduced Pressure Operation. In one type of unit, the crystallizer consists of two main parts, namely, a lower suspension vessel and an upper flash chamber which is maintained under vacuum.[26] Mother liquor circulates from the former to the latter, either thermodynamically, or by means of an external pump, and after flashing, it is returned to the lower part of the suspension vessel via a central dip-pipe. The ammonia and sulfuric acid are added to the circulating line where they react and mix with the mother liquor which becomes superheated prior to flashing, because of the reaction heat generated.

Water is lost in the flash chamber, which makes the liquor supersaturated with respect to the ammonium sulfate present, and when this liquor is brought into contact with fresh nuclei and small crystals in the suspension vessel, further growth takes place. Undesirable nuclei and fragments are destroyed during circulation by the heat of reaction from the ammonia and acid. Controlled nucleation and crystallization are thus ensured, as well as some classification in accordance with the shape of the suspension vessel and the external means of separation and recycling provided. Thus, by skilled design and careful operation, all the desiderata of crystallization can be met by this type of crystallizer, which was pioneered by Isaacssen and Jeremiassen, and led to the well-known "Krystal" series of units.[21, 34, 52]

A flow diagram for a flash crystallizer installation is shown in Figure 11.2. The acid and ammonia flow must be controlled to maintain a pH of 3.0

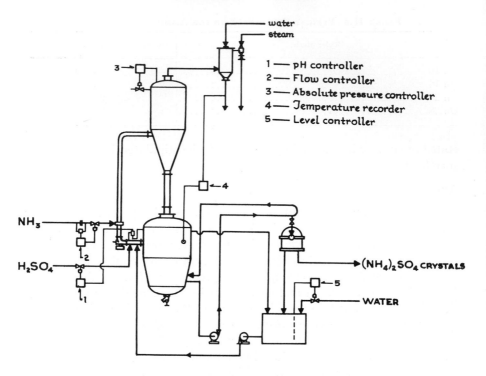

Figure 11.2. Krystal-type evaporator/crystallizer unit for ammonium sulfate production. (*Courtesy Struthers Wells Corp.*)

to 3.5, as a lower pH produces long thin needlelike crystals and a higher pH results in loss of ammonia as well as crystals inferior in shape and size, as can be seen from a comparison of crystals in Figure 11.3.

In another design of crystallizer (and various forms of evaporator-reactor-crystallizers) known as the draft-tube-baffle (DTB) type,[22] an impeller is used to induce a strong internal upflow of slurry, via a baffle tube, from the lower region of the crystallizer to the upper flash area. In this way, growing crystals are brought to the boiling surface where supersaturation and crystal growth are at maximum values. Furthermore, sufficient seed surface is provided in the boiling region to minimize the deposition of scale inside the vessel. Figure 11.4 shows a DTB unit producing by-product ammonium sulfate from caprolactam liquor in Japan.

Atmospheric Pressure Operation. Several processes for producing ammonium sulfate under atmospheric pressure are in use. Some of these combine neutralization and crystallization in one vessel, while others employ a separate neutralizer. Cooling is furnished by evaporation of water, as

Figure 11.3. Various ammonium fertilizer salts produced in "Krystal" units. Top left, Normal ammonium sulfate made from virgin acid and NH_3. Middle left, Ammonium sulfate made from by-product capraolactam liquor. Lower left, Ammonium nitrate made from virgin acid and NH_3. Top right, Ammonium sulfate made at low pH from virgin acid and NH_3. Middle right, Ammonium sulfate made from by-product gypsum. Lower right, Diammonium phosphate made from furnace-grade phosphoric acid and NH_3.

Figure 11.4. Draft tube baffle evaporator/crystallizer.
(*Courtesy Swenson Evaporator Co.*)

well as air-blowing in some cases, to maintain a crystallization temperature
of 63° to 66°C, which represents an optimum balance between the energy
required for cooling air and the crystal yield. One type of atmospheric-
pressure process is shown diagrammatically in Figure 11.5.

Ammonia-Containing Gas.   One of the earliest methods of making ammonium sulfate on a commercial scale, and which is still in wide use, is
based on washing coal gas and coke-oven gas with sulfuric acid in specially
designed saturators. High-temperature carbonization of coal gives a gas
with a free ammonia content of about one per cent by volume (or approximately 0.5 lb of ammonia per 1000 cu ft), which can cause corrosion and
plugging troubles unless removed from the gas before distribution.

Older recovery methods are of an indirect nature; hot foul gas from the
ovens is cooled and washed with water to remove some of the tar and other
impurities. The wash liquors are distilled with steam and "sprung" with
alkali to release ammonia. The ammonia-containing vapor is passed into

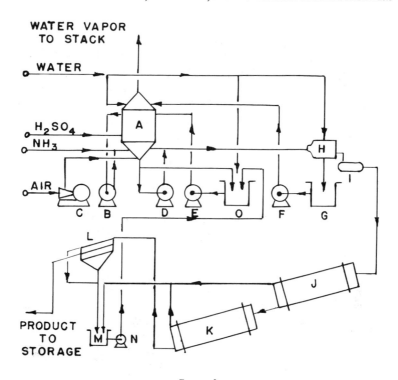

Legend:

A. Crystallizer
B. Circulating pump
C. Cooling-air blower
D. Circulating pump
E. Return liquor pump
F. Mother liquor pump
G. Mother liquor tank
H. Centrifuges

I. Belt conveyor
J. Dryer
K. Cooler
L. Cooler
M. Slurry tank
N. Slurry pump
O. Sump tank

Figure 11.5. Atmospheric-pressure process for ammonium sulfate production.

a reactor-crystallizer containing weak sulfuric acid of about 5 per cent concentration, and the ammonium sulfate crystals formed are centrifuged, washed, and dried. In more recent methods, the gas is cooled and passed directly into washer-saturators containing weak sulfuric acid before proceeding to further processing and distribution. Ammonium sulfate crystals formed in the saturator are recovered and washed in batch or continuous centrifuges, dried, and sent to storage.

Various designs of washer-saturators are used, such as the Wilputte packed-column type, the Koppers (which employs a submerged cracker type) and the Otto (which is based on spray-washing). In some installations,[31] separate evaporator-crystallizers, such as the Krystal and Draft-Tube types, are used in conjunction with washers to improve crystal size and purity. A large Otto unit is shown in Figure 11.6 and a flow diagram for a typical saturator-evaporator installation is given in Figure 11.7.

These plants can also be adapted to produce mono- and diammonium phosphate, according to the availability of furnace-grade phosphoric acid and market conditions. Various combinations of ammonium sulfate and ammonium phosphate can also be made.

By-Product Acids and Waste Streams. Spent sulfuric acid from alkylation or other units in oil refineries, chemical plants, can also be used in some cases for ammonium sulfate production, provided associated foaming and corrosion problems are not too great, or that impurities do not

Figure 11.6. Otto absorber-saturator unit for ammonium sulfate production from coke oven gas. (*Courtesy Otto Construction Co. and Bethlehem Steel Co.*)

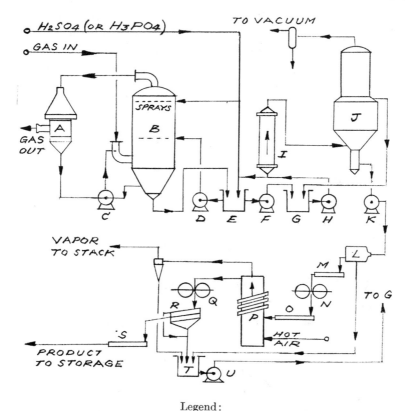

Legend:

A. Acid catcher
B. Absorber
C. Spray pump ⅊1
D. Spray pump ⅊2
E. Overflow tank
F. Slurry pump ⅊1
G. Mother liquor tank
H. Crystallizer feed pump
I. Heater
J. Evaporator-crystallizer
K. Slurry pump ⅊2

L. Centrifuges
M. Screw conveyor
N. Compactor
O. Vibrating conveyor
P. Vibrating dryer
Q. Granulator
R. Screens
S. Product conveyor.
T. Reslurry tank
U. Slurry pump ⅊3

Figure 11.7. Flow diagram for production of dry ammonium sulfate from coke oven gas.

spoil the yield and structure of the crystals produced. When these difficulties are severe, it may be preferable to burn the sludge and produce new acid prior to ammoniation. Appreciable tonnages of ammonium sulfate are recovered from caprolactam, acrylonitrile[7] and other processes[2, 43] in USA,

Europe, and Japan. However, in USA, because of economic factors, unless waste streams contain at least 30 per cent ammonium sulfate, recovery may not be economically justified. Figure 11.8 shows a large ammonium sulfate evaporator-crystallizer operating on caprolactam by-product liquor in the United States.[19]

As an alternative to producing crystalline ammonium sulfate from spent sulfuric acid, a method of using sludge acid to make a granular product has been proposed, whereby the sludge is first ammoniated and added to a recycling granular stream, similar to a method employed for making ammonium phosphate from wet-process phosphoric acid. It is claimed that this process enables granular ammonium sulfate to be produced from

Figure 11.8. 650 T P D ammonium sulfate unit operating on caprolactam by-product liquor. (*Courtesty Allied Chemical Co., Hopewell, Va., and Struthers Wells Corp., Warren, Pa.*)

sludges containing as much as 40 per cent carbonaceous material. Recycle ratios of the order of 1.5 to 4.0 based on the weight of the feed are indicated.[60]

Calcium Sulfate. In Europe and India,[3, 4] large tonnages of ammonium sulfate are made by reacting ammonium carbonate with calcium sulfate, according to the reaction:

$$2NH_3 + H_2O + CO_2 + CaSO_4 \cdot 2H_2O \rightarrow$$
$$(NH_4)_2SO_4 + CaCO_3 + 2H_2O \quad (11.2)$$

Some of these plants use by-product gypsum from phosphoric acid installations, either alone or in conjunction with natural gypsum or anhydrite, and in several cases outputs are in the region of 1000 tons per day. Ammonia and carbon dioxide are made from synthesis-gas sources, and the by-product calcium carbonate can also be used for fertilizer purposes, either to produce calcium nitrate, or it can be applied as a land plaster, according to local needs. This method of producing ammonium sulfate[20, 36] has found favor where it has been desired to avoid the production of large tonnages of sulfuric acid, or to recover the sulfur value of by-product gypsum from a phosphoric acid plant.[28] In addition, cost-free carbon dioxide from synthesis-gas plants and flue gases can be advantageously utilized. A schematic flow diagram of this process is given in Figure 11.9.

When by-product gypsum from a phosphoric acid plant is used, this is first slurried, washed, and dewatered, prior to reaction with ammonium carbonate liquor previously made from ammonia and carbon dioxide.[30] The reaction slurry is filtered and washed on rotary vacuum filters, and the clear liquor is neutralized before evaporation and crystallization in multiple-effect, Krystal-type units. (In some well-designed and operated plants, the ammonium sulfate content of the evaporator feed liquor may be as high as 40 to 42 per cent.) Ammonium sulfate crystals are withdrawn from the salt catchers, dewatered and washed on continuous centrifuges, dried, cooled and sent to storage. Typical crystal-size data relating to ammonium sulfate produced in parallel-flow, multiple-effect, Krystal-type evaporator-crystallizers are given in Table 11.4.

An interior view of a large ammonium sulfate plant using gypsum as a raw material is shown in Figure 11.10.

Spray Tower. In Japan amorphous ammonium sulfate has been made for many years from anhydrous ammonia and sulfuric acid from chamber- or contact-type plants in spray towers. In this process, the heat of reaction removes all water present and the dry, fine product is continuously removed from the base of the tower and sent to storage. Ammonium sulfate in this form is used to a great extent in the production of dry-mixed and granular

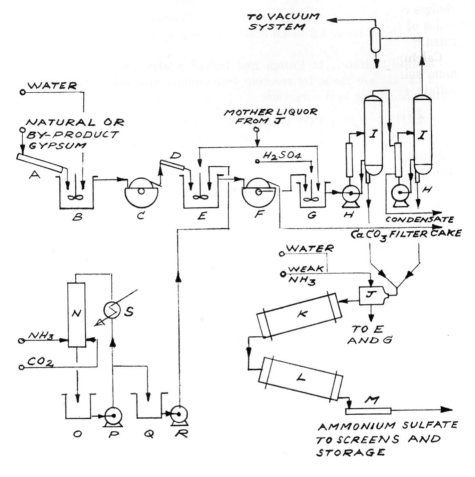

Figure 11.9. Flow diagram for ammonium sulfate production from gypsum.

Legend:

A. Gypsum conveyor
B. Gypsum wash tank
C. Gypsum filter
D. Gypsum conveyor
E. Reactor
F. Chalk filters
G. Evaporator feed tank
H. Evaporator circulation pumps
I. Evaporator crystallizers
J. Centrifuges

K. Dryer
L. Cooler
M. Sulfate conveyor
N. Carbonator
O. Recycle tank
P. Recycle pump
Q. Carbonate tank
R. Carbonate pump
S. Cooler

TABLE 11.4. CRYSTALLINE AMMONIUM SULFATE TYPICAL SIZE ANALYSES:
EX-CRYSTALLIZERS

Cumulative Per Cent Over-Size (mm)						Mean Aperture* (mm)	CV** (%)	Remarks
2.5	2.0	1.5	1.0	0.5	0.2			
Triple-effect Plant with Feed Liquor from Gypsum								
	7	37	80	97		1.37	33	
	6	36	74	97	99.8	1.35	35	
5	13	36	80	98.5		1.34	36	
6	18	51	90	99.5		1.52	31	
4.4	13.3	34.5	72	96	99.8	1.30	38	
Single-effect Plant with Feed Liquor from Caprolactum								
20	50	82	95	99		2.0	25	increased retention time from reduced production rate

* MA, the mean aperture, is defined as that sieve aperture through which 50 per cent by weight of the material will pass.
** CV, the coefficient of variation, is defined as the standard deviation × 100 and divided by mean aperture.

fertilizers. When required, it can be granulated or compacted to increase particle size. A spray-tower installation is shown in Figure 11.11.

In-Situ Methods. Large tonnages of ammonium sulfate are produced simultaneously with other ammonium salts in the manufacture of granular fertilizers, as described elsewhere in this volume. For example, in the well known "ammophos" (16-20-0) about two-thirds of this material is ammonium sulfate, the balance being ammonium phosphate. In some processes, ammonia, sulfuric acid, together with phosphoric acid and/or other acids, are combined in a preneutralizer before granulation, while in others these reactions are undertaken in the granulator. The production of granular ammonium sulfate alone is also undertaken to a limited degree by similar means.

Storage of Ammonium Sulfate

Storage properties of ammonium sulfate, as for other materials, are greatly improved by ensuring a uniform product size. In addition, the free moisture content must be reduced to a minimum, since a figure greater than 0.1 per cent may result in caking difficulties. It is also essential to remove all but traces of free acid, which is done in some cases by washing

Figure 11.10. "Krystal"-type evaporator/crystallizers in a large gypsum-ammonium sulfate plant. (*Courtesy Sindri Fertilizer Plant Govt. of India, and Power-Gas Corporation Ltd., London, England*)

with weak ammonia during centrifuging or filtration. Cooling with dry air prior to bulk storage is essential in some locations where high humidities are prevalent. Otherwise, hot air trapped in the storage pile may cool below its dew point and deposit water on the crystal interfaces, causing solidification.

Certain anti-caking agents[12] can also be used to minimize storage problems in bulk and bagged form. These can be either of the inert dusting type, such as diatomaceous earth, or of the organic type based on fatty acids or naphthalene sulfonates. However, some organic anti-caking agents can create foaming problems or interfere with crystal growth if accidentally allowed to enter crystallizing vessels; suitable precautions must therefore be taken in the plant to prevent trouble arising from this source.

Figure 11.11. Spray tower for ammonium salt production.
(*Courtesy Nissan Chemical Industries Ltd., Tokyo, Japan*)

Recovery from Stack Gases

Although the washing of ammonia-containing gas with mineral acids is a highly developed practice based on over a century of experience, little has been achieved regarding the scrubbing of sulfur-containing stack and flue gases with ammonia for the dual purpose of reducing air pollution and producing useful by-products. On a world-wide basis, the potential value of materials at present lost to the atmosphere is enormous, and the harmful effects caused by pollution are probably even more costly.

However, some suggestions for using flue gases as a raw-material source

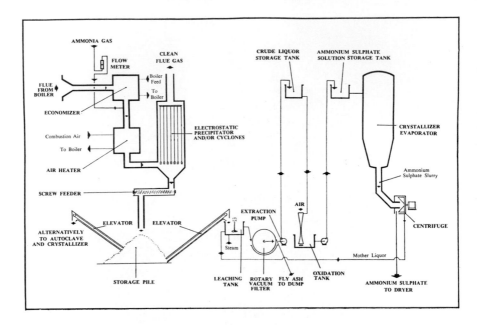

Figure 11.12. Flow diagram for production of ammonium salts from stack gases. (*Courtesy Chemical Construction Corp., and "Nitrogen", London*)

for fertilizers have been made,[15, 56] and one proposed process designed to minimize air pollution and to recover simultaneously by-products via ammoniation is illustrated in Figure 11.12. It is said that ammonium bisulfite, ammonium sulfate, and other compounds can be recovered economically by such means, according to the source of the stack gas.

AMMONIUM NITRATE

General

Several processes have been developed for ammonium nitrate manufacture, according to the type of product desired.[6, 32, 48, 61] Large tonnages of crystalline, prilled, and granular material are used in mixed fertilizers and for blasting purposes, while another major outlet is in the form of nitrogen solutions,[13, 14] often in conjunction with ammonia, urea, ammonium phosphate, and micronutrient salts. Some is also used for conditioning snow for winter sports. These products have largely superseded the earlier "grained" material[39] which is made by rolling the semimolten salt in horizontal pans, sometimes with the aid of resinous binders.

Properties

Pure ammonium nitrate has the properties given in Table 11.5.

At 84.2°C and 32.1°C, sudden expansion takes place in the solid material, which may cause problems in processing and storage, unless suitable provisions are made. Ammonium nitrate exhibits a negative heat of solution in water. For example, 60 parts of salt dissolved in 100 parts of water by weight will give a temperature reduction from 13.6°C to −13.6°C. This heat of solution must be anticipated when designing nitrogen solution units. The system NH_4NO_3—NH_3—H_2O has been investigated by Schultz and Elmore[46] and others.[45, 61]

The basis of virtually all ammonium nitrate processes is a reaction between ammonia and nitric acid according to the following equation:

$$NH_3(g) + HNO_3(aq) \rightarrow NH_4NO_3(aq) - 26,000 \text{ cal/gram mole} \quad (11.3)$$

Decomposition of ammonium nitrate by heat takes place at 200° to 250°C on the following lines:

$$NH_4NO_3(s) \rightarrow N_2O(g) + 2H_2O(g) - 6720 \text{ cal/gram mole} \quad (11.4)$$

Under physical shock, aided by heat and/or the presence of organic material, violent detonation can take place,[35, 37, 54] i.e.,

$$NH_4NO_3(s) \rightarrow N_2 (g) + H_2O (g) + 1/2 O_2 (g)$$
$$- 26,700 \text{ cal/gram mole} \quad (11.5)$$

From the solubility values in Table 11.5 it can be seen that ammonium nitrate is hygroscopic, thus necessitating suitable precautions during manufacture and storage.[38]

Neutralization

In some processes, neutralization[29] according to Eq. (11.3) is performed under vacuum[40, 44] or atmospheric pressure, while in others, pressures of 3 to 5 atm are used, depending on local conditions and the concentration of nitric acid available. If this is above 50 per cent HNO_3, enough steam is usually generated when a pressure neutralizer is used to preheat the incoming ammonia and nitric acid, as well as to concentrate the ammonium nitrate solution in an associated unit. For example, use of a 64 per cent HNO_3 produces about one ton of steam per ton of ammonia neutralized.[17] However, if ample free or low-cost steam is available from other processes, it may be preferable to install an atmospheric pressure neutralizer instead,

TABLE 11.5. PROPERTIES OF PURE AMMONIUM NITRATE

Color	white
Molecular weight	80.05
Nitrogen content	35%
Density 20°/4°C	1.725

Solubility	°C	Gm NH_4NO_3 Per 100 Gm H_2O
	0	118
	20	187
	40	297
	60	410
	80	576
	100	843

Melting point	170.4°C

Crystal states	State	Temp. °C	System
	liquid	169.6	—
	1	169.6 to 125.2	cubic
	2	125.2 to 84.2	tetragonal
	3	84.2 to 32.1	rhombic
	4	32.1 to −18	rhombic
	5	Below −18	tetragonal

since capital costs are usually lower and the plant is simpler in design and operation.

Major Processes

Crystallization. Crystalline ammonium nitrate[41] is made from a direct reaction between virgin acid and anhydrous ammonia in equipment similar to that used for ammonium sulfate production. A variety of processes is available, operating under vacuum, or at atmospheric or higher pressures, and either a combined neutralizer-crystallizer or separate units can be used. In the latter method, a solution of approximately 60 per cent concentration is made by direct reaction in a neutralizer followed by evaporation to about 83 per cent concentration in a vacuum crystallizer-evaporator at 95 to 98°F to give crystals of the size and shape desired. The slurry containing about 60 per cent mother liquor is centrifuged, and the crystals are sent to a rotary dryer where the free moisture is reduced from about 1.0 to 0.1 per cent. Following drying and cooling, the product is coated with

Kieselguhr, calcium carbonate, or other anti-caking agent;[53] bagged; and sent to storage. Alternatively, the evaporated liquor can be used to prepare nitrogen solutions.

Prilling. Prilled ammonium nitrate is made by cooling a hot solution of about 95 to 99 per cent concentration in a rising stream of air in a tower,[9] the prills being dried and cooled prior to coating and bagging. A typical flow diagram for this type of process is shown in Figure 11.13 which also provides for the production of nitrogen solutions. Superheated ammonia vapor and strong, aqueous nitric acid are reacted in a pressure neutralizer, the steam produced being used to evaporate the ammonium nitrate solution to 95 per cent concentration in a separate vacuum evaporator. Traces of ammonia vapor in the condensate are recovered in a flash vessel and are returned to the process. The 95 per cent liquor is prilled or used to prepare nitrogen solutions as required. In some plants, a further concentration in a wiped film evaporator is undertaken prior to prilling. A view of an ammonium nitrate prilling tower is shown in Figure 11.14.

Melt Processes. In the Bamag Process, gaseous anhydrous ammonia and concentrated nitric acid are pumped into a melt of ammonium nitrate at about 150°C, which is subsequently cooled and converted to the type of product required. In the Stengel Process,[5, 25, 32, 47, 51] illustrated in Figure 11.15, superheated ammonia vapor at about 145°C and hot 60 per cent nitric acid at 165° to 170°C are reacted in a packed, stainless steel vessel. Molten ammonium nitrate and water vapor leave the reactor at 200 to 205°C and are separated in a cyclone. Air is blown through the molten salt to reduce the moisture content to about 0.25 per cent, prior to cooling on a steel-belt chiller, fragmenting, coating, and bagging.

Granulation. In some plants, ammonium nitrate solutions from the concentrator are granulated instead of being crystallized or prilled. This is undertaken either in a drum granulator or a pugmill, and the latent heat of crystallization provides most or all of the heat required to dry the product. In one process,[17] two-stage granulation is used; pregranulation is undertaken in a pugmill, followed by hardening and drying in an air-swept rotary drum.

A comparison of some fertilizer grades of ammonium nitrate is given in Table 11.6.

Nitro-Chalk. Powdered limestone or calcium carbonate is frequently added to ammonium nitrate to increase stability and to improve storage properties.[18] The product, termed nitro-chalk, usually contains about 20 to 21 per cent N, compared to 33.5 per cent N available in most commercial grades of ammonium nitrate. The addition is made either to the concentrated nitrate solution before prilling, or to the mixture of slurry and recycled fines entering the granulator, according to the type of product made.

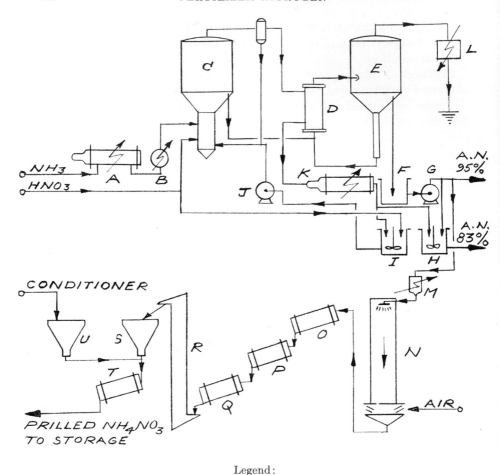

Legend:

A. Ammonia heater
B. NH₃ superheater
C. Neutralizer
D. Evaporator heater
E. Evaporator
F. 95% A.N. Tank
G. 95% A.N. Pump
H. 83% A.N. Mixer
I. Reclaim tank
J. Reclaim pump
K. NH₃ flash tank

L. Evap'r. condenser
M. Film evaporator
N. Prilling tower
O. Pre-prill dryer
P. Prill dryer
Q. Prill cooler
R. Prill elevator
S. Prill bin
T. Coating drum
U. Conditioner bin

FIGURE 11.13. Pressure neutralizer/concentrator process for prilled ammonium nitrate and ammonium nitrate solutions.

Figure 11.14. Ammonium nitrate prilling tower. (*Courtesy Armour Agricultural Chemical Company and Chemical Construction Corp.*)

AMMONIUM CHLORIDE

General

Although ammonium chloride can be more corrosive than other ammonium fertilizers under humid conditions and also may increase the residual chloride content of some soils, it is popular in the Far East as a fertilizer for rice, paddy, and some field crops. One reason is that a rice fungus which reduces ammonium sulfate to toxic sulfides does not affect ammonium chloride. In addition, when used in conjunction with calcium cyanamide and calcium silicate, ammonium chloride is of assistance in preventing

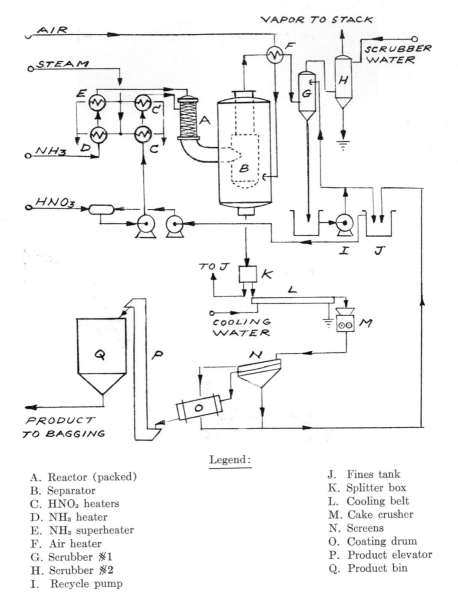

Legend:

A. Reactor (packed)
B. Separator
C. HNO₃ heaters
D. NH₃ heater
E. NH₃ superheater
F. Air heater
G. Scrubber #1
H. Scrubber #2
I. Recycle pump

J. Fines tank
K. Splitter box
L. Cooling belt
M. Cake crusher
N. Screens
O. Coating drum
P. Product elevator
Q. Product bin

Figure 11.15. Stengel process for ammonium nitrate.

plant disease. Another contributory factor is that ammonium chloride provides a useful outlet for surplus chlorine or hydrochloric acid which, instead of being a nuisance factor, helps to produce a fertilizer containing
about 26 per cent nitrogen.

TABLE 11.6. COMPARISONS OF SOME FERTILIZER GRADES OF AMMONIUM NITRATE

	Stengel	Prills	Crystalline (Oslo Krystal)
Product Type:			
Nitrogen content, %................	33.5	33.5	33.0
Bulk density, lb/ft³..............	56	45–52	72
Moisture, %......................	0.2–0.4*	0.2–0.6	0.1
Coating agent, %.................	2.0–3.0	2.7–3.5	3.0–4.0
*Screen Analysis, Weight %**:*			
+5, Mesh.........................	0.1	0.1	0
−5, +10 Mesh....................	75.0	12.7	0
−10, +14 Mesh..................	13.9	76.2	0.1
−14, +20 Mesh..................	10.0	10.0	23.0
−20 Mesh.......................	1.0	1.0	76.9

* Can be controlled to desired value.
** U. S. Standard Sieve Series.

Properties

Pure ammonium chloride has properties as shown in Table 11.7.

On heating, ammonium chloride sublimes at 520°C, but begins to decompose at 350°C.

Major Processes

Direct Reaction. Although not the most widely used method, ammonium chloride is produced in some plants by direct neutralization of ammonia with hydrochloric acid in accordance with the following equation:

$$NH_3(g) + HCl(g) \rightarrow NH_4Cl(s) - 42,000 \text{ cal/gram mole} \quad (11.6)$$

This process is advantageous when surplus hydrochloric acid is available, and the reaction is usually undertaken in vacuum crystallizers. In one method, gaseous ammonia enters the saturator near the base and chlorine-free hydrochloric acid gas diluted with three to four volumes of air (for agitation purposes) is sparged into the solution. A pH of about 8 is maintained and the reaction is controlled by the addition of water. Slurry is continually withdrawn from the saturator and centrifuged, the crystals being washed and then dried by warm air. Vapor from the saturator is scrubbed with water, which is recycled to the saturator to recover small amounts of ammonia and ammonium chloride present in the exhaust, prior to being vented to atmosphere. The product is stored and shipped in moisture-proof bags.

Salting-Out Process. The major process for ammonium chloride manufacture is the salting-out, or double-salt process, which is used extensively

TABLE 11.7. PROPERTIES OF PURE AMMONIUM CHLORIDE

Color	white
Molecular weight	53.50
Density 20°/4°C	1.526
Nitrogen content	26 per cent

	°C	Gm NH_4Cl in 100 Gm H_2O
Solubility	0	29.4
	20	37.2
	40	45.8
	60	55.3
	80	65.6
	100	77.3
	115.6 (b. pt.)	87.3

in Japan, and to some extent in India. This method is a modification of the Solvay ammonia-soda process used for producing sodium carbonate (soda ash) on the lines of Schreib's method, which offers higher economies by salting out the ammonium chloride, and recovering all of the sodium bicarbonate in solution.

In the Solvay process, a 30 per cent sodium chloride solution is ammoniated and then treated with carbon dioxide in a carbonating tower, thereby converting the ammonia into ammonium carbonate:

$$2NH_3 + H_2O + CO_2 \rightarrow (NH_4)_2CO_3 \tag{11.7}$$

Further treatment yields ammonium bicarbonate:

$$(NH_4)_2CO_3 + H_2O + CO_2 \rightarrow 2NH_4HCO_3 \tag{11.8}$$

The ammonium bicarbonate reacts as it is formed with sodium chloride to give sodium bicarbonate and ammonium chloride:

$$NH_4HCO_3 + NaCl \rightarrow NaHCO_3 + NH_4Cl \tag{11.9}$$

Equilibrium is normally reached in the Solvay process at about 75 per cent completion of Eq. (11.9). The sodium bicarbonate is separated by centrifuging or filtration, washed and calcined to produce sodium carbonate. The mother liquor is treated with calcium hydroxide to recover the ammonia, and the calcium chloride is either sold or discarded, i.e.,

$$2NH_4Cl + Ca(OH)_2 \rightarrow CaCl_2 + 2H_2O + 2NH_3 \tag{11.10}$$

In the double-salt process, ammonium chloride regenerated in the liquor after separation of the sodium bicarbonate is salted out by ammoniating the mother liquor, cooling below 15°C, and adding washed solid sodium chloride. In some plants the operations of initial cooling, nucleation, and final crystallization are undertaken in separate crystallizers of special design, which enable oolitic crystals of ammonium chloride 2 to 3 mm in diameter to be continuously made. Slurry from the final crystallizer is dewatered on centrifuges and dried to a final moisture content of about 0.25 per cent by heating to about 105°C in a rotary dryer. The product is packed in moisture-proof bags prior to storing and shipping. The mother liquor from the centrifuges is carbonated, centrifuged to remove the following crop of sodium bicarbonate, reammoniated, and returned to the salt reactor. The process is illustrated in Figure 11.16.

Other Methods. Limited amounts of ammonium chloride are also produced by other means, according to available raw or by-product materials and market conditions. One method is based on the addition of sodium chloride to ammonium sulfate, followed by crystallization, centrifuging, and drying, i.e.,

$$(NH_4)_2SO_4 + 2NaCl \rightarrow Na_2SO_4 + 2NH_4Cl \qquad (11.11)$$

When by-product sulfite liquor or SO_2 is available, addition of ammonia and sodium chloride will yield sodium sulfite and ammonium chloride which can be separated by crystallization and centrifuging in accordance with the following reaction:

$$SO_2 + 2NH_3 + H_2O + 2NaCl \rightarrow Na_2SO_3 + 2NH_4Cl \quad (11.12)$$

The use of polyacrylamides as crystallization aids for ammonium chloride processes has been reported.[42]

HIGH-NITROGEN GRANULATED SALTS

A recent TVA development of significance to the fertilizer industry is a pan-granulation process for making high nitrogen compounds from mixtures of ammonium salt slurries or concentrated solutions. In this method, the requisite quantities of sulfuric, nitric and/or phosphoric acids are first ammoniated, and the resulting solutions are evaporated to about 95 to 98 per cent concentration. The hot melt or slurry is sprayed over a rolling bed of recycled fines in a pan granulator. Material leaving the pan is screened to remove on-size product (which is usually in the 6 to 10 mesh range), while the oversize is crushed, combined with fines, cooled, and returned to

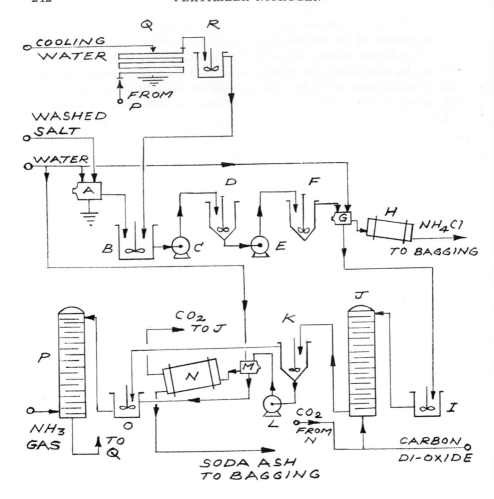

Legend:

A. Washed salt centrifuge
B. Reactor
C. Separator pump
D. Separator
E. Concentrator pump
F. Concentrator #1
G. Centrifuge
H. NH₄Cl dryer
I. Mother liquor tank

J. Carbonating tower
K. Concentrator #2
L. Bicarb feed pump
M. Bicarb centrifuge
N. Bicarb calciner
O. Mother liquor tank
P. Ammoniation tower
Q. NH₃-brine cooler
R. NH₃-brine tank

Figure 11.16. Double-salt process for ammonium chloride production.

the pan granulator. On-size material is dried, cooled, and coated before bagging and dispatch.

An interesting feature of this process when products containing substantial amounts of ammonium nitrate are made is the precooling of the on-size material to a temperature below the ammonium nitrate transition point of 32.1°C before final drying. In this way, rapid drying of the product to a moisture content below 0.1 per cent becomes possible. The flow diagram for this process is given in Figure 11.17 and an illustration (rear view) of a pan-granulator used for this purpose is shown in Figure 11.18. Typical capacities of these machines are in the region of one ton per hour per 15 sq ft, and in some plants, pans of 14 ft diameter are used.

Details of the crystallographic properties of some of these mixed salt compounds have recently been reported.[56a]

Some of the grades made by this process include: ammonium nitrate (33 to 34% N), ammonium nitrate sulfate (21 to 35% N), ammonium phosphate nitrate[49] (30-10-0), compound fertilizers (such as 17-17-17, 21-0-21, 24-6-12, 25-25-0).

Complete NPK compounds can be made by adding potash to the last neutralizer or (preferably) to the stream of recycled fines. For many formulations, recycle requirements are below 1:1 product; in fact, on-size

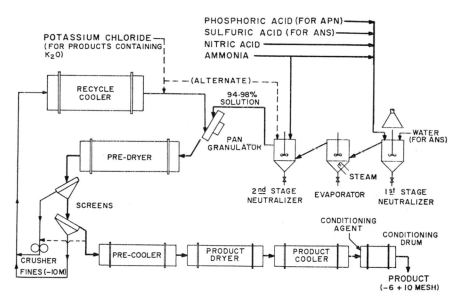

Figure 11.17. Flow diagram of pan-granulation process for production of granular high-nitrogen fertilizers. (*Courtesy TVA*)

Figure 11.18. Rear view of 14 feet diameter pan granulator. (*Courtesy Dravo Corp.*)

material may have to be crushed and returned to the pan to maintain satisfactory granulation. In view of the relative simplicity and flexibility of
this process, a widespread adoption within the next few years is most
probable.

REFERENCES

1. Anon., *Chem. Eng.*, 99 (April 1948).
2. Anon., *Ind. Eng. Chem.*, 2241 (Nov. 1950).
3. Anon., *Brit. Chem. Eng.*, 384 (April 1952).
4. Anon., *Chem. Eng.*, 242 (June 1952).
5. Anon., *Chem. Eng.*, (Aug. 1952).
6. Anon., *Ind. Eng. Chem.*, **44,** 1912 (Aug. 1952).
7. Anon., *Chem. Eng.*, 288 (Sept. 1955).
8. Anon., *Chem. Eng. News*, 25 (August 1958).
9. Anon., *Chem. Eng. News*, **50,** 25 (August 1958).
10. Anon., *Chem. Eng.*, 72 (Oct. 1958).
11. Anon., *Chem. Eng.*, 78 (Dec. 1958).
12. Anon., *Chem. Eng.*, 68 (May 1959).

13. Anon., *Fert. Feedingstuffs J., London,* 17 (June 1959).
14. Anon., *Nitrogen, London,* 37 (Sept. 1959).
15. Anon., *Nitrogen, London,* 34 (Dec. 1959).
16. Anon., *Nitrogen, London,* 36 (Dec. 1959).
17. Anon., *Nitrogen, London,* 28 (March 1960).
18. Anon., *Nitrogen, London,* 37 (March 1960).
19. Anon., *Ind. Eng. Chem.,* **53,** 2, 157 (Feb. 1961).
20. Anon., *European Chem. News,* 23 (Nov. 1962).
21. Bamforth, A. W., *Teknillisen Kemian Aikakauslehti,* 18, 20, Finland (1961).
22. Bennett, R. C., *Chem. Eng. Progress* (Sept. 1962).
23. Buckley, H. E., "Crystal Growth", New York, John Wiley & Sons, 1951.
24. *Chem. Trade J.,* London, 18 (Jan. 1963).
25. Dorsey, J. J., *Ind. Eng. Chem.,* 11 (1955).
26. Enyedy, G., "Applied Mathematics in Chem. Eng.", CEP Symposium Series 37-S (May 1962).
27. Ettle, G. W., *Proc. Fert. Soc., London,* 20 (Jan. 1949).
28. Hardy, W. L., *Ind. Eng. Chem.,* **2,** 574 (1957).
29. Harvey, S. A. and Ewald, P. P., *Instruments,* **19,** 500 (Sept. 1946).
30. Hatch and Pigford, *Ind. Eng. Chem.,* 209F (1962).
31. Hazel, J. B., *Blast Furnace and Steel Plant,* 1445 (Dec. 1944).
32. Hester, *et al., Ind. Eng. Chem.,* 622 (1954).
33. Imamura, M., *Ind. Eng. Chem.,* **54,** 34 (Feb. 1962).
34. Jeremiassen, F., and Svanoe, H., *Chem. Met. Eng.,* **39,** 594 (1932).
35. Johnson, R., *et al.,* Proc. 48 Nat. Meeting, Am. Inst. Chem. Eng., Denver (Aug. 26–29, 1962).
36 Larson, M. M., and Baylan, D. R., *J. Agr. Food Chem.,* **7,** 408 (Sept. 1959).
37. Manual on "Explosives and Other Dangerous Articles", U.S. Coast Guard, Washington, D. C.
38. Manual Sheet A-10, Manuf. Chem. Assoc., Washington, D. C. (1960).
39. Miller, P., *et al., Ind. Eng. Chem.,* **38,** 709 (July 1946).
40. Miller, P., and Saeman, W. C., *Chem. Eng. Progress,* **43,** 667 (Dec. 1947).
41. Miller, P., and Saeman, W. C., *Ind. Eng. Chem.,* **40,** 154 (Jan. 1948).
42. Panov, V. I., USSR Pat. 142-641, Buyl Izobret 2228 (1961).
43. Robinson and Roberts, *Com. J. Chem. Info.* (Oct. 1957).
44. Saeman, W. C., *et al., Ind. Eng. Chem.,* **44,** 1912 (Aug. 1952).
45. Sanders, B. H., and Young, D. A., *Ind. Eng. Chem.,* 1430 (1951).
46. Schultz, J. F., and Elmore, G. V., *Ind. Eng. Chem.,* **38,** 296 (March 1946).
47. Sharp, J. C., "Chemistry and Technology of Fertilizers," Ed. V. Sauchelli, New York, Reinhold Pub. Corp., 10 (1960).
48. Shearon, W. H., and Dunwoody, W. B., *Ind. Eng. Chem.,* 496 (1953).
49. Siegel, M. R., *et al., J. Agr. Food Chem.,* **10,** 350 (Sept./Oct. 1962).
50. Smith, J. P., *J. Agr. Food Chem.,* **10,** 1 (Jan./Feb. 1962).
51. Stengel, L. A., U.S. Pat. 2568901.
52. Svanoe, H., *Ind. Eng. Chem.,* **32,** 6363 (1940).
53. Sykes, W., and Meyers, S., Proc. 48 Nat. Meeting Am. Inst. Chem. Eng., Denver, (Aug. 26–29, 1962).
54. Sykes, W. G., *et al., Chem. Eng. Progress,* **59,** 1, 67 (Jan. 1963).
55. Tans, A. M. P., *Ind. Eng. Chem.,* 971 (1958).
56. Tarbutton, G., *et al., Ind. Eng. Chem.,* 372 (1957).

56a. Tennessee Valley Authority Proc. 4th Demonstration, 61 (1962).
57. Ting, H. H., and McCabe, W. L., *Ind. Eng. Chem.*, **26,** 1201 (1934).
58. Waters, C. E., Proc. Fert. Round Table, 60 (1960).
59. Wethly, F., *Blast Furnace and Steel Plant* (Aug. 1945).
60. Wilson, F. J., US Pat. 3,035,899 (May 20, 1962).
61. Worthington, *et al.*, *Ind. Eng. Chem.*, 910 (1952).

12

Chemistry and Processing of Urea and Ureaform

R. J. Church

E. I. du Pont de Nemours & Company. Inc.

UREA

In 1773 Rouelle separated a crystalline substance from the urine of an animal. On bacterial fermentation, this crystalline material gave ammonia and carbon dioxide. Fourcroy and Vauquelin continued the investigation of this unknown substance, and in 1822 Prout separated the pure, crystalline urea from the urine. Wöhler in 1828 performed the now classical synthesis which gave urea (an organic compound) on heating ammonium cyanate (an inorganic compound).

$$NH_4CNO \xrightarrow{\text{heat}} NH_2CONH_2$$

$$\underset{cyanate}{\underset{ammonium}{}} \qquad urea \qquad\qquad\qquad (12.1)$$

This synthesis of urea is considered to be the beginning of synthetic organic chemistry. Until 1828 many chemists believed that only the living processes could produce organic compounds such as urea.[48]

The I. G. Farbenindustrie[46] in Germany in 1920 was the first company to synthesize urea commercially from ammonium carbamate. The first major production of urea in the United States was pioneered by Du Pont in the early 1930's at Belle, W. Va. After World War II, the use of urea in the United States expanded rapidly. Production facilities for the manufacture of urea showed about a five-fold increase over the period from 1945 to 1962. It is estimated that the total capacity for the production of urea will reach 1,100,000 tons for 1962. The growth of the production of urea in the United States since 1956 is illustrated in Figure 12.1.

A tabulation of the urea producers, plant locations, estimated plant capacities, and processes employed for the production of urea in the United States is shown in Table 12.1.

The geographical location of the producing plants and the processes employed are illustrated in Figure 12.2.

Physical and Chemical Properties

Some of the more important physical and chemical properties of urea are detailed in Tables 12.2 and 12.3.

Urea, a diamide of carbonic acid, is a white crystalline water-soluble compound having a total nitrogen content of 46.6 per cent. It sublimes readily under reduced pressure at temperatures just below and up to its melting point of 132.7°C. Urea is hygroscopic; thus, it absorbs moisture from the air when the relative humidity is 72 per cent or greater at 86°F. When the relative humidity of the air is less than 72 per cent, at 86°F urea will lose moisture to the air.

Neutral solutions of urea hydrolyze very slowly in the absence of bacteria and/or enzymes. However, hydrolysis of urea to form ammonia and carbon dioxide may be initiated by increasing the temperatures, combined with the addition of acids or bases or in the presence of bacteria or enzymes (i.e., urease). Urea may also be converted directly to nitrogen, carbon di-

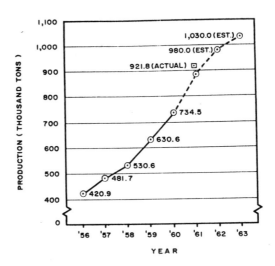

Figure 12.1. U.S. urea production [Chem. Week, p. 129, Feb. 17, 1962]. (Source: U.S. Tariff Commission 1956–1960; C. W. Estimates 1961–1963)

TABLE 12.1. U. S. UREA CAPACITY 1962[a]

Process	Company	Location	Estd. Capacity (Tons/Yr.)
Allied	Allied Chemical Co.	La Platta, Neb.	110,000
		South Point, Ohio	110,000
Chemico	Coop. Farm Chem. Co.	Lawrence, Kansas	23,000
	Monsanto Chem. Co.	El Dorado, Ark.	35,000
Du Pont	Du Pont	Belle, W. Va.	205,000
Dutch State Mines	Solar Nitrogen Chem.	Joplin, Mo.	52,000[b]
Inventa	Hercules Powder Co.	Hercules, Calif.	20,000
	Mississippi Chem. Co.	Yazoo City, Miss.	33,000
	Mississippi Chem. Co.	Pascagoula, Miss.	33,000
	Solar Nitrogen (Sohio)	Lima, Ohio	40,000
	Southern Nitrogen Co.	Savannah, Ga.	24,000
Montecatini	Armour Ag. Chem. Co.	Sheffield, Ala.	17,000
	Shell Chem. Co.	Ventura, Calif.	50,000
	Spencer Chem. Co.	Vicksburg, Miss.	10,000
	Spencer Chem. Co.	Henderson, Ky.	33,000
	Sun Olin Chem. Co.	N. Claymont, Del.	73,000
Pechiney	John Deere & Co.	Pryor, Okla.	95,000
	W. R. Grace & Co.	Memphis, Tenn.	120,000
(Undisclosed)	Escambia Chem. Co.	Pace, Fla.	20,000
	Hawkeye Chem. Co.	Clinton, Iowa	—[c]
	Hercules Powder Co.	Louisiana, Mo.	—[d]
	Nitrin Chem. Co.	Cordova, Ill.	—[e]

[a] *Chem. Week*, 129 (Feb. 17, 1962).
[b] *Chem. Processing*, 19 (Sept. 24, 1962).
[c] *Chem. Week*, 44 (June 16, 1962).
[d] *Chem. Week*, 82 (June 9, 1962).
[e] *Croplife*, 2 (Aug. 1962).

oxide, and water by the action of nitrous acid, alkaline hypochloride, hypobromide, or acid permanganate solutions.[28]

$$NH_2—CO—NH_2 + 3NaOBr + 2NaOH \rightarrow$$
$$N_2 \uparrow + Na_2CO_3 + 3NaBr + 3H_2O \quad (12.2)$$

Methods of Analysis

A method for the rapid volumetric analysis of the total nitrogen content of urea was described by Fox and Geldard in 1923.[16] Their method of analy-

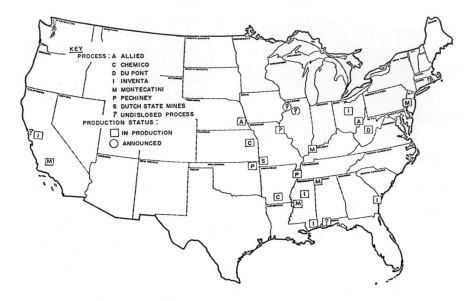

Figure 12.2. U.S. urea production plants 1962.

sis was adapted by the AOAC* [35] for use in the determination of urea in mixed fertilizer products. A description of the AOAC method is as follows:

A 10 ± 0.01 gm sample of mixed fertilizer is transferred to a 15 cm Whatman No. 12 fluted filter paper. The sample is leached with ca 300 ml H_2O into a 500 ml volumetric flask. Add 75 to 100 ml saturated $Ba(OH)_2$ solution to precipitate the phosphates present in the sample. Allow solution to settle and test for complete precipitation of the phosphates by adding a few extra drops of the saturated $Ba(OH)_2$ solution. Add 20 ml of 10 per cent Na_2CO_3 solution to precipitate the excess Ba and any soluble Ca salts. Allow the solution to settle and test for complete precipitation by adding a few drops of the 10 per cent Na_2CO_3 solution. Dilute the solution to volume, mix well, and filter through a 15 cm Whatman No. 12 fluted filter paper. Transfer a 50 ml aliquot (equivalent to 1 gm of sample) to a 200 or 250 ml erlenmeyer and add 1 to 2 drops of methyl purple indicator. Acidify the solution with $2N$ HCl and add 2 to 3 drops in excess. Neutralize the solution with $0.1N$ NaOH to the first change in color of the indicator. Add 20 ml of a neutral urease solution (see below), close flask with rubber stopper, and allow the flask to stand for 1 hr at 20 to 25°C. Cool the flask in an ice-water slurry and titrate at once with $0.1N$ HCl to the full purple color of the indicator, and then add ca 5 ml excess. Record the total volume of HCl added. Back titrate the excess HCl with $0.1N$ NaOH to the neutral end point of the indicator.

* Association of Official Agricultural Chemists.

TABLE 12.2. PHYSICAL PROPERTIES OF UREA

Molecular weight................................60.06
Total nitrogen content..........................46.6%
Color..White crystals
Melting point..................................132.7°C (270.9°F)
Specific gravity 20°/4°C........................1.335
Heat of solution (in water).....................−60.1 cal/gm (−108 Btu./lb)
Apparent density (loosely packed)...............42 lb/cu ft

TABLE 12.3. PROPERTIES OF AQUEOUS SOLUTIONS OF UREA

Temperature		Solubility		Approximate % in Volume of Water on Saturation
°C	°F	gm/100 gm water	lb/gal water	
0	32	66.7	5.57	49
10	50	85.2	7.11	63
20	68	108.0	9.01	82
30	86	135.0	11.3	103
40	104	167.0	13.9	129
50	122	203.0	16.9	158
60	140	251.0	20.9	198
70	158	360.0	25.9	245
80	176	400.0	32.4	319
90	194	525.0	43.8	338
100	212	733.0	64.5	591

Calculations:

$$\text{per cent urea} = \frac{(\text{ml } 0.1N \text{ HCl} - \text{ml } 0.1N \text{ NaOH}) \times 0.3003}{\text{wt. of sample}}$$

Preparation of the Neutral Urease Solution:

Shake 1 gm of jack bean meal with 100 ml H_2O for 5 min. Transfer 10 ml of solution to a 250 ml erlenmeyer flask, dilute with 50 ml H_2O, and add 4 drops of methyl purple. Titrate with $0.1N$ HCl to a reddish purple color, then back-titrate to a green color with $0.1N$ NaOH. From the difference in ml, calculate the amount of $0.1N$ HCl required to neutralize the remainder of the solution (usually ca 2.5 ml/100 ml), and add this amount of acid and shake well.

The above analytical method may be easily adapted for use in the analysis of the concentrated urea products such as the crystalline or prilled types. For example, a 0.5 to 1.0 gm sample is used in place of the 10 gm sample of mixed fertilizer. Secondly, one may eliminate the steps required for the precipitation of the soluble phosphates and subsequently the soluble Ba and Ca salts, where these salts are not present in the sample.

Manufacture[15, 52]

Chemical Reactions. The commercial production of urea is based on the exothermic synthesis of ammonium carbamate with its subsequent dehydration to urea. For example,

$$2NH_3 \;+\; CO_2 \;\rightleftarrows\; NH_2COONH_4 \qquad\qquad (12.3)$$

ammonia   carbon   ammonium
dioxide   carbamate

$$NH_2COONH_4 \rightleftarrows NH_2CONH_2 + H_2O \qquad\qquad (12.4)$$

ammonium   urea   water
carbamate

Ammonia and carbon dioxide are reacted together in a pressure reactor to form a melt containing urea, ammonium carbamate, and water, along with some unreacted ammonia. Depending upon the particular process used, the temperature of the melt in the reactor is maintained between 175°C and 210°C and the pressure between 170 atm and 400 atm.

Selection of the best operating conditions for the manufacture of urea is normally a compromise between several competing factors.[9] For example, the process conditions most suited for high yields of urea are high pressure, high temperature, and a minimum excess of ammonia. These very conditions, however, are most conducive to the acceleration of corrosion of the urea reactor equipment. The use of special alloys, silver, or stainless steel liners for the reactors are the most common answers to combat the corrosion. The Dutch-State-Mines and the Lonza (Swiss) processes claim the addition of air or oxygen in their processes minimize the corrosion in the reactor, while the Pechiney process claims the use of a light paraffin oil in the process aids in minimizing corrosion.

Table 12.4 illustrates the compromise in operating conditions for eight processes used in the manufacture of urea.

Raw Materials.[42] The primary sources of raw materials for the synthesis of urea today are natural gas, air, and water. Carbon dioxide of suitable quality is usually available from anhydrous ammonia production. Often, however, it is desirable to pass the carbon dioxide over a catalyst to remove any traces of oxygen, which is considered to be a major source of corrosion in the synthesis reactor of some processes. The anhydrous ammonia, as produced, is of high purity and seldom requires any pretreatment prior to its introduction into the synthesis process.

Synthesis.[9, 46] The method of treating the off gases (ammonia and carbon dioxide) from the carbamate-urea reactor represents the major differences among the variety of competing processes for the manufacture of urea. The choice of the particular process depends upon, to some degree,

TABLE 12.4. COMPARISON OF EIGHT UREA PROCESSES

Operating Characteristics	Chemico[a]	Du Pont[a]	Dutch State Mines[b]	Inventa[a]	Lonza[c]	Montecatini[a]	Pechiney[a]	Monsanto[d] (Pilot Plt. Stage)
Type of operation	Absorption of CO_2	Recycle of carbamate in H_2O-NH_3 solution	Recycle of carbamate in H_2O NH_3 solution	Absorption of NH_3	Recycle of carbamate in H_2O NH_3 solution	Recycle of carbamate in H_2O-NH_3 solution	Recycle of carbamate in slurry of light oil	Recycle of NH_3-H_2S in methanol
Reactor conditions:								
Temperature °C	175–185	200–210	180–185	180–200	160–220	180	180	100
Pressure, atm	170	400	200	200	200–350	200	200	15–20
Reactor lining	silver	silver	stainless steel	—	stainless steel	stainless steel	lead	stainless steel
NH_3:CO_2:H_2O ratio	6:1:0	5:1:0.73	—	2+:1:0	—	3.4:1:0.84	2:1:0	—
CO_2 conversion in autoclave	76%	70%	—	50%	77%	52%	50%	CO conversion 95–99%
Total	76%	70%	98–99%	50%	99%	88%	50%	99%
NH_3 conversion in autoclave	25%	24%	—	50%	—	30–32%	50%	60–65%
Total	73%	24%	99%	50%	99%	72.5%	50%	99%

a Chem. Week, 90 (Nov. 27, 1954).
b Chem. Processing, 19 (Sept. 24, 1962).
c Hydrocarbon Processing & Petroleum Refiner, 40, 305 (1961).
d Chemical & Engineering News, 51 (December 19, 1960). Hydrocarbon Processing & Petroleum Refiner, 40, 307 (1961). (A Process using NH₃-CO-S in Methanol.)

253

the particular objectives to be obtained and the location of the plant. For example, the Total Recycle Process may be best suited in the case where it is undesirable to integrate the urea operation with a nitric acid plant or some similar facility for the complete utilization of ammonia. On the other hand, the Partial Recycle Process or the Once-Through Process may have certain advantages where part or all of the off-gas ammonia is to be used in the production of nitric acid or for the reaction with the specific acid to form its ammonia salt, i.e., sulfuric, nitric, or, phosphoric acid. In one process, the off-gases are reacted with calcium sulfate to produce calcium carbonate and ammonium sulfate. Still another process (a Japanese patent) proposes the preparation of ammonium bicarbonate from the off-gases.

The principal advantage of the Once-Through Process lies in the relatively low capital investment for equipment, as there is no need to invest in equipment for the recycle of the off-gas. There are, however, certain drawbacks to this process and, for the process to be economical, there must be:

(1) a means of utilizing the ammonia in the off-gas;
(2) the process of utilizing the ammonia must also tolerate the presence of CO_2 as well as being as corrosion-free as possible; and
(3) the carbon dioxide must be available to the urea synthesis unit at essentially no cost, i.e., as a by-product from another process.

The Once-Through Process is illustrated in Figure 12.3.

The Partial Recycle Process is basically an equipment expansion of the Once-Through Process. In the Partial Recycle Process, normally the ammonia is recycled back to the urea reactor with the possible use of the carbon dioxide elsewhere in the plant system. The availability and economics involved at the particular plant will dictate which of the two gases will be recycled.

There are two versions of the Partial Recycle Process. The first process

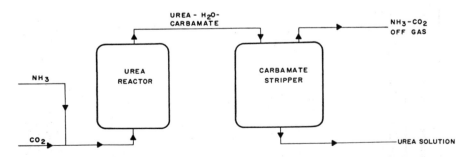

Figure 12.3. Sketch of once-through process.

entails the absorption of the carbon dioxide in monoethanolamine, thus leaving the ammonia free for recycle to the reactor, as illustrated in Figure 12.4.

Another version of the process involves the absorption of ammonia in a urea-nitrate solution, thus allowing the carbon dioxide to pass freely from the process stream. The ammonia is subsequently released from the urea-nitrate solution in a desorber unit and then recycled back to the urea reactor as illustrated in Figure 12.5.

In the Total Recycle Process, the ammonia and carbon dioxide are returned to the reactor as ammonium carbamate, either dissolved or slurried in a solvent such as water or a light paraffin oil. The use of a solvent to carry the ammonia and carbon dioxide as ammonium carbamate eliminates the major problem encountered in the so-called Hot-Gas Recycle Process, as once used by the Badische Anilin und Soda Fabrik. High capital costs, considerable operating difficulties, and severe corrosion of equipment were

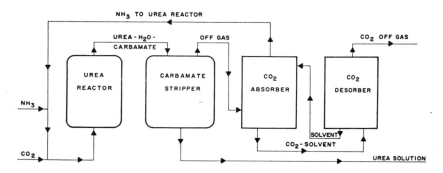

Figure 12.4. Sketch of partial recycle process. (Absorption of carbon dioxide)

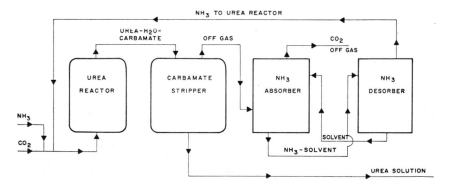

Figure 12.5. Sketch of partial recycle process. (Absorption of Ammonia)

the basic factors which worked against the possible commercial utilization of this process (the Hot-Gas Recycle Process).

The Total Recycle Process may be illustrated as in Figure 12.6.

Solid Urea Products. The aqueous solution of urea from any of the above processes must be concentrated to remove the excess synthesis water as well as traces of dissolved synthesis gases and then filtered to remove any solid impurities. The solution of urea is then ready for its final step in the preparation of the solid product.

The crystalline product is prepared by further concentration or evaporation of the solution followed by separation of the crystals of urea from the mother liquor. The crystals are subsequently dried to a moisture content of less than 0.5 per cent.

The process for manufacture of the crystalline product is illustrated in Figure 12.7.

The prilled or shotted urea product is prepared by concentrating the solution of urea to 98 to 99 per cent solids. The hot molten urea melt is then pumped through spray nozzles located at the top of a tower, as illustrated in Figure 12.8. A stream of air is circulated through the tower to assist in cooling the newly formed prills or shots. The product is passed through a dryer, coater, deduster, cooler, and finally into storage.

Biuret ($NH_2CONHCONH_2$) may be formed by the decomposition of urea during the concentration and the evaporation steps in the preparation of either the crystalline or prilled product. Normally little, if any, biuret (<0.5 per cent) is found in the crystalline product. A biuret content of less than 1 per cent for the prilled or shotted product is attainable by care-

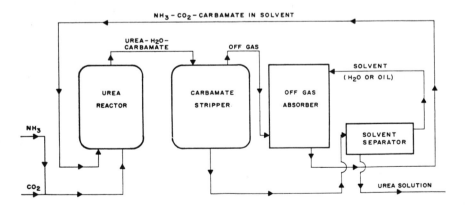

Figure 12.6. Sketch of total recycle process.

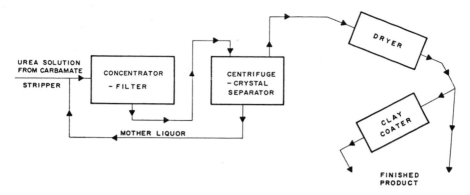

Figure 12.7. Sketch of manufacturing process for crystalline urea product.

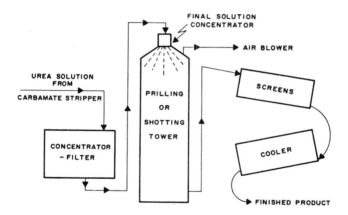

Figure 12.8. Sketch of manufacturing process for prilled or shotted urea product.

ful control of the concentration and evaporation steps just prior to the prilling operation.

Urea in Agriculture[30, 46]

Economic Aspects. Tests conducted by the various agricultural experiment stations since the late 1930's have shown urea to be equal to and, in some cases, superior to other forms of nitrogen for fertilizers. Urea has the highest nitrogen content (containing either 45 per cent or 46 per cent total nitrogen) of any of the solid products; it is easy to handle in conventional fertilizer-spreading equipment; it has good leach resistance in soils, leaves no residue in soils, and is noncorrosive to equipment used in its application. Urea enjoys wide-spread use in foliar sprays, in irrigation feeding of certain crops, in direct application to the soil, and in the standard ammoniating solutions used in the manufacture of the NPK-type fertilizer formulations.

A pound of urea with a 45 per cent nitrogen content gives 35 per cent more nitrogen than does ammonium nitrate and more than twice as much as ammonium sulfate. This illustrates the economics in the use of urea, which provides more efficient utilization of storage areas, of shipping, and of application equipment.

Use

Soil Applications.   The prilled urea may be applied to a variety of agricultural crops by the use of the standard types of application equipment. It may be applied by airplane, and recent developments in high speed spreaders or distributors enable one to spread the prilled type urea at a rate 4 to 8 times faster than is possible with conventional equipment. Important cost-saving advantages are obvious to the applicator and purchaser. For example, with the new spreading equipment, it is possible to cover up to sixty or more acres in 1 hr, thus offering a per-acre reduction in application costs.

A second, and rapidly developing field is in the bulk blending of the NPK raw materials for subsequent application to the soil. Urea may be used to advantage in certain mixtures of ammoniated phosphates and potash salts. Where the nonammoniated normal superphosphate (ROP) or triple superphosphate (CSP or TSP) are used, it is well to mix with hydrated lime before adding the prilled urea. The hydrated lime not only aids in neutralizing the free acids in the superphosphates and in reducing the free water content of the superphosphates but also minimizes the pickup of moisture by the urea.

Foliar Application.[45]   Urea is readily absorbed by the leaves of most plants and subsequently utilized for the production of proteins by the plants. Fruit trees, in general, give almost immediate nitrogen response, and this enables the growers to control the nitrogen feeding and thereby produce fruit of superior quality.

The concentration of the sprays may vary from regular strength solutions that have 5 to 15 lb of prilled urea per 100 gal of water to the more concentrated sprays containing from 40 to 60 lb of urea per 100 gal of water. Experience has shown that good quality prilled agricultural-grade urea is very satisfactory in most commercial applications. There are exceptions to the use of the prilled urea where the biuret content may be greater than 0.25 per cent. For example, citrus fruit, pineapple, coffee, and certain types of cherry trees have a very limited tolerance of biuret, thus requiring the use of a urea product having a biuret content of less than 0.25 per cent.

Irrigation Applications.   Urea performs well when distributed in irrigation waters. The urea is completely soluble in water and moves quickly down to the root zone of the plant, where it is converted to ammonia nitrogen by the soil bacteria. There it is held by the soil particles, which resist leaching losses from the percolation of water down through the soil.

Concentrated solutions made from the prilled urea are introduced into the irrigation water at the suction side of a water pump; however, by the use of pressure equipment, the concentrated urea solution may be injected into the irrigation water on the discharge side of the pump. Where the gravity-flow ditches are used, the concentrated urea solution may be metered into the water at the head gate or weir box. Usually the solution of urea is added during the first half of the irrigation cycle, but in the case of the ditch-type irrigation the urea solution may be fed to the water over most of the entire cycle.

Urea Solutions.   A variety of aqueous solutions containing urea are employed in the agricultural field. For example, the range of solutions might be summarized as follows:

(1) Nonpressure type (not containing ammonia)
    (a) Urea-water solutions
    (b) Urea-ammonium nitrate-water solutions
(2) Pressure type (fertilizer ammoniating solutions)
    (a) Urea-ammonia-water solutions (with or without carbon dioxide)
    (b) Urea-ammonia-ammonium nitrate-water solutions

The nonpressure type of solutions are applied directly to the soils as the so-called direct application solutions. Certain of these solutions are prepared simply by dissolving solid urea in water (see Table 12.5). Other more concentrated solutions (see Table 12.6) are made from the urea solution obtained from the process streams in the urea manufacturing plant, as described above. The manufacture of these solutions basically involves

TABLE 12.5. CHARACTERISTICS OF DILUTE UREA-WATER SOLUTIONS

Urea Solution (lb/gal)	Per cent Increase in Volume of Urea Solution (25°C)	At 25°C, Each Gallon of Solution Contains		Temperature at Which Solution is Saturated with Urea (°F)
		lb Urea	lb Nitrogen	
1	11	0.90	0.41	
2	19	1.68	0.76	
4	36	2.94	1.32	5
6	54	3.89	1.75	34
8	71	4.68	2.11	56

TABLE 12.6. CHARACTERISTICS OF CONCENTRATED UREA WATER SOLUTIONS

Total Nitrogen (%)	Composition Parts/100			Physical Properties	
	Water	Urea	NH_4NO_3	Density (15°C)	Salting-out Temp. (°F)
23.3	50	50	—	1.14	64
18.6	60	40	—	1.11	33
28.0	30	31	39	1.28	0
30.0	25.1	32.7	42.2	1.30	15
32.0	20.3	35.4	44.3	1.33	32

dilution of the concentrated urea solution to meet the required specification of total nitrogen and freezing point of the final solution. Dilution may be accomplished simply by adding water. In the manufacture of the urea-ammonium nitrate-water solutions, the urea solution may be mixed directly with a concentrated solution of ammonium nitrate, and again the proportions of ingredients used will depend upon the specifications of total nitrogen and freezing point for the final product.

The urea-water solutions are essentially noncorrosive and may be used safely in mild steel equipment. Solutions containing ammonium nitrate are corrosive to mild steel equipment, and should be employed only where aluminum equipment or other corrosion-resistant equipment is available.

The pressure type of urea solutions are primarily made for use as ammoniating solutions in the manufacture of the various types of NPK fertilizer products. These solutions may be used in either the batch or continuous ammoniation processes for the manufacture of either the pulverized or granular type of fertilizer products.

The aqueous urea-ammonia solutions (see Table 12.7) are prepared by the appropriate adjustment of the composition of the urea synthesis stream. Such solutions contain a certain quantity of ammonium carbamate, which decomposes to ammonia and carbon dioxide during the fertilizer ammoniation process. Other urea-ammonia solutions are made by the addition of ammonia to the concentrated urea solution as produced in the urea synthesis process.

The second type of solutions contain ammonium nitrate with a small quantity of urea, usually from 6 to 15 per cent by weight (see Table 12.8). These solutions are quite popular as they have relatively higher fixed nitrogen ratios (more solid nitrogen to free ammonia) and lower amounts of water. The corrosion characteristics of these solutions is the same as that for the regular ammonium nitrate solutions and, as such, must be handled in similar corrosion-resistant equipment.

TABLE 12.7. COMPOSITION AND PHYSICAL PROPERTIES
OF UREA-AMMONIA-WATER SOLUTIONS

Total Nitrogen	Composition (parts/100)			Physical Properties			Ratio of fixed N to free N
	Ammonia	Urea	Water	Specific Gravity (60°F)	Approx. Vapor Pressure Psig (104°F)	Approx. Salting-out. Temp. (°F)	
21.0	4.3	37.5	58.2	1.09	2	33	4.94
35.1	19.6	40.6	39.8	1.02	58	9	1.17
37.1ᵃ	25.0	35.3	23.3	1.09	20	34	0.8
43.0ᵇ	27.5	39.3	13.7	1.13	50	20	0.9
45.3	30.6	43.1	26.3	0.97	48	46	0.8
45.4	36.8	32.5	30.7	0.93	57	16	0.5
45.5ᶜ	36.8	32.5	23.3	1.00	64	5	0.5
45.5ᵈ	30.5	43.3	16.2	1.06	50	34	0.8
46.0	37.3	32.9	29.8	0.93	70	1	0.5
46.0	31.1	43.8	25.1	0.97	60	41	0.8
50.0	40.6	32.9	23.7	0.92	100	25	0.5
51.0	34.7	48.3	17.0	0.97	95	42	0.79

ᵃ Contains a compound which forms insoluble methylene urea during manufacture of mixed fertilizers, also contains 8.4 per cent carbon dioxide in the form of ammonium carbamate.

ᵇ Contains 9.5 per cent carbon dioxide as ammonium carbamate and 10 per cent as ammonium sulfate.

ᶜ Contains 7.4 per cent carbon dioxide as ammonium carbamate.

ᵈ Contains 10 per cent carbon dioxide as ammonium carbonate.

Finally, the urea-ammonia-water solutions may be modified by the addition of water for the preparation of a low-pressure solution for use as a direct application solution. Such solutions may be employed in the standard low pressure type of application equipment. These solutions exhibit the same noncorrosive properties of the standard urea-water or urea-ammonia-water solutions.

UREAFORM

A nitrogen fertilizer with a controlled availability for feeding plant life over a prolonged time was the goal of researchers in the agricultural field for many years. Natural organic materials have been widely employed through the years as a source of slowly available nitrogen. Unfortunately, most of the available nitrogen for the natural organic materials is converted rapidly to the nitrate form, while much of the remaining nitrogen is unavailable for productive use by growing plants.[43]

In the late 1930's, a fertilizer-ammoniating solution was developed which was capable of producing a slowly available or water-insoluble urea-form-

Table 12.8. Composition and Physical Properties
of Urea-Ammonia-Ammonium Nitrate Solutions

Total Nitrogen	Composition Parts/100				Physical Properties			Ratio of fixed N to free N
	Ammonia	Water	Ammonium Nitrate	Urea	Specific Gravity (60°F)	Approx. Vapor Pressure Psig (104°F)	Approx. Salting-out Temp. (°F)	
41.4	19.0	9.4	65.6	6.0	1.18	13	35	1.66
43.0	20.0	6.0	68.0	6.0	1.18	12	39	1.63
42.0	19.5	8.2	66.3	6.0	1.18	10	34	1.16
44.0	22.0	6.0	68.0	6.0	1.158	17	14	1.44
45.2	29.9	13.1	51.0	6.0	1.06	27	−8	0.84
44.4	24.5	9.5	56.0	10.0	1.11	22	−15	1.20
44.4	25.0	10.0	55.0	10.0	1.11	22	−20	1.15
41.0	19.0	12.0	58.0	11.0	1.16	10	7	1.63
49.5	37.0	12.0	40.0	11.0	1.04	10	—	0.63
44.4	26.0	12.0	50.0	12.0	1.08	25	−7	1.08
49.0	33.0	8.9	45.1	13.0	1.03	51	−17	0.8
49.1	34.0	10.0	43.0	13.0	1.01	52	−5	0.75
44.0	28.0	17.0	40.0	15.0	1.05	29	1	0.91
45.5	26.0	11.0	45.0	18.0	1.09	28	15	1.13
23.0	4.7	52.9	5.5	36.9	1.10	0	30	4.95

aldehyde-type nitrogen product. This slowly available source of nitrogen was formed during the normal process of ammoniating superphosphate in the manufacture of a mixed fertilizer.[19] The value of this slowly available nitrogen as a useful source of nitrogen was demonstrated in the early 1940's when it was compared to the molding-powder type of urea-formaldehyde resinous products obtained from the plastic-manufacturing industry and other natural organic fertilizers.[29] The amount of urea-formaldehyde product obtained from this ammoniating solution is relatively small; for example, only 20 per cent of the nitrogen from the ammoniating solution is capable of forming the slowly available urea-formaldehyde source of nitrogen.

The use of a concentrated urea-formaldehyde solution, with additional urea, is a later approach to the manufacture of urea-formaldehyde products in mixed fertilizers. A typical concentrated solution would contain 25 per cent urea, 60 per cent formaldehyde, and 15 per cent water. Compared to the ammoniating-solution route described above, the concentrated solutions may provide more water-insoluble nitrogen, i.e., up to about 40 per cent of the total nitrogen in the mixed fertilizer. Difficulty in proper control of the urea-formaldehyde condensation reaction during the conventional manufacture of the mixed fertilizer, however, presents serious problems in the proper development or formation of the desired type of urea-formaldehyde nitrogen.

Work at the U. S. Department of Agriculture, Beltsville, Md., in 1946, showed that a solid water-insoluble nitrogen product having a well-defined controlled availability could be made from the reaction of urea with formaldehyde.[53] Additional process information on the urea-formaldehyde reaction was reported by the USDA in 1948.[6] At this time, they proposed the generic name "ureaform" for this type of urea-formaldehyde product.[47] Extensive laboratory studies continued at the Beltsville station. The variables in the manufacturing process were studied to determine their influence on the nitrogen availability of the ureaform. Other studies involved plant-growth measurements under greenhouse and field conditions as well as the microbiological aspects of the ureaform nitrogen and its rate and manner of breakdown and conversion in the soil.[5, 8, 17]

The Association of American Fertilizer Control Officials adopted[3] the following as a definition of the ureaform fertilizer: "Urea-formaldehyde fertilizer materials are reaction products of urea and formaldehyde containing at least 35 per cent nitrogen, largely in insoluble but slowly available form. The water-insoluble nitrogen in these products shall not test less than 40 per cent active by the nitrogen activity index for urea-formaldehyde compounds as determined by the appropriate AOAC method."

In 1955 ureaform became commercially available to the specialty fertilizer market. Since that time it has found growing use in the turf and ornamental markets, either as the directly applied product or mixed into the standard NPK type specialty fertilizer products.

Chemical and Physical Properties

Ureaform is an odorless, white, granular solid containing about 38 per cent nitrogen. It is largely a mixture of methylene urea polymers having a range of molecular weights and thus a range of solubilities in aqueous solutions. It also contains small quantities of unreacted urea and methylol ureas. Ureaform is a stable product under normal conditions of storage and use. When placed in an aqueous environment, such as found in the fertilizer mixing process, ureaform is capable of continued polymerization[11] at elevated temperatures and over a wide range of pH, i.e., pH 2 to 11. Where there is no control over the conditions of pH and temperature, the resulting ureaform product usually has little, if any, remaining agronomic value. Ureaform exhibits only a slight tendency toward being hygroscopic. This is due primarily to the presence of the unreacted urea remaining in the commercial product after manufacture.

The properties of a typical commercial ureaform product are illustrated as follows:

Total nitrogen 38%
Activity index...55
Cold water-insoluble nitrogen 28%
Urea nitrogen..1.5%
Bulk density..40 lb/cu ft
Moisture content..3%

Agronomic Aspects of Ureaform

The agronomic value of any given ureaform, as a source of long feeding nitrogen, depends upon two factors:

(1) the *quantity* of cold water insoluble nitrogen which is the source of the slowly available nitrogen, and

(2) the *quality* of the cold water-insoluble nitrogen as determined by its activity index (AI), which reflects the rate at which the cold water-insoluble nitrogen will become available.[8, 23, 31]

Numerical values for these two factors are obtained by the laboratory procedures delineated in the next section.

That AI is a reliable indicator of the availability of the cold water-insoluble nitrogen has been amply demonstrated on field-grown turf, in the greenhouse, and by nitrification studies in the laboratory.[1, 2, 13, 32, 40, 51]

Figure 12.9 shows the relationship of the AI of a ureaform to its measured nitrification rate under controlled test conditions. In this study, each of the ureaform samples was washed with cold water in order to remove the soluble and therefore readily available nitrogen prior to the tests.

Leading authorities have found, and AAFCO (American Association of Fertilizer Control Officials) has established an AI of 40 as the minimum for acceptable plant response.

Other nitrification studies (Figure 12.10) show the relative nitrification rates for a variety of nitrogenous compounds.[23] These particular samples were not washed prior to the nitrification test.

The influence on the pH of the soil on the nitrification of ureaform is illustrated in Table 12.9. These data show that nitrification takes place most rapidly where the pH of the soil is slightly acidic—a pH environment which is also generally described as the most desirable for optimum plant growth.[50]

In the nitrification of ureaform the soil microorganisms convert the urea-formaldehyde nitrogen to nitrates in presumably the normal manner. The presence of formaldehyde has never been detected during the course of a nitrification test.[17] Apparently formaldehyde, as such, is either not liberated during the nitrification process or, if liberated, it is promptly

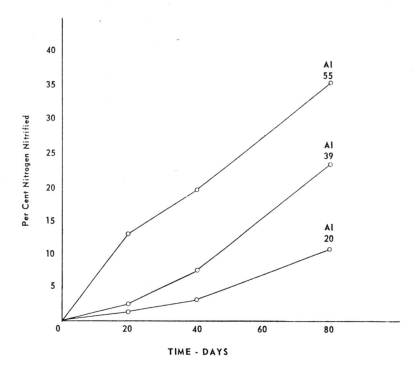

Figure 12.9. Relationship of AI to nitrification rate for water insoluble fractions of ureaform.

utilized by the soil organisms. As such, the carbon of the ureaform may be available for microbial activity as that present in the normal soil organic matter.

The effect of the soil moisture content on the rate of nitrification of ureaform[21] is shown in Table 12.10. A 50 per cent saturation level seems to favor the nitrification of ureaform. This level of saturation is usually best for normal plant growth. Nitrification at reduced rates does occur, however, even though the remaining conditions are relatively severe.

Finally, since ureaform supplies only the nitrogen requirements of the plant, optimum conversion of the ureaform nitrogen to the available nitrate form occurs when there are adequate amounts of other plant nutrients.

Method of Analysis

Analysis of ureaform involves the determination of the total nitrogen, the cold and hot water-insoluble nitrogen used in the calculation of the activity index (AI), and urea. The official AOAC Improved Kjeldahl

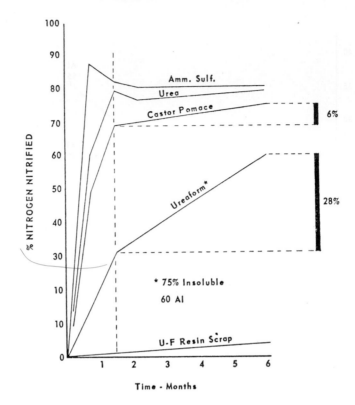

Figure 12.10. Relative nitrification rates of nitrogenous compounds.

Method for Nitrate-Free Samples[36] is used in the determination of the total nitrogen and the nitrogen present in both the cold water-insoluble nitrogen (CWIN) and the hot water-insoluble nitrogen (HWIN) residues remaining after the appropriate treatment with either cold[37] or boiling water.[38]

The official AOAC method for the determination of the CWIN or WIN is described as follows:

Place a 1 or 1.4 gm sample (previously prepared) in a 50 ml beaker, wet with alcohol, add 20 ml water ($25 \pm 2°C$), and let stand for 15 min, stirring occasionally. Transfer the supernatant liquor to an 11 cm Whatman No. 2 paper in a 60° long-stem funnel 2.5 in. in diameter, and wash the residue 4 or 5 times by decanting with water ($25 \pm 2°C$). Finally, transfer all the residue to the filter paper and complete the washing until the filtrate measures 250 ml. Determine the nitrogen in the residue using the official AOAC Improved Kjeldahl Method for Nitrate-Free Samples.

TABLE 12.9

Test Number	Initial Soil pH	Total Nitrogen Nitrified (%)		
		21 days	42 days	84 days
1	5.0	19.5	25.0	45.0
2	6.1	33.5	51.5	69.5
3	7.3	21.0	37.5	48.5

TABLE 12.10

Sample No.	Water Content of soil*	% Nitrogen Nitrified			
		3 weeks	6 weeks	12 weeks	26 weeks
1	25	0	5	22	37
2	50	6	25	45	56
3	75	2	12	11	16

* Per cent of total water-holding capacity.

The official AOAC method (as modified) for the determination of HWIN is as follows:

Place accurately weighed sample containing 0.1200 gm WIN in a 200 ml tall-form beaker (for mixed fertilizers add approx. 0.5 gm $CaCO_3$). From a supply of boiling buffer solution add 100 ml by graduate to the sample, stir, cover, and immerse *promptly* in a boiling water bath so that the liquid in the beaker is below H_2O line in bath. Maintain bath at 98° to 100°C. (Check with thermometer.) Stir at 10 min intervals. After *exactly* 30 min remove beaker from bath and filter *promptly* through 15 cm Whatman No. 12 fluted paper. If more than 4 min are required to filter the original solution, discard and weigh a new sample. Repeat the extraction process and just prior to removal of the beaker from the water bath introduce with stirring 1 gm "Celite" filter aid into the hot extraction mixture. Filter as before. Wash the insoluble residue completely onto the paper with hot (boiling) H_2O and continue washing residue with hot H_2O until total wash water is 100 ml. Washing should be completed before the filtrate becomes cloudy or its temperature drops below 60°C. Determine the nitrogen in the residue using the official AOAC improved Kjeldahl Method for nitrate-free samples. In the case where $CaCO_3$ has been used in the determiantion, add 35 ml instead of 25 ml conc. H_2SO_4 in the digestion step for the analysis of total nitrogen.

The activity index (AI) of the ureaform is calculated as follows:

$$AI = \frac{\% \text{ CWIN} - \% \text{ HWIN}}{\% \text{ CWIN}} \times 100 \qquad (11.5)$$

Thus, AI reflects the amount of CWIN that is soluble in boiling water.

Figure 12.11 illustrates how a change in the composition of the CWIN is directly reflected in a change of the AI of the ureaform. Bar A represents a sample of ureaform having a total nitrogen content of 38 per cent and a CWIN content of 28 per cent. Bars B, C, and D are represented to show AI values of 25, 50, and 75, respectively. As illustrated, ureaforms having a low AI have undesirably larger quantities of HWIN than do ureaforms having a high AI.

Manufacture of Ureaform

Chemical Reaction. To produce consistently high quality solid ureaform, the following variables must be controlled:[6, 7] pH, temperature, reaction time, initial urea-formaldehyde mole ratio, degree of dilution of the reaction system, and catalyst used for initiating condensation reaction.

Several patents relating to various aspects of ureaform manufacture have been issued.[7, 10, 14, 20, 22, 25, 26, 33, 34, 39, 41, 49]

The following brief summary of the chemistry involved in the ureaformaldehyde reaction leading to solid ureaform shows how and why

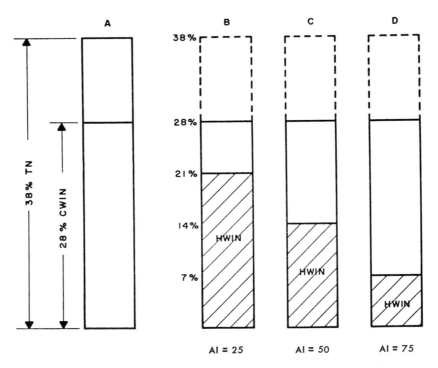

Figure 12.11. Relationship of AI to hot water-insoluble nitrogen in ureaform.

product quality depends on manufacturing conditions. The principal reactions are assumed to proceed through the following series of equations (see Figure 12.12).

In Reaction 1, one mole of urea reacts with one mole of formaldehyde to form monomethylol urea.[11, 12, 18, 44, 54] The reaction is carried out in an aqueous system at the appropriate temperature by the use of an acid catalyst. The condensation reactions then develop, forming a variety of methylene urea polymers having varying chain lengths as shown in Reactions 2, 3, and 4. By appropriate adjustment of the pH and temperature of the system, these condensation reactions may be continued, retarded, or stopped.[6] It is important to understand, however, that the primary reaction of urea with formaldehyde (Reaction 1) is reversible[11] over a pH range from 2.0 to 11.0. Thus, dimethylol urea could be formed (Reaction 5) with the eventual formation of long-chain methylene urea products such as are illustrated by the Reaction 6.[24, 27] The rate and extent of reaction is influenced and controlled by pH and temperature, provided that the variables of time and initial urea-to-formaldehyde mole ratios are the same at the start of each new preparation of product.

The initial urea-to-formaldehyde mole ratio is also one of the more important variables. For example, with the same reacting conditions, an

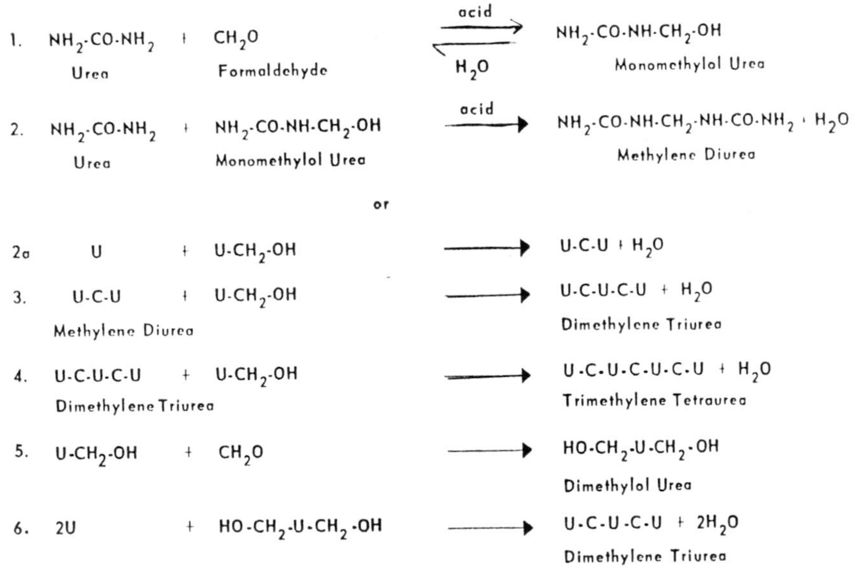

1. $NH_2 \cdot CO \cdot NH_2$ + CH_2O $\xrightleftharpoons[H_2O]{acid}$ $NH_2 \cdot CO \cdot NH \cdot CH_2 \cdot OH$
     Urea   Formaldehyde   Monomethylol Urea

2. $NH_2 \cdot CO \cdot NH_2$ + $NH_2 \cdot CO \cdot NH \cdot CH_2 \cdot OH$ $\xrightarrow{acid}$ $NH_2 \cdot CO \cdot NH \cdot CH_2 \cdot NH \cdot CO \cdot NH_2$ + H_2O
     Urea   Monomethylol Urea   Methylene Diurea

or

2a.   U   + $U \cdot CH_2 \cdot OH$ $\longrightarrow$ $U \cdot C \cdot U$ + H_2O

3. $U \cdot C \cdot U$ + $U \cdot CH_2 \cdot OH$ $\longrightarrow$ $U \cdot C \cdot U \cdot C \cdot U$ + H_2O
     Methylene Diurea   Dimethylene Triurea

4. $U \cdot C \cdot U \cdot C \cdot U$ + $U \cdot CH_2 \cdot OH$ $\longrightarrow$ $U \cdot C \cdot U \cdot C \cdot U \cdot C \cdot U$ + H_2O
     Dimethylene Triurea   Trimethylene Tetraurea

5. $U \cdot CH_2 \cdot OH$ + CH_2O $\longrightarrow$ $HO \cdot CH_2 \cdot U \cdot CH_2 \cdot OH$
                                                  Dimethylol Urea

6. $2U$ + $HO \cdot CH_2 \cdot U \cdot CH_2 \cdot OH$ $\longrightarrow$ $U \cdot C \cdot U \cdot C \cdot U$ + $2H_2O$
                                                  Dimethylene Triurea

Figure 12.12. U-F condensation reaction.

initial urea-to-formaldehyde mole ratio of 1:1 will react more rapidly and to a much greater degree than will a 4:1 urea-to-formaldehyde mole ratio. Another feature of these reactions to be considered is the liberation of a mole of water for each mole of formaldehyde used. In more practical terms, this would mean that 60 lb of water are released for every 100 lb of formaldehyde employed in the initial reaction, provided the condensation reaction has proceeded beyond the methylol urea step shown in Reaction 1.

Manufacturing Process. The processes for the manufacture of ureaform are generally divided into two categories, i.e., the dilute- or the concentrated-solution processes.[6] In most cases the processes require an acid to catalyze the urea-formaldehyde condensation; however, the condensation reaction may be initiated by utilizing an alkaline catalyst with the subsequent employment of an acid catalyst as the reaction proceeds. In all processes, the initial reacting mole ratio of urea to formaldehyde is greater than 1.

The dilute-solution process involves the use of an acid catalyst and mild temperatures for the condensation of a dilute solution of urea with formaldehyde. In this process, the reaction proceeds at a moderate rate and, at an appropriate point, the acidic aqueous reaction solution is neutralized. The ureaform, as a suspended reaction product, is then filtered, granulated, and dried. The mother liquor of unreacted urea, formaldehyde, methylol ureas, and short-chain water-soluble methylene ureas is recycled back to the reaction vessel for further reaction.

The advantages of the dilute-solution process lie in the uniformity, through good process control, of the quality or AI of the product and in consistently higher yields of CWIN. Also the granular ureaform product exhibits certain end-use advantages over the solid-flake product as made in the concentrated-solution process. The disadvantages of this process are in the necessity for recycling the unconverted reactants, for filtering of the solid reaction product, and for extra drying to produce the finished product.

In the concentrated-solution process, crystalline urea is added to an aqueous solution of formaldehyde. The mixture is made slightly alkaline and is heated to accelerate the condensation of urea with formaldehyde. After allowing appropriate time for condensation, acid is added continuously to this mixture while the mixture is poured onto a heated surface such as a tray, moving belt, or rotating drum. After a second time cycle, the solid ureaform is neutralized, dried, and made ready for packaging and distribution.

The advantages of the concentrated solution process are (1) the relatively short reaction time, (2) the relatively simple processing equipment, and (3) the minimum requirements for product-drying equipment. On the other hand, the inherent difficulty in controlling the condensation reaction is the major drawback to the process. Because of this, the resulting ureaform product exhibits wide variations in AI as well as CWIN and urea content. In general, ureaform products prepared by the concentrated-solution process having a high AI will have a correspondingly low CWIN content and, conversely, where the AI is low the CWIN content will be high.

Ureaform in Mixed Fertilizers[4]

Ureaform is employed successfully in the normal fertilizer products, such as the dry-mix or mix-to-grade types, and in either the batch or continuous processes. In these fertilizers, ureaform offers the fertilizer manufacturer flexibility in formulation, good mixing and storage characteristics, and uniform quality and quantity of the insoluble nitrogen. Its use in mixed fertilizers, however, still requires careful control of pH, temperature, and time throughout the various processing steps, whether in the conventional mixing or granulating equipment.

An example of how the pH of the final fertilizer mixture can affect the AI of the ureaform is illustrated in Table 12.11.

The two 10-6-4 grade fertilizers were prepared by the dry-mix process and stored under similar conditions prior to analysis. "Uramite" * ureaform fertilizer was used as the source of the ureaform nitrogen in both formulas. The important difference is the use of nonammoniated superphosphate (ROP) in Formula 1 versus ammoniated superphosphate with hydrated

TABLE 12.11. EFFECT OF pH ON AI OF UREAFORM IN A MIXED
FERTILIZER PRODUCT

Materials	10-6-4 Grade (Dry-Mix Type)	
	Formula 1	Formula 2
"Uramite" ureaform fertilizer	290 lb	290 lb
Ammonium sulfate	409	200
6-16-0 base	—	750
ROP	600	—
Muriate of potash	135	135
Organic (natural)	100	100
Dolomite	466	500
Hydrated lime	—	25
	2000 lb	2000 lb
Analysis:		
AI	27.1	43.9
pH	3.8	5.4

* Registered Trademark of E. I. du Pont de Nemours & Co. (Inc.).

lime in Formula 2. Note that the analysis of Formula 1 shows the AI is 27.1 with a pH of 3.8, while in Formula 2 the AI is 43.9 at a pH of 5.4. A pH between 5.4 and 6.2 has been found best for maintaining the AI of ureaform in complete fertilizer mixtures.

The effect of temperature on the AI of ureaform is illustrated by the use of the following formula for a 12-8-4 grade fertilizer:

"Uramon"* ammonia liquor-37	173 lb
"Uramite" ureaform fertilizer	380
Ammonium sulfate	175
ROP	800
Muriate of potash	134
Dolomite	373
Hydrated lime	20
	2055 lb

In this formula "Uramon" ammonia liquor-37, "Uramite" ureaform fertilizer, and ammonium sulfate are the sources of nitrogen. Hydrated lime is used to adjust the pH of the product during processing. The results are shown in Figures 12.13 and 12.14.

The data in Figure 12.13 were obtained while holding the fertilizer in a laboratory type rotary dryer where the exit air temperature was held constant at 350°F for 25 min. The AI decreases sharply as the product temperature increases above 200°F.

Figure 12.14 shows the accelerated degradation of AI when the exit air temperature was 400°F. The 50° higher temperature accelerated the degradation of the AI so that the ureaform became agronomically worthless in 25 min, even though the pH of the mixture was within the proper range.

The following recommendations detail the steps to be taken in order to maintain the quality of the ureaform nitrogen during the manufacture of a specialty fertilizer. These recommendations may be modified, to a certain extent, depending upon the specific equipment and raw materials available.

The types of fertilizers and mixing operations discussed are dry-mix, nongranular, granular, and light-weight formulations.

The formulas of typical dry mixtures are shown in Table 12.12. "Uramite" ureaform fertilizer is the source of the ureaform nitrogen in both formulas. In Formula 1, urea supplies the remainder of the nitrogen, and triple superphosphate supplies the phosphate requirements. In Formula 2, the remainder of the nitrogen is supplied by three sources: (1) a natural organic-type nitrogen, (2) an ammoniated base which also supplies the

* Registered Trademark, E. I. du Pont de Nemours & Co. (Inc.).

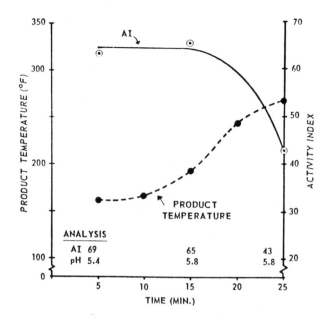

Figure 12.13. Effect of temperature on ureaform 12-8-4 grade fertilizer. (Dryer exit gas temperature at 350°F)

phosphate requirements, and (3) urea. Hydrated lime is used in both formulas to adjust the pH for protection of the AI of the "Uramite."

Recommendations for manufacture of these dry mixtures are as follows:

(1) use urea for source of supplemental nitrogen;

(2) add 10–25 lb of hydrated lime to formula when employing a well-ammoniated base, or

(3) add 25–50 lb of hydrated lime in the case where a nonammoniated superphosphate is utilized;

(4) mix the hydrated lime with the superphosphate source prior to adding the ureaform and urea;

(5) minimize segregation by using raw materials having similar particle size and bulk densities; and

(6) maintain the product temperature at less than 100°F during storage.

A typical 10-5-5 grade fertilizer is illustrated in Table 12.13 for the nongranular type of product.

Hydrated lime is not needed, as the proper pH range of 5.4 to 5.6 can be obtained by the utilization of the appropriate ammoniation rate for the phosphate source. The following suggestions apply to the manufacture of nongranular products:

(1) employ a urea-ammonia-water type of ammoniating solution;

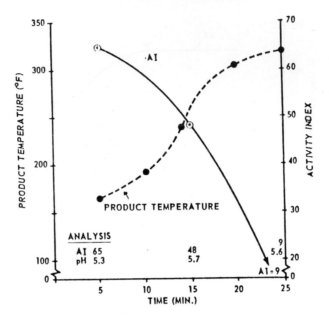

Figure 12.14. Effect of temperature on ureaform 12-8-4 grade fertilizer. (Dryer exit gas temperature at 400°F)

TABLE 12.12. DRY-MIX FORMULATIONS (10-6-4 GRADE)

Materials	Formula 1	Formula 2
"Uramite" ureaform fertilizer	300 lb	300 lb
Urea	200	94
Organic (natural)	—	110
6-16-0 base	—	750
Triple super	270	—
Muriate of potash	140	140
Filler	1040	581
Hydrated lime	50	25
	2000 lb	2000 lb

(2) use urea for supplemental nitrogen;
(3) utilize a 6 to 6.5 lb ammoniation rate for normal superphospate or a 3 to 4 lb rate for triple superphosphate;
(4) use dolomitic limestome as filler, fine particle size preferred; and
(5) cool and store product below 100°F.

TABLE 12.13. NONGRANULAR FORMULATION (10-5-5)

"Uramon" ammonia liquor-37	140 lb
"Uramite" ureaform fertilizer	290
Ammonium sulfate	180
ROP	540
Muriate of potash	170
Dolomite	680
	2000 lb

The fine pulverized type of dolomitic limestome has been proved an excellent aid for maintaining the proper pH of the product during processing. The product should be cooled and stored so that its final temperature will be below 100°F.

To obtain a granular product, water should be added before or during normal ammoniation, followed by drying and cooling. The temperature of the product leaving the dryer should not exceed 200°F, followed by cooling and storing at 100°F or less. It is highly desirable to keep the recycle of product to a minimum in order to avoid degradation of the AI of the ureaform by repeated exposure of the product to high temperatures in the dryer. Thus if a granular type of mixture is desired,

(1) add 6 to 8 per cent water prior to ammoniation;
(2) keep product temperature at 170 to 190°F in dryer for no more than 15 min;
(3) cool and store below 100°F; and
(4) keep recycle to a minimum.

Typical formulas for granular products are shown in Table 12.14.

Only 60° Bé sulfuric acid is used in these specialty fertilizer formulas; 66° Bé is not advisable because it is extremely difficult, if not impossible, to protect the AI of the ureaform from degradation by this more concentrated acid.

Suggestions for making granular formulations by the batch process are as follows:

(1) select urea as the preferred source of supplemental nitrogen;
(2) use 50 lb of hydrated lime;
(3) employ dolomitic limestone as the major source of the filler; and
(4) use a 6 to 6.5 lb ammoniation rate for normal superphosphate or a 3 to 4 lb rate for triple superphosphate;
(5) for processing, add the water required for granulation, followed by one-third of the ammoniating solution;
(6) add the acid simultaneously with the remaining solution; and

TABLE 12.14. GRANULAR FORMULATIONS

Materials	10-6-4	12-6-6	14-7-7
"Uramon" ammonia liquor-37.......	300 lb	259 lb	302 lb
"Uramite" ureaform fertilizer.......	257	296	345
Urea..............................	—	69	81
ROP..............................	600	600	700
Muriate of potash..................	134	200	233
H_2SO_4-60°Bé......................	150	108	126
Filler.............................	576	460	221
Hydrated lime.....................	50	50	50
	2067 lb	2042 lb	2058 lb

(7) add the ureaform and continue mixing to end of normal mixing cycle;

(8) keep product temperature exit the dryer below 200°F;

(9) cool and store below 100°F; and

(10) keep recycle to a minimum.

Suggestions for the continuous ammoniation process are as follows:

(1) select urea as the preferred source of supplemental nitrogen;

(2) use 50 lb of hydrated lime;

(3) employ dolomitic limestone as the major source of the filler;

(4) use a 6 to 6.5 lb ammoniation rate for normal superphosphate or a 3 to 4 lb rate for triple superphosphate;

(5) mix the ureaform with the dry raw materials;

(6) either partially or completely neutralize the acid with the ammoniating solution prior to addition to the ammoniator;

(7) where required add the remainder of the solution to the ammoniator;

(8) keep product temperature exit the dryer below 200°F;

(9) cool and store below 100°F; and

(10) keep recycle to a minimum.

Formulas for typical light-weight products are shown in Table 12.15.

Phosphoric acid, either the electric furnace or wet process type, furnishes the phosphate requirements of the formula, and fixes the free ammonia from the ammoniating solution. Phosphoric acid may be introduced into the ammoniator through the normal sparger pipe system. With the recommended ammoniation rates, the resulting mixture of ammoniated phosphates provides the ideal pH range of 5.8 to 6.2 for the protection of the AI of the ureaform.

For manufacture of these products, a batch or continuous process may

TABLE 12.15. LIGHT-WEIGHT FORMULATIONS

Materials	16-8-8	18-8-5	20-10-5
"Uramon" ammonia liquor-37	257 lb	257 lb	322 lb
"Uramite" ureaform fertilizer	410	468	515
Urea	152	192	187
H_3PO_4 75%	294	294	367
Muriate of potash	267	167	167
Light-weight filler	709	710	561
	2089 lb	2088 lb	2119 lb

be employed. Urea and a urea-ammonia-water type ammoniating solution are the preferred sources of nitrogen. A light-weight filler, such as vermiculite, should be utilized, and for the electric furnace phosphoric acid use an 8 lb ammoniation rate, or a 7.2 lb ammoniation rate for the wet-process phosphoric acid. Water should be added prior to or during the ammoniation to minimize the loss of the free ammonia from the ammoniating solution. The acid and ammoniating solution should be added in such a manner as to prevent any accumulation of free acid in the product. To preserve the light-weight feature of these products, several recommendations are pertinent: (1) for the batch process use a 1000 lb to 1500 lb batch; (2) for the continuous process operate at a reduced production rate, such as 10 to 12 tons per hr; and (3) avoid large bulk storage of the final product. Maintain the product temperature at less than 200°F exit the dryer, cool and store the product below 100°F, and keep recycle of the product to a minimum.

Uses

Direct Application. Ureaform is an ideal source of nitrogen for any plant having a steady and prolonged period of nitrogen demand. Its high nitrogen content of 38 per cent, ease of application, and unique feature of slow, gradual release of nitrogen (as well as its safe, nonburning characteristics) make it well suited for turf grass, ornamental plants, and certain cash crops. For example, application of ureaform once or twice per year can provide the entire season's feeding requirements for turf grass areas such as golf courses, athletic fields, park and highway areas, and home lawns. Also, ornamental plants such as flowers, foilage plants, shrubs, and trees—grown in or outdoors—may be easily supplied with an entire season's nitrogen feeding requirements. An application of 2 to 5 lb of ureaform per 100 sq ft of planting area is adequate for most ornamental plants. For greenhouse or potting soils, 2½ to 5 lb of ureaform per cu yd of soil has been found to be adequate for most applications.

Mixed Fertilizers

Ureaform has found increasing use as a supplemental source of nitrogen in the NPK type of fertilizers. These fertilizer products are primarily employed in the large, growing, specialty home-lawn and commercial-grower fertilizer markets. Specialty fertilizers of the 2-1-1, 4-2-1, 5-3-2, etc., NPK ratios that utilize ureaform may be easily produced, as previously discussed, by the various commercial fertilizer manufacturing processes. The use of ureaform enables the manufacturer to incorporate the desired higher quantity of nitrogen in the particular specialty formula without encountering the usual "burning" characteristics normally associated with the high-nitrogen fertilizers which contain only the soluble, readily available sources of nitrogen. These specialty fertilizers are also employed for grasses on highway slopes, field-grown ornamental plants, and certain other cash crops.

REFERENCES

1. Armiger, W. H., Forbes, I., Wagner, F. E., and Lunstrom, F. O., *J. Amer. Soc. Agron.*, **40**, 342 (1948).
2. Armiger, W. H., Clark, K. G., Lunstrom, F. O., and Blair, A. E., *J. Amer. Soc. Agron.*, **43**, 123 (1951).
3. Association of American Fertilizer Control Officials, No. 8, 1954.
4. Church, R. J., and Lewis, J. W., "High Quality Ureaform Fertilizers", paper presented at 142nd American Chemical Society Meeting, Atlantic City, N. J., 1962.
5. Clark, K. G., *Amer. Soc. Agron. Crops and Soils*, p. 14 (June–July 1952).
6. Clark, K. G., Yee, J. Y., and Love, K. S., *Ind. Eng. Chem.*, **40**, 1178 (1948).
7. Clark, K. G., Yee, J. Y., Love, K. S., and Boyd, T. A., *Ind. Eng. Chem.*, **43**, 871 (1951).
8. Clark, K. G., Yee, J. Y., Gaddy, V. L., Lunstrom, F. O., *Agr. Food Chem.*, **4**, No. 2, 135 (1956).
9. Cronan, C. S., "Urea Processes Face Bright Future", *Chem. Eng.* (Jan. 26, 1959).
10. Darden, E. T., U. S. Patent 2,766,283 (1956).
11. de Jong, J. I., and de Jonge, J., *Rec. Trav. chim. Pays-Bas*, **71**, 643 (1952).
12. Ibid, **71**, 661 (1952).
13. Duich, J. M., and Musser, H. B., Penn. State Univ. Prog. Rept. 214, April 1960.
14. Ettle, G. W., and Arkless, K., British Patent 172,178 (1954).
15. Frejacques, M., *Chim. & Ind.* (Paris), **60**, 22 (1948).
16. Fox, E. J., and Geldard, W. J., *Ind. Eng. Chem.*, **15**, 743 (1923).
17. Fuller, W. H., and Clark, K. G., *Proc. Soil Sci. Soc. Amer.*, **12**, 198 (1947).
18. Kadowaki, H., *Bull. Chem. Soc. Japan*, **11**, 248 (1936).
19. Keenen, F. G., and Sachs, W. H., U. S. Patents 2,255,026; 2,255,027 (1941).
20. Kise, M. A., U. S. Patent 2,644,806 (1953).
21. Kolterman, D. W., Proc. Penn. State Silver Anniv. Turf Conf., 1956.
22. Kralovec, R. D., and Huffman, R. L., U. S. Patent 2,592,809 (1952).

23. Kralovec, R. D., and Morgan, W. A., *Agr. Food Chem.*, **2**, 92 (1954).
24. Kuriyama, S., Hamada, H., and Takenouchi, M., *J. Chem. Soc. Japan Industri, Chem. Sect.*, **55**, 38 (1952).
25. Kvalnes, H. M., and Darden, E. T., *Can.* **550**, 618 (1957).
26. Long, D. R., U. S. Patent 2,810,710 (1957).
27. Long, M. I. E., and Winsor, G. W., *J. Sci. Food Agr.* **11**, 441 (1960).
28. Lucas, H. J., Organic Chemistry, page 302, New York, American Book Co., 1935.
29. McCool, M. M., *Contrib. Boyce Thompson Inst.*, **11**, 393 (1941).
30. Moore, R. L., and Parks, R. Q., "Urea—Growing Over Capacity Problems," *Chem. & Eng. News*, (Nov. 23, 1959).
31. Morgan, W. A., and Kralovec, R. D., *J. Assoc. Office Agr. Chem.* **36**, No. 3, 907 (1953).
32. Musser, H. B., Watson, J. R., Stanford, J. B., and Harper, J. C., *Bull. Pa. Agric. Exp. Sta.*, No. 542 (1951).
33. O'Donnell, J. M., U. S. Patent 2,830,036 (1958).
34. O'Donnell, J. M., U. S. Patent 2,916,371 (1959).
35. Official Methods of Analysis of the Association of Official Agricultural Chemists, Method 2.055, 9th ed., 1960.
36. Ibid, Method 2.036.
37. Ibid, Method 2.047.
38. Ibid, Method 2.053.
39. Patry, M., Dhers, M., and Paul, C., French Patent 956,459 (1950).
40. Pereira, R. L., and Smith, J. B., "Nitrification of Urea-Formaldehyde Fractions Soluble in Hot or Cold Water", paper presented at 76th Association of Official Agricultural Chemists Meeting, Oct. 16, 1962.
41. Rohner, L. V., and Wood, A. P., U. S. Patent 2,415,705 (1947).
42. Rooseboom, A., *Chem. Eng.*, **58**, 111 (1951).
43. Rubins, E. J., and Bear, F. E., *Soil Sci.*, **54**, 411 (1942).
44. Straudinger, H., and Wagner, K., *Mikromol. Chem.*, **12**, 168 (1954).
45. "The Chemistry and Technology of Fertilizers", ACS Monograph ≠148, p. 47, New York, Reinhold Publishing Corp., 1960.
46. *The Magazine of World Nitrogen*, **2**, (May 1959).
47. U. S. Dept. Agricultural Press Release, April 11, 1947.
48. Werner, E. A., *The Chem. of Urea*, London (1923).
49. Whynes, A. L., British Patent 789,075 (1958).
50. Winsor, G. W., and Long, M. I. E., *J. Sci. Food Agr.*, **9**, 185 (1958).
51. Wisniewski, A. J., DeFrance, J. A., *et al.*, *Agron. J.*, **50**, 575 (1958).
52. Wolf, F. A., and O'Flynn, D. J., *Encyclopedia of Chemical Technology*, Vol. 14, pp. 458–466, New York, Interscience Publishers, Inc., 1955.
53. Yee, J. Y., and Love, K. S., *Proc. Soil Sci. Soc. Amer.*, **11**, 389 (1946).
54. Zigeuner, G., Pitter, R., Berger, H., and Rauch, H., *Mh. Chem.*, **86**, 165 (1955).

13

The Girdler–Toyo Koatsu Urea Processes*

J. C. REYNOLDS AND C. R. TRIMARKE

Girdler Corporation

The recent introduction of the Girdler–Toyo Koatsu urea total-re-cycle process represents one of the high points of a long history of develop-ment of urea engineering techniques pioneered by Toyo Koatsu Industries, Inc., Tokyo, Japan.

The Claude Nitrogen Industry Co., a predecessor of Toyo Koatsu In-dustries, conducted research on the synthesis of urea as early as 1926. By 1937 the first Japanese urea plant using ammonia and carbon dioxide as raw materials was placed into production by Toyo Koatsu.

The first commercial urea fertilizer plant in Japan was completed at Sunagawa, Hokkaido by Toyo Koatsu in August 1948. The Sunagawa plant was based on a once-through urea process developed by Toyo Koatsu. The use of excess ammonia in the reactor eliminated the necessity of internal and/or external cooling, thus decreasing plant investment, and it simplified operating techniques.

Further development, based on results obtained at Sunagawa and addi-tional research, led to the completion of a partial-recycle plant at Omuta, Kyushu in November 1950. The Omuta plant featured the use of excess ammonia and a recovery system to permit recycling of a large percentage of the excess ammonia back to the reactor. In 1955 a urea plant using this Toyo process was built by Showa Denko at their Kawasaki plant.

In 1953 prilled urea was first introduced in Japan by a Toyo Koatsu developed process and was incorporated in their Sunagawa plant. The Sunagawa urea plant was converted from a once-through to an ammonia-partial-recycle plant in 1952, and in 1954 provisions for total recycle via a gas-separation system were added. Due to the relatively high utility and

---

*This section first appeared in *Hydrocarbon Processing and Petroleum Refiner* and is reproduced with its permission and that of its authors.

investment costs in gaseous recycle systems, Toyo Koatsu felt that the development of a total-recycle system based on solution recycle was necessary for a more economical process.

The Toyo-Gas-Chemicals-Company partial-recycle urea plant in Niigata was placed on stream in May of 1958. The plant featured the first Toyo Koatsu–developed solution-partial-recycle system.

In July of 1958 the Chiba plant of Toyo Koatsu was placed in operation. This plant, with a nominal capacity of 75,000 short tons/yr, featured a highly developed total-recycle process employing solution recycle. Further development work, based on plant operating data and additional research, led to the erection of a second total recycle plant using solution recycle at Chiba. The new total recycle process emphasized high product qualities, lower raw material and utilities consumption, and decreased plant investment. The new total recycle urea plant was completed in mid October of 1960, and the full production capacity of 75,000 tons per year was achieved by early November, 1960. At the end of 1962 plants utilizing the various Toyo Koatsu processes had a combined capacity of 740,000 short tons/yr, and by the end of 1963, this value will have increased to 1,380,000 short tons per yr when plants currently under construction are completed.

In 1961 the Girdler Corporation, a subsidiary of the Chemical and Industrial Corporation, entered into a licensing arrangement allowing Girdler to offer urea plants incorporating the process features of the Toyo Koatsu urea processes. Girdler has since designed urea production facilities via the Girdler–Toyo Koatsu processes which include the (1) once-through process, (2) ammonia-partial-recycle process, (3) solution-partial-recycle process, and (4) total-recycle process.

DESCRIPTION OF THE PROCESSES

Introduction

Urea is produced ultimately from the reaction of CO_2 and ammonia under conditions of high temperature and pressure. The ammonia and CO_2 entering the reactor are converted initially into ammonium carbamate. A substantial fraction of the carbamate in the reactor dehydrates to form urea and water. The fraction which dehydrates is determined by the ratios of the various reactants, the operating temperature, and the residence time in the reactor. The operating pressure slightly exceeds the combined effect of the decomposition pressure of the ammonium carbamate and the vapor pressure of the aqua ammonia present. Pressures substantially higher than this have little or no effect on the equilibrium or on the fraction converted to urea. The reaction products consist of urea, water, free ammonia, and ammonium carbamate which was not dehydrated. This mixture is separated in the recovery system where the ammonium carbamate is separated from the urea by decomposing the ammonium carbamate back to gaseous CO_2 and ammonia in successively lower stages of pressure. The free ammonia and water are removed by boiling, evaporating, crystallization, and drying. The decomposed ammonium carbamate may be recovered by absorption at various pressure levels in an aqueous solution, and then returned to the reactor. Much of the free ammonia can be recovered as essentially pure ammonia by condensation in water-cooled condensers and returned to the ammonia feed pump.

Urea Production Processes

The Once-Through Process. The production of urea by the once-through process is illustrated in Figure 13.1. Gaseous CO_2 is compressed directly into the reactor. (Liquid CO_2 may be used if desired.) Liquid ammonia is pumped into the reactor which operates in the temperature range of 355 to 365°F and at a pressure of about 3800 psig. The ratio of ammonia

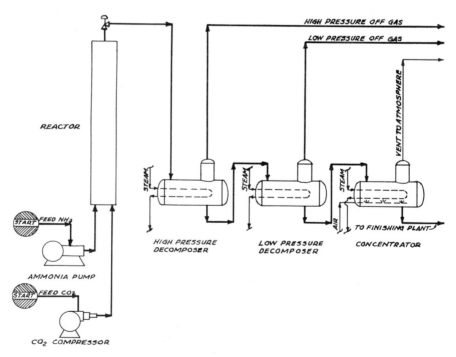

Figure 13.1. Once-through process.

to CO_2 is such that the reactor operates adiabatically. No internal cooling coils or external cooling jackets are required. The excess ammonia is around 120 per cent. Under these conditions the conversion ratio of CO_2 to urea in the reactor is about 70 to 75 per cent.

The reaction products flow from the reactor, through a letdown valve and into a steam heated high pressure decomposer where most of the excess ammonia is flashed off and where some carbamate is decomposed. The high ammonia content and high pressure level of this gas stream make it suitable for use as feed ammonia for a nitric acid plant and as a neutralizer for making ammonium nitrate or sulfate. The solution from the high pressure decomposer flows to a steam-heated low pressure decomposer where the decomposition of the carbamate is essentially completed. The off-gas stream from this decomposer is suitable for use in a neutralizer or in a complex fertilizer plant. The solution from the low pressure decomposer is about 80 to 82 per cent weight urea and can be utilized directly in nitrogen solutions. If prills or crystals are desired, the urea is concentrated to 85 to 92 per cent weight in an air-blown steam-heated concentrator before flowing to the crystallizer in the finishing section.

The over-all ammonia conversion to urea is about 32 per cent while that for carbon dioxide is around 73 per cent.

More than 75 per cent of the ammonia in the off gases is contained in the high pressure stream. If the entire quantity of ammonia in the off-gas streams is converted to ammonium nitrate, about 5.7 tons of ammonium nitrate will be produced per ton of urea.

If the ammonia is converted to ammonium sulfate, about 4.7 tons of ammonium sulfate, will be produced per ton of urea. The use of the once-through process requires fairly large tonnages of ammonium nitrate or sulfate in addition to the urea. The tonnages of nitrate and sulfate produced from the off gases can be reduced by 50 to 60 per cent by the use of the ammonia-partial-recycle process.

The Ammonia-Partial-Recycle Process. The ammonia partial recycle process is illustrated in Figure 13.2. It is a refinement of the once-through process in which about 66 to 75 per cent of the excess ammonia is recovered as an essentially anhydrous liquid and recycled back to the ammonia pump. This increases the over-all conversion of ammonia to urea from about 32 per cent up to 50 to 56 per cent. The reactor conditions are very similar to those used in the once-through process. The reaction products flow from the reactor, through the letdown valve, and into the excess ammonia separator where CO_2-free ammonia vapor is taken overhead and condensed in water-cooled condensers. A small reflux of liquid ammonia prevents CO_2 contamination of the overhead ammonia vapor. Also, the

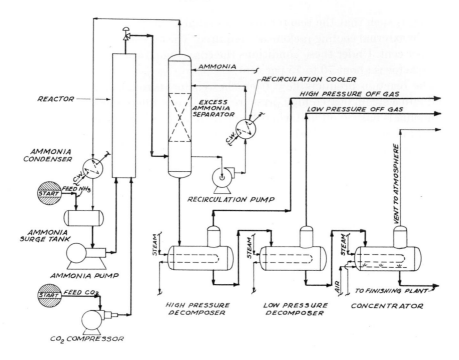

Figure 13.2. Ammonia partial-recycle process.

gases flashed from the reaction products are cooled as they flow up the tower by a liquid recirculation system. The solution from the excess ammonia separator flows to the high pressure decomposer. The decomposition section of the ammonia-partial-recycle process is similar to that used in the once-through process except that the quantity of ammonia in the off gas from the high pressure decomposer is about one-third as much as in the case of the once-through process. If the entire quantity of ammonia contained in the off-gas streams is converted to ammonium nitrate, about 2.1 to 2.7 tons of ammonium nitrate will be produced per ton of urea. If converted to ammonium sulfate, about 1.75 to 2.2 tons of ammonia sulfate will be produced per ton of urea. The tonnages of nitrate and sulfate produced can be reduced by 60 to 75 per cent by the solution-recycle process.

The Solution-Partial-Recycle Process.   The solution-partial-recycle process is illustrated in Figure 13.3. It differs from the ammonia-partial-recycle process by the addition of solution-recycle equipment, thus permitting an increase in the over-all conversions of ammonia and carbon dioxide to urea.

Gaseous carbon dioxide, liquid ammonia, and recycle solution are fed

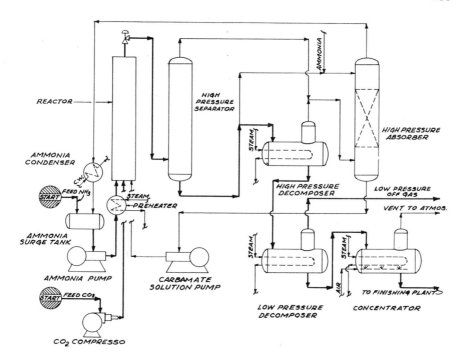

Figure 13.3. Solution partial-recycle process.

into a reactor operating at 355 to 370°F and about 3800 psig. The ratio of feed materials is based on the reactor heat balance and the desired conversion of CO$_2$ to urea in the reactor which ranges from 70 to 80 per cent. Excess ammonia in the reactor ranges from 110 to 125 per cent.

Reaction products from the reactor letdown valve discharge into a high pressure separator where excess ammonia is flashed off. The solution from the separator flows into the high pressure decomposer where a large fraction of the ammonium carbamate is decomposed. Vapors from the high pressure separator and high pressure decomposer are sent to the high pressure absorber for recovery. The solution from the high pressure decomposer flows to the low pressure decomposer where the remaining ammonium carbamate is decomposed. Vapors from the low pressure decomposer are made available for off-site utilization. The urea solution from the low pressure decomposer is suitable for utilization in nitrogen solutions. If solid urea is preferred, the urea solution is usually concentrated to 85 to 92 per cent before being sent to the urea finishing section.

Effluent gases from the high pressure separator and decomposer are contacted with an ammonia-urea solution in the high pressure absorber. Vaporizing ammonia serves as the cooling medium in the absorber, thus eliminating the necessity of expensive heat-exchange equipment. Pure ammonia vapor from the top of the absorber is condensed and recycled to the ammonia pump. Ammonium carbamate solution from the base of the absorber is recycled to the reactor by means of a high pressure pump.

Process variables make possible a range of over-all ammonia conversions to urea from 56 to 80 per cent with over-all carbon dioxide conversions to urea ranging from 80 to 95 per cent.

Utilization of off gases from the solution-partial-recycle process is limited to low pressure recovery operations such as the production of ammonium sulfate, ammonium nitrate, and complex fertilizers. Off-gas utilization in ammonium sulfate production would yield 0.4 to 1.0 tons of sulfate per ton of urea produced. The use of off gas for the production of ammonium nitrate would produce 0.485 to 1.21 tons of nitrate per ton of urea.

The Total-Recycle Process. The production of urea by the total-recycle process is illustrated in Figure 13.4. Gaseous CO_2 is compressed

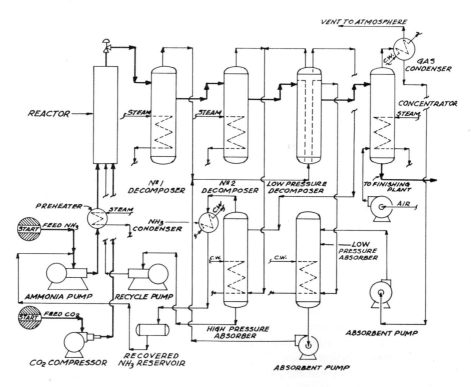

Figure 13.4. Total recycle process.

directly into the reactor. Simultaneously, liquid ammonia and recovered ammonium carbamate solution are pumped separately into the reactor where urea is formed. Reaction conditions in the reactor are maintained at approximately 365°F and 3300 psig. Carbon dioxide conversion to urea ranges from 58 to 60 per cent per pass. The mole ratio of total equivalent ammonia to carbon dioxide in the reactor is about 3.5. The products from the reactor flow through a letdown valve into the No. 1 decomposer where much of the excess ammonia flashes out of solution, and a portion of the ammonium carbamate is decomposed. This decomposer operates at a high pressure, the heat of decomposition being supplied by steam. The solution then passes to the No. 2 decomposer, which is also steam heated and which operates at a lower pressure than the No. 1 decomposer. In the No. 2 decomposer further decomposition of the ammonium carbamate takes place. The solution from the No. 2 decomposer then passes to the low pressure decomposer where the decomposition of ammonium carbamate is essentially completed. In the tube side of the low pressure decomposer a portion of the gaseous ammonia and CO_2 from the No. 1 decomposer is absorbed in and reacts in the aqueous solution from the low pressure absorber. The resulting heats of reaction supply the heat for decomposition for the solution in the shell side of this unit. The gases from the overhead of the No. 2 decomposer and those from the tube side of the low pressure decomposer which were not absorbed are sent to the high pressure absorber where they are recovered. The aqueous solution from the low pressure decomposer then flows to the concentrator where some of the water and the last traces of free ammonia are stripped from the solution by steam heating and air blowing.

From the concentrator, urea-water solution containing 75 to 80 per cent urea is made available for processing in the finishing section for production of solid urea. The over-all conversion of ammonia and carbon dioxide to urea approaches 100 per cent in the total-recycle process.

The gases from the low pressure decomposer are recovered in the low pressure absorber where they are absorbed in an aqueous solution. The heat of absorption and reaction is removed by cooling water. The solution from the low pressure absorber is then pumped to the same pressure as exists in the No. 1 decomposer in order that it may join the gases from this unit as described earlier. The solution resulting from this absorption operation is used as the absorbent in the high pressure absorber where the gases from the No. 2 decomposer are absorbed and reacted. Here, also, the heats of absorption and reaction are removed by cooling water. The overhead vapor from the high pressure absorber is essentially pure ammonia which is condensed in water cooled condensers and recycled to the process as the excess ammonia required to obtain a high conversion to urea. The solution from the high pressure absorber is the recovered aqueous ammonium carbamate solution which is recycled to the reactor.

Urea Finishing Processes

Generally, urea finishing refers to the processing steps by which a urea-water solution is transformed into a usable form of solid urea. The nature of these processing steps is dependent on the character of the solution to be processed, the purity and form of the final product, and over-all process economics.

Figures 13.5 and 13.6 represent two of the most popular and versatile finishing schemes available for the Girdler–Toyo Koatsu urea processes.

The Atmospheric Crystallization Process. The atmospheric crystallization process is illustrated in Figure 13.5, and can be used in conjunction with any of the four urea processes.

Urea water solution from the concentrator containing 85 to 92 per cent weight urea is pumped continuously into Swensen-Walker-type crystal-

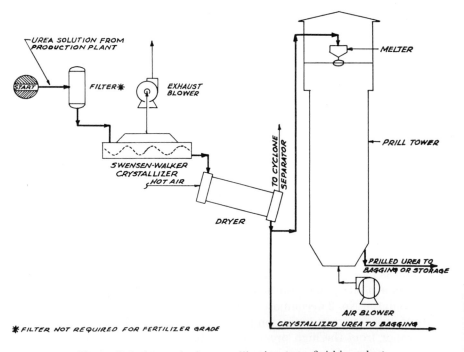

Figure 13.5. Atmospheric crystallization type finishing plant.

lizers. These crystallizers are equipped with low speed spiral agitators which provide contact between crystals and mother liquor. The sensible heat in the feed and the heat of crystallization of urea are sufficient to vaporize most of the water in the inlet solution. An exhaust blower establishes a flow of air within the crystallizer, thus facilitating the removal of water vapor. Almost complete crystallization of urea takes place within the crystallizer which eliminates the need for additional equipment to recover the mother liquor. The wet crystals from the crystallizer are conveyed to a rotary drier where their moisture content is reduced to the desired level by a stream of hot air.

Crystalline urea, with a moisture content of less than 0.3 per cent weight from the drier outlet is suitable for use in adhesives, animal feed, and fertilizers. Filtration prior to crystallization is sometimes required for improved product quality.

If prilled urea is desired, the dry crystals are lifted to the top of the prill tower by means of a bucket elevator where they are melted in steam heated melters of a special design. The molten urea is then prilled through multiple spray heads. Molten urea prilled in this manner has a much lower tendency to stick to the walls of the prilling tower than does urea which is prilled prior to the drying operation. In addition, the drying of prilled urea tends to weaken the physical structure of the prill, and also destroys the effectiveness of the glossy outer surface of the prill. The prills are cooled to near ambient temperature at the base of the prill tower by a unique system and are then available for bulk storage or bagging.

The Vacuum-Crystallization Process. The vacuum crystallization process is illustrated in Figure 13.6 and is used when crystals or prills of the highest obtainable quality are desired. Urea solution from the concentrator containing 75 to 80 per cent urea is pumped continuously through precoat-type filters for removal of contaminants. The filtration step removes traces of oil and oxidized metals and improves the color and turbidity of the final product. Filtered urea solution flows to a vacuum crystallizer where much of the remaining water is vaporized. Sensible heat in the urea solution and the heat of crystallization of urea provide sufficient heat to vaporize most of the water which passes overhead to the vacuum generation equipment. Recirculation and sufficient holding time in the crystallizer provide for adequate crystal growth.

Urea slurry from the crystallizer is pumped into a continuous-type centrifuge where the crystals and mother liquor are separated by centrifugal force. The mother liquor portion of the slurry is returned to the crystallizer. Urea crystals containing a small quantity of water are conveyed to a

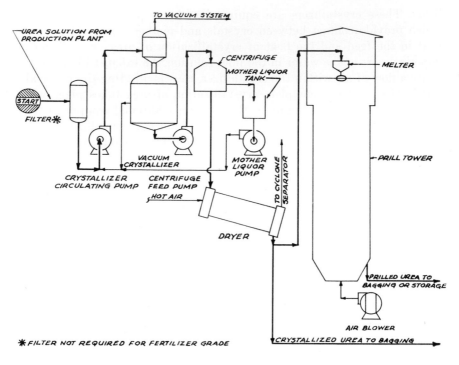

Figure 13.6. Vacuum-crystallization type finishing plant.

rotary drier where the moisture content is reduced to less than 0.3 per cent by a stream of hot air. The dry crystalline urea is of the highest quality and may be used in the manufacture of plastics as well as in its other normal applications.

Prilled urea containing less than 0.4 per cent weight biuret may be produced from these crystals by the melting and prilling process described under the atmospheric crystallization process. The vacuum-crystallization finishing process was originally developed for use in conjunction with the total-recycle process. However, in the very near future, a partial-recycle plant will start up which will use vacuum crystallization.

RAW MATERIAL AND UTILITY REQUIREMENTS

The raw material and utility requirements for the Girdler–Toyo Koatsu urea processes are given in Table 13.1. These requirements, particularly steam, are lower for making crystalline urea than for making prilled urea by each process shown in the table.

TABLE 13.1. TYPICAL RAW MATERIAL AND UTILITY REQUIREMENTS FOR
THE GIRDLER–TOYO KOATSU UREA PROCESSES

Urea Process	Units per Short Ton of Uncoated Prilled* Urea			
	Once-Through	Ammonia partial recycle	Solution partial recycle	Total recycle
Liquid ammonia				
In urea and losses, tons	0.572	0.574	0.576	0.585
In off gases, tons	1.216	0.574	0.187	—
Fresh feed, tons	1.788	1.148	0.763	0.585
Gaseous carbon dioxide**				
In urea and losses, tons	0.749	0.749	0.760	0.768
In off gases, tons	0.270	0.270	0.066	—
Fresh feed, tons	1.019	1.019	0.826	0.768
Electric power, KWH	185	185	160	175
Steam, (185 psig) lb	2200	2200	2700	3700
Cooling water, (20°F rise) GPM	3000	11,000	14,000	29,000

* Not including bulk storage and bagging.
** At atmospheric pressure and ambient temperature.

PRODUCT SPECIFICATIONS

The processing steps used in the finishing section determine the quality of the final products. Below are typical product analyses from a total-recycle plant using filtration and vacuum crystallization in the finishing section.

	Crystal Urea	Uncoated Prills
Nitrogen content, %w	46.5	46.4
Moisture content, %w*	0.3	0.3
Biuret, %w**	0.1	0.4
Free ammonia, ppm	30	150
pH (10% solution)	7.2	9.0
Ash, ppm	20	20
Iron content, ppm	2	2
Particle size (Tyler sieve)	90% through 20 on 80 mesh	95% through 8 on 20 mesh

* By Karl Fischer method.
** By tartrate or copper complex salt method.

Below are typical product analyses from a partial-recycle plant using filtration and atmospheric crystallization in the finishing section.

	Crystal Urea	Uncoated Prills
Nitrogen content, %w....	46.5	46.4
Moisture content, %w*...	0.3	0.3
Biuret, %w**............	0.5	0.8
Free ammonia, ppm......	90	200
pH (10% solution)........	9.0	9.3
Ash, ppm................	20	20
Iron content, ppm........	2	2
Particle size (Tyler sieve).	90% through 30 on 100 mesh	95% through 8 on 20 mesh

* By Karl Fischer method.
** By tartrate or copper complex salt method.

PLANT INVESTMENT AND MANUFACTURING COST

The economic comparison of the manufacturing cost of the various urea processes shown in Table 13.2 is based on the raw material and utility requirements given in Table 13.1. Also, it is based on a battery-limits plant

TABLE 13.2. MANUFACTURING COST FOR THE GIRDLER–TOYO KOATSU UREA PROCESSES

Urea Process	Cost Per Short Ton of Uncoated Prilled Urea			
	Once-through	Ammonia partial recycle	Solution partial recycle	Total recycle
Plant investment.....................	$1,650,000	$1,800,000	$1,950,000	$2,700,000
Operating costs				
Ammonia—$60/short ton............	$34.32	$34.44	$34.56	$35.10
CO_2, $3/short ton.................	3.06	3.06	2.48	2.30
Steam, $0.50/1000 lbs..............	1.10	1.10	1.35	1.85
Electric power, $0.010/KWH........	1.85	1.85	1.60	1.75
Cooling water, $0.020/1000 gal........	0.06	0.22	0.28	0.58
Maintenance, 6% of investment......	2.00	2.18	2.36	3.27
Operating labor, $2.50/man hour.....	1.55	1.55	2.00	2.65
Administration and general, 100% of				
operating labor....................	1.55	1.55	2.00	2.65
Fixed costs				
Taxes and insurance, 2.5% of invest-				
ment............................	0.83	0.91	0.98	1.36
Depreciation, 10% of investment.....	3.33	3.64	3.94	5.45
Manufacturing cost $/short ton........	$49.65	$50.50	$51.55	$56.96

(which does not include bagging or storage) for producing 150 short tons of uncoated prills per operating day and on 330 operating days per year.

DISCUSSION OF ADVANTAGES

The Girdler–Toyo Koatsu urea processes offer to the urea producer a wide range of processing conditions from which to choose. If the producer requires a rather small quantity of urea solution for blending into his nitrogen solutions, a once-through plant may be the most economical choice since the off gases can be used for producing ammonium nitrate and the once-through plant is lowest in first cost. Two types of partial-recycle processes are available at a slightly higher first cost for the producer who requires more urea and cannot utilize as much off gas as comes from the once-through process. Finally, the total-recycle process is available for the producer who requires a completely independent urea production facility. The urea prill producer has further versatility in the fact that the entire plant output or any fraction of it may be taken as crystalline urea with no increase in investment cost.

In addition to a wide range of processing conditions and product versatility, the Girdler–Toyo Koatsu processes offer the following advantages.

(1) A prilled urea of unexcelled quality, that is 0.4 per cent weight biuret and 0.3 per cent weight moisture, is produced in normal operation with the vacuum-crystallization system. This biuret content is guaranteed to be within ±0.1 per cent weight of this value, and is exceptionally low. The prills are also hard and free-flowing. They may be stored in bulk, and coating is not required.

(2) By the combination of mild operating conditions, along with substantial excess ammonia and special materials of construction, the corrosion problems are essentially eliminated.

(3) No cooling equipment is required to control the temperature within the reactor. This simplifies reactor design and operations, and reduces plant investment.

(4) The conversion of CO_2 to urea is always high even in the once-through and partial-recycle processes; the amount of ammonium carbamate to be decomposed is small which results in smaller equipment and lower plant investment.

(5) The urea for prilling undergoes its final drying operation before the prilling step. This procedure of prilling a dry melt greatly reduces the tendency of the prills to stick to the walls of the prilling tower. Since the prills do not have to be dried, their hard glossy surface is not damaged, and no fines are created either by attrition or by water vapor escaping from the prills.

(6) A crystalline urea for plastics use that is noncaking in storage can be manufactured by a special processing technique (not clay-coated) with a negligible increase in investment cost.

BIBLIOGRAPHY

Physical and Chemical Properties

Frejacques, M., *Chim. and Ind. (Paris)*, **60**, 22 (1948).

Wolff, F. A., and O'Flynn, D. J., "Encyclopedia of Chemical Technology." Vol. 14, New York, Interscience, 1955.

Raw Materials

Rooseboom, A., *Chem. Eng.*, **58**, 11 (1951).

Processes

Cook, L. H., *Chem. Eng. Progress* **50**, 327 (1954).

Kolterman, D. W., and Rennie, W. W., in "The Chemistry and Technology of Fertilizers," Ed. V. Sauchelli, New York, Reinhold, 1960.

Vancini, Carlo A., "La Sintesi dell'Ammoniaca," Milano, Hoepli, 1960.

14

Chemistry and Utilization of Ammonia Solutions in Fertilizer Manufacture

E. D. CRITTENDEN

Allied Chemical Corporation

Developments which completely alter an entire industry are uncommon. However, as previously noted, the fertilizer industry has been totally changed by the synthesis and use of ammonia and ammoniacal salt solutions (ordinarily called nitrogen solutions). Although the tonnage of these materials being utilized in the early 1930's was minor, they had attained a major role by 1961 in the provision of nitrogen, both for fertilizer manufacture and for direct application. The story of this development in the United States is told by Figure 14.1.[4, 5, 17]

Of the almost three million tons of total nitrogen consumed in agriculture in the United States in the fertilizer year ending June 30, 1961, about 54 per cent came from ammonia and nitrogen solutions. In manufactured fertilizers these materials furnished around 63 per cent of the total N; the next largest source of nitrogen being ammonium sulfate. Ammonia consumed largely in the anhydrous form came to about 85 per cent for direct application and 15 per cent for fertilizer manufacture; while in the case of solutions about two-thirds was used in fertilizer manufacture and the other third in direct-application outlets.

Economic, technical, and agronomic factors—each favorable to the ammoniation development—could only have occurred after the synthesis of ammonia on a large scale was an accomplished fact. With lower cost nitrogen available in abundance as ammonia, it was natural that the major ammonium salts and urea would become competitive with it. Moreover, the combination of ammonium salts and urea with ammonia to produce nitrogen solutions was also a natural development stemming from the

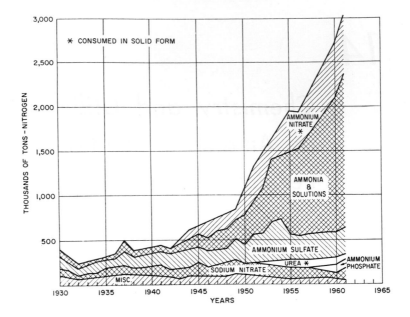

Figure 14.1. Nitrogen consumption in agriculture in the United States 1930–1961.

availability of low cost ammonia. These solutions provided fertilizer nitrogen in a form easy to manufacture, transport, store, and utilize, and they possessed the desirable property of neutralizing acid materials in complete fertilizer manufacture. Today it is estimated that about 90 per cent of all the fertilizer grades made in the United States are formulated with ammonia and ammoniacal salt solutions.

Ammoniation of fertilizers has been almost strictly an American development and is based soundly on the proven fact that so-called citrate soluble P_2O_5 gives excellent agronomic response in the growing of our major crops. However, in much of the world outside of the United States, legislation provides that water-soluble P_2O_5 must be used.

SOLUTIONS CHEMISTRY

Ammonia and several of the ammonium and nitrate salts have been known for centuries. The first systematic, although qualitative, study of the solubility relations in the systems involving ammonia and nitrogen salts, however, was not made till the early 1870's.[20] More extensive studies were undertaken near the close of the 19th century, but the practical and quantitative chemistry of nitrogen solutions did not develop rapidly in the

United States until between the middle 1920's and the middle 1930's. The principal systems in which the nitrogen solutions have been developed commercially are ammonia-ammonium nitrate-water and ammonia-urea-water. The solubility relations in these three-component systems are given in the ternary diagrams in Figures 14.2 and 14.3.[51, 59] It is obvious that a multitude of three-component solutions are possible chemically, but, as will be brought out, the practical development of nitrogen solutions involved both chemical and physical properties, of which solubility is only one major factor. A number of the practical ammoniacal salt solutions today involve solubility systems with more components than the ternary type. Outstanding examples are from the ammonia-ammonium nitrate-urea-water, and the ammonia-urea-formaldehyde-water systems. A few five-component systems furnish ammoniacal solutions designed for specific fertilizer requirements.

The most important practical chemical and physical properties of ammonia and examples of three important types of nitrogen solutions are given in Table 14.1. Excellent tabulations giving the compositions and principal

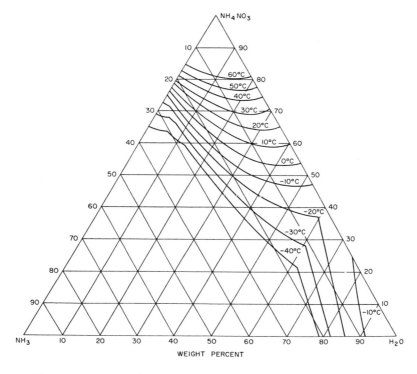

Figure 14.2. Solubility in system ammonium nitrate-ammonia-water.

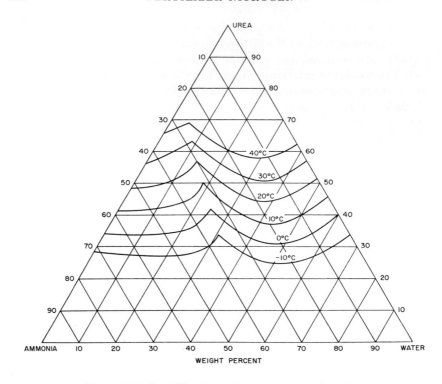

Figure 14.3. Solubility in system urea-ammonia-water.

properties of nitrogen solutions have been published,[1, 2, 3] and several of the principal suppliers of the solutions offer comprehensive brochures covering the physical chemistry of their products.[6]

Over eighty ammoniacal nitrogen solutions are available today to the fertilizer industry. However, this list is constantly changing to meet technological changes in the industry. Table 14.2 summarizes the range of compositions (with their principal properties) now on the American market. Certain trends in the compositions have taken place since the first nitrogen solutions were put on the market in the early 1930's. The principal ones are (1) higher nitrogen content, (2) lower water content, and (3) more components to meet special requirements. Since some nitrogen solutions are no longer on the market, it seems doubtful that strong reasons exist for having so many separate compositions, many of which differ only in minor ways from others. The future may well see a reduction in the number of solutions.

Registered trade names have been adopted for specifying particular solutions such as "Arcadian", "Uramon", "Sohiogen", etc., and these are

TABLE 14.1. TYPICAL AMMONIATING LIQUID COMPOSITIONS

	Anhydrous Ammonia	30% Aqua	Nitrana 3 M	Urana 10	Urea Ammonia Liquor
	822 (100-0-0)	247 (30-0-0)	440 (28-60-0)	444 (25-56-10)	455 (31-0-43)
Composition by weight:					
Ammonia, free, %	100	30	28	24.5	30.5
Ammonium nitrate, %	—	—	60	56.0	—
Urea, %	—	—	—	10.0	43.3
Water, %	—	70	12	9.5	16.2
Nitrogen by weight:					
Ammonia N, free, %	82.25	24.68	23.02	20.14	25.09
Ammonia N, combined, %	—	—	10.50	9.80	—
Total ammonia N, %	82.25	24.68	33.52	29.94	25.09
Nitrate N	—	—	10.50	9.80	—
Urea N	—	—	—	4.66	20.05
Total N	82.25	24.68	44.02	44.40	45.14
Sp.g. at 60°F/60°F	0.618	.896	1.083	1.108	1.06
Lb/gal at 60°F	5.15	7.47	9.03	9.24	8.85
Lb/N per gal at 60°F	4.24	1.84	3.98	4.10	4.07
Vapor pressure, psig at 104°F	211	11.4	25	22	50
Salting-out temp., °F	−108	−112	−36	−15	34

accompanied by a registered type designation such as "Nitrana", "Urana", etc. Certain literature has carried the designation further to indicate low pressure, medium pressure, and high pressure types.[1, 8, 43] Attempts have been made to use a coding system which would employ the company trade name; the per cent total nitrogen with the period omitted; and the percentage composition with respect to NH_3, ammonium nitrate, and urea as whole numbers and in that order in brackets. As an example the "Urana 10" composition in Table 14.1 would be designed 444(25-56-10). This coding system has not been accepted by all ammoniating solutions producers.

Many patents have been issued on ammoniacal salt solutions, particularly up to 1940. Typical United States patents are shown in the bibliography.[7, 12, 13, 14, 22, 26, 29, 36, 37, 40, 42, 45, 54] Methods for sampling and for analysis of nitrogen solutions have been developed and perfected since their commercial advent and represent an important contribution to the manufacture and use of these materials.[21, 46, 49]

TABLE 14.2. AMMONIATING SOLUTIONS

	Anhydrous NH_3, %	Nitranas, %	Uranas, %	Urea-Ammonia, %	Urea-Ammonium Nitrate-Ammonia %
Nitrogen content.....	82.2	41–58.5	41–49	37–46	37–37.1
Ammonia............	99.9	19–50	19–33	25–37.3	13.3–26.0
Ammonium nitrate...	—	49.5–75.5	40–68	—	29.0–53.4
Urea................	—	—	6–18	26.5–43.8	15.9–40.0
H_2O	0.1	0.5–18.2	6–17	16.2–39.8	8.4–23.3
CO_2................	—	—	—	4.9–8.6	—
Formaldehyde.......	—	—	—	—	7.4–16.0
Sp.g. (60°F).........	.618	.93–1.194	1.033–1.180	.93–1.06	1.051–1.235
SOT,* °F	−108	−52 to +61	−17 to +39	1–58	34–55
Vap. pressure, psig, 104°F	211	1–144	10–51	20–70	0–24

* SOT = Salting out temperature.

Seven highly significant chemical and physical features of ammoniacal salt solutions involved in their manufacture, specifications, and use are discussed below:[18]

Nitrogen Content

The total nitrogen content of ammoniating solutions for fertilizer manufacture varies from a low of about 37 per cent N to a high of 58.5 per cent N with anhydrous ammonia having 82.2 per cent N. The largest tonnage solutions have nitrogen contents between 37 and 49 per cent.

Nitrogen Sources and Forms

Ammonia is always one source of nitrogen and varies in content from a low of about 13 per cent to the peak value of 99.9 per cent in anhydrous ammonia. Ammonium nitrate (AN) and urea are the principal combined forms of nitrogen besides ammonia, and these components vary for AN from 29 to 75.5 per cent and for urea from 6 to about 44 per cent. Other sources of nitrogen are ammonium sulfate and historically sodium nitrate.

Other Components

Water, except in the case of anhydrous ammonia, is an important component varying from below 1.0 to around 40 per cent. In recent years, formaldehyde has become an important component of nitrogen solutions for providing, along with urea, a source of nitrogen having agronomically desirable slow release properties.

Specific Gravity

This property is very important in controlling the manufacture of the nitrogen solutions and in making fertilizers with them. Specific gravities at 60°F vary from 0.618 for NH_3 to 1.235 for the most dense solution.

Salting-Out Temperature (SOT)

This descriptive, rather than precise, term is commonly used to designate the temperature, usually in °F, at which solid phase first appears as the solutions are cooled slowly. Due to the inherent tendency of some nitrogen solutions to supercool, a fictitious freezing point is sometimes evident. Practically, all temperatures below the SOT must be avoided in storage and use to avoid salt formation which has adverse effects in handling and manufacturing operations. From Table 14.2 it will be seen that SOT's vary from −108°F for anhydrous NH_3 to +61°F for the salt solutions. The solutions with higher SOT's require special care for successful winter use in the northern states and often are avoided in the colder months.

Vapor Pressure

This property is important in providing proper equipment for manufacturing and utilizing ammonia and the nitrogen solutions. The values of vapor pressure range from 0 psig to 211 psig at 104°F.

Corrosiveness

An outstanding chemical property which has an important practical bearing is corrosiveness. Franklin[20] pointed out many years ago that many metals are attacked by ammoniacal salt solutions and that the action closely resembles the action of acids in water solutions, except that the reactions in ammoniacal liquids are generally more sluggish. This characteristic persists in compositions containing water and is no better, and often enhanced, in mixed salt solutions. Davis *et al.*[20] showed in the early 1920's that ammonium nitrate in ammonia attacked iron and steel to some extent.

Proper selection of materials to use with ammoniacal salt solutions has long been an enigma both to producers and to users. Iron and steel would be preferred materials and even today are used to some extent, especially for anhydrous NH_3. Corrosion behavior, however, is erratic and has led to the wide adoption of aluminum and its alloys.[19] Stainless steel and rubber show low attack, but in many instances have been ruled out on cost even for lined equipment. Quite recently some polyester resins have shown encouraging chemical and mechanical behavior.

Much research has been devoted to studying the mechanism of corrosion by ammoniacal salt solutions and to finding and perfecting corrosion inhibitors. The most satisfactory single inhibitor is ammonium thiocyanate in small concentrations, and its inhibiting action is enhanced by minor additions of sodium arsenate. A list of important references and patents is given in the bibliography.[9, 10, 11, 33, 39] The problem of inhibitors is complicated by the wide diversity of materials employed throughout the industry for manufacturing, handling, and using the nitrogen solutions. At best inhibitors alleviate the situation but are not a perfect cure.

The best current knowledge on materials of construction for handling nitrogen solutions is summarized in Table 14.3.[6] Selection of the material best suited for a given purpose depends on both technical and economic factors in a particular job, and no general prescription can be given for all cases.

Manufacture

The manufacture of ammoniacal salt solutions is relatively simple technically. These solutions are produced most often at ammonia synthesis plants but recently some nitrogen solutions are being made from ammonia shipped from other locations for conversion to these products. The ammonium nitrate and urea are utilized most frequently as aqueous solutions of various concentrations depending on the commercial solution produced. Other nitrogen materials like ammonium sulfate and urea-formaldehyde solutions are employed as slurries or liquids.

Batch manufacture in several tank car lots is usually employed but continuous processing is easily adaptable and could be automated. Mixing of ingredients produces heat, and provision for cooling is necessary. The principle controls in manufacture are total nitrogen content, specific grav-

TABLE 14.3. BEHAVIOR OF AMMONIACAL SALT SOLUTIONS TOWARD
VARIOUS CONSTRUCTION MATERIALS

Suitable; Minor Corrosion Attack	Useable, Some Corrosion Attack	Unsuitable, Destroyed Rapidly
Aluminum and aluminum alloys (3003, 3004, 5052, 5154 and 6061) Stainless steels, (303, 304, 316, 347, and 416) Rubber and neoprene Polyethylene, vinyl, and some polyester resins Glass Asbestos gaskets JM 60 or equal	Carbon steel Cast iron	Copper, brass, bronze, monel, zinc, galvanized metals, concrete, usual die castings

ity, and the desired proportions of urea and free and combined ammonia forms.

Nitrogen solutions may be loaded as made into tank cars or tank trucks, or may be placed in storage for later shipment. These solutions for shipping purposes are known as fertilizer ammoniating solutions containing free ammonia and are classed as a nonflammable gas and shipped with green ICC lable.[16] Safety in fertilizer manufacture is covered by a National Plant Food Institute publication.[48]

AMMONIATED FERTILIZERS

The ammoniated phosphate fertilizers have already been discussed at length in Chapter 10a. The types, grades, and formulations of ammoniated fertilizers are now considered.

Types

Four major types of mixed fertilizers are available on the world markets today, namely, pulverized, semigranular, granular, and liquid. Ammoniation is practiced on all four types in the United States. The earliest noticeable improvement in fertilizers occurred in the pulverized type as ammoniation was more and more widely adopted. Granular fertilizers were slower to develop, but in recent years this type comprises at least 30 per cent of the total mixed fertilizers in the United States and yearly increases are significant.[47] The present trend is to develop means for making semigranular fertilizers with improved storage and handling characteristics. Significant advances are already evident and other changes may be expected. Liquid fertilizers[1] became popular in the mid-fifties and are steadily attaining increased commercial stature (see also Chapter 17).

The rapidly growing urban requirements for lawn and garden fertilizers has provided an increasing market for specialty products. The most widely recognized are the low bulk density (lightweight) fertilizers having part of their nitrogen in a form more slowly acting and persistent that than coming from highly soluble nitrogen materials. In many of these special formulations, expanded vermiculite or lightweight organic residues like wood bark are employed to provide the bulking factor.

Grades

The number of solid mixed fertilizer grades produced in the United States in recent years exceeds 1800.[1] Broadly, the grades are classified by their principal plant food ingredients; namely, NPK, NP, NK, and PK. Better that 90 per cent of the total tonnage contains nitrogen and, with only minor exceptions, part or all of this nitrogen is derived from ammonia and nitrogen solutions as stated above. The largest use is in NPK (so-called complete) fertilizers although appreciable tonnages are employed in N-P and N-K grades, particularly when the expanding production of ammonium phosphates and nitrophosphates utilizing ammonia is included.

Fertilizers are further categorized by the ratios of N to P to K, for example 1:1:1 signifies that the units of N, P_2O_5, and K_2O are equal. The bulk of the grade ratios with respect to nitrogen vary from those containing much more N than P_2O_5 to those with only a small nitrogen content compared to P_2O_5 content; for example, 30-10-0 down to 2-12-12.

Formulations

Successful fertilizer formulation requires skillful manipulation of a set of checks and balances to provide the product wanted. Major factors in formulation are agronomic requirements, market requirements, material sources and availability, equipment capacity and limitations, and lowest manufactured cost compatible with other factors.

There has been considerable advance in fertilizer formulation, but even today it is largely an art and requires a skillful blending of technology and economics. Several excellent presentations have been made on formulating ammoniated fertilizers.[15, 28, 41, 52, 60] Nitrogen solutions have provided a new and highly flexible source of nitrogen in liquid form for producing fertilizers and have furnished a sound basis for making higher analysis grades with improved properties. It is highly significant that of the three major plant foods, nitrogen is the only one which is adaptable to making high analysis liquid products in the practical range.

CHEMISTRY OF AMMONIATION

Chemically and physically nitrogen solutions accomplish four main purposes in fertilizer manufacture.

(1) They neutralize the free acids and acidic materials present in the superphosphates employed or added as supplementary materials. Put another way, the pH of the fertilizer is adjusted to a more favorable practical and agronomic range, say around 4.5 to 6.0.

(2) They provide the conditions for desirable secondary reactions such as double decomposition, hydration, and polymerization.

(3) They supply the additional nitrogen in the form in which it is needed in fertilizer formulations, particularly for high analysis grades.

(4) They furnish a proper and controlled liquid phase situation which has made possible the outstanding improvements in fertilizer properties (such as granule size and type) in the past 30 years in the fertilizer industry.

The principal chemical reactions in ammoniation are represented by the following equations:

Involving phosphate materials

$$H_3PO_4 + NH_3 \rightarrow NH_4H_2PO_4 \tag{14.1}$$

$$Ca(H_2PO_4)_2 + NH_3 \rightarrow CaHPO_4 + NH_4H_2PO_4 \tag{14.2}$$

$$NH_4H_2PO_4 + CaSO_4 + NH_3 \rightarrow Ca_3(PO_4)_2 + (NH_4)_2SO_4 \tag{14.3}$$

$$2CaHPO_4 + CaSO_4 + 2NH_3 \rightarrow Ca_3(PO_4)_2 + (NH_4)_2SO_4 \tag{14.4}$$

$$NH_4H_2PO_4 + NH_3 \rightarrow (NH_4)_2HPO_4 \tag{14.5}$$

$$3CaHPO_4 + 2NH_3 \rightarrow Ca_3(PO_4)_2 + (NH_4)_2HPO_4 \tag{14.6}$$

Involving double decomposition and hydration

$$NH_4NO_3 + KCl \rightarrow NH_4Cl + KNO_3 \tag{14.7}$$

$$(NH_4)_2SO_4 + KCl \rightarrow NH_4Cl + K_2SO_4 \tag{14.8}$$

$$CaH_4(PO_4)_2 + (NH_4)_2SO_4 \rightarrow CaSO_4 + 2NH_4H_2PO_4 \tag{14.9}$$

$$CaSO_4 + 2H_2O \rightarrow CaSO_4 \cdot 2H_2O \tag{14.10}$$

$$CaHPO_4 + 2H_2O \rightarrow CaHPO_4 \cdot 2H_2O \tag{14.11}$$

$$MgNH_4PO_4 + 6H_2O \rightarrow MgNH_4PO_4 \cdot 6H_2O \tag{14.12}$$

Involving decomposition and polymerization

$$CO(NH_2)_2 + H_2O \rightarrow 2NH_3 + CO_2 \tag{14.13}$$

$$(NH_4)_2HPO_4 \rightarrow NH_3 + NH_4H_2PO_4 \tag{14.14}$$

$$4CO(NH_2)_2 + 3HCHO \rightarrow \tag{14.15}$$

$$H_2O + NH_2(CONHCH_2NH)_3CONH_2$$

trimethylene tetra urea

In a few other areas of the chemical industry are so many actual and po-

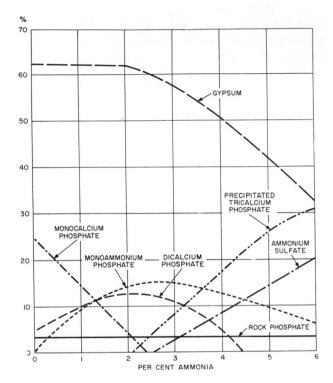

Figure 14.4. Changes in composition of typical super-phosphate with increasing ammoniation. [Keenen, F. G. Ind. Eng. Chem. **22** 1378 (1930)].

tential chemical reactions involved as in making ammoniated mixed fertilizers. In view of this it is an outstanding tribute to fertilizer technology and technologists that such marked success has been attained in making fertilizers with such outstanding qualities.

The effect of an increasing addition of NH_3 on a typical ordinary super-phosphate had been worked out by the early 1930's[30, 31, 32] and is shown in Figure 14.4. It is generally considered that Eq. 14.1, 14.2, 14.5, and 14.6 represent the limit for the addition of free neutralizing NH_3 to triple superphosphate, and Eq. 14.1 to 14.4 represent a similar limit for ordinary superphosphate, although with the growth of ammoniation these limits are exceeded under special conditions even with the loss of some NH_3. The course and extent of the many reactions are dependent on a number of important factors, major ones being temperature and moisture. Not all reactions are favorable or desired, and the practical application involves a set of checks and balances to avoid undesired results. Undue reversion of the P_2O_5 which was in highly available and water-soluble form in the original superphosphates must be avoided for agronomic reasons. The definition and limits of reversion were developed as an early part of ammoniation practice[27, 31, 58] and are the basis for present AOAC control methods.[49]

The increased commercial availability of urea and formaldehyde has brought into greater prominence Eqs. 14.13 and 14.15 which have required additional controls in fertilizer manufacture to utilize successfully the nitrogen solutions containing urea and likewise urea and formaldehyde.[38]

Chemical Heat Effects

Each of the reactions represented by Eq. 14.1 to 14.15 involves heat to a greater or lesser extent. The principal reactions with significant positive heats are those involving neutralization, hydration, and polymerization, while the decomposition reaction (Eq. 14.13) is the principal negative heat producer. The heat developed by the neutralizing reactions of NH_3 with superphosphates has been found to be in the range of 775 to 795 cal/gm of anhydrous NH_3 absorbed.[23] From the standpoint of practical value, a temperature rise of 1.7 to 2.0°F occurs in a ton of fertilizer per lb of free NH_3 absorbed by superphosphates. Moisture evaporation with its cooling effect is one of the principal means for attaining the proper heat balance in ammoniated fertilizer manufacture. With the increasing production of high analysis fertilizers containing nitrates and chlorides in relatively large concentrations, it has been necessary to take extra precautions to avoid the large heat effects induced by their interreaction.[57]

Ammoniation Rates

Ammoniation rates vary widely in the fertilizer industry and are dependent on many factors. The most widely used values are approximately as follows:[28]

Ordinary superphosphate (20 per cent P_2O_5)

Usual rate—5.5 to 6.0 lb neutralizing NH_3 per unit P_2O_5 (20 lb)
Upper limit—up to 8 to 10 lb per unit P_2O_5
(Special cases)

Triple superphosphate (45 to 48 per cent P_2O_5)

Usual rate—3.0 to 4.0 lb neutralizing NH_3 per unit P_2O_5
Coarse grade—2.5 to 3.0 lb NH_3
Granular—1.0 lb NH_3

PROCESSING OF AMMONIATED FERTILIZERS

The early utilization of ammonia and ammoniacal salt solutions for making ammoniated fertilizer was done largely by adaptation of existing fertilizer plants to handle nitrogen source materials in liquid rather than solid forms. As use increased and the benefits of ammoniation became more generally recognized, additional changes in processes occurred so that to-day there are fertilizer plants adapted for the utilization of solutions, as well as an increasing number of plants designed specifically to meet the popular demand for granular high analysis fertilizers.[28] Today, ammoniation technology is putting into practice the results of much research aimed at developing better techniques[50, 56] and equipment for mixing and conditioning fertilizers. Out of the many processing improvements which have been developed and applied to ammoniation in the past thirty years, the one which stands high above the others is the accurate control today of the liquid phase during the manufacture of solid mixed fertilizers. This important factor required extensive basic and applied research to perfect the technique.[24, 53]

The major processes for mixed fertilizer manufacturing are shown in Figure 14.5. The types of process in use are batch, semicontinuous, and continuous. These processes may be operated as once-through, as in the case of pulverized and semigranulated fertilizers, or as recycle operations in which part of the product is screened out and returned for further processing.

Major processing steps are ammoniation, drying, cooling, storage, and shipping. The heart of each process is the ammoniation step, while the other major steps are usually handled quite conventionally. Generally, the liquid nitrogen materials used in ammoniation are fed to ammoniation direct from tank cars or storage tanks.

Major equipment categories in fertilizer ammoniation plants are nitrogen-materials supply and handling units; control and recording instruments; the ammoniator (often acting as granulator); the dryer; the cooler; solids-handling units including elevators, screens, holding bins, etc.; storage buildings; and weighing and bagging units.

The units are sized to meet hourly production rates which vary in the fertilizer industry from about 10 to 60 tons/hr of finished fertilizer. As in industry generally, attempts are continually being made to obtain greater production from given units, often leading to poor and unsatisfactory results in product quality.

Ordinarily, the equipment is fabricated from the lowest cost materials of construction such as steel, and there is an increasing trend towards special materials, particularly in critical equipment units such as those for adding and distributing the nitrogen solutions to the ammoniator. Recently, aluminum alloys are being used more commonly, and some of the newer plastics are also being adapted. Corrosion in ammoniation plants is a tantalizing factor, since it is generally not unduly high but is sufficient to cause

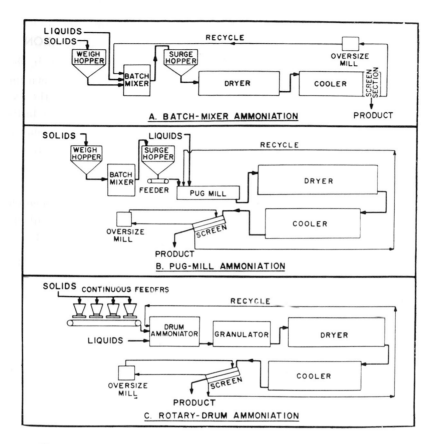

Figure 14.5. Fertilizer granulation process. (Hignett, T. P., Am. Chem. Soc. Monograph 148).

concern for the life of some equipment units. It can be reduced by good housekeeping practices, particularly during stand-by periods.

Successful operation of ammoniation processes depends upon careful and accurate control of many variables. The more important variables which require accurate control are the measurement of solid and liquid ingredients; the timing of addition of solutions; the time in the ammoniator and other units; the moisture content of ingredients; the original, attained, and final temperatures in ammoniation, drying, and cooling; the liquid phase in the ammoniator and in drying; and product shrinkage and undue losses.

With proper control, the processes will produce products meeting the market criteria as to type, grade, physical form, and condition.

BROAD EFFECTS OF AMMONIATING SOLUTIONS AND AMMONIATION

The advent of synthetic ammonia and ammoniacal salt solutions in the late 1920's and early 1930's at prices far below those previously known for nitrogen source materials played an important role in triggering the extensive changes which have occurred in the manufacture of mixed fertilizers in this country in the past 30 yr.[44] This price situation is clearly shown by the data in Table 16.3 in Chapter 16. The rather wide price differences between solid and liquid nitrogen materials has persisted since the marketing of liquids began and still exists in today's market.

The fact that the new nitrogen materials were liquids rather than solids likewise had a major influence on mixed fertilizer manufacture particularly in control of operating conditions and in grade formulation. It must be remembered that the mixed fertilizer industry was well established processwise by 1930, and was based exclusively on unit operations involving the handling of solids in the case of all three major plant foods, NPK. While the adaptation of fertilizer manufacture to utilize liquids appears to be relatively simple, on the surface, many detailed changes were required. It is interesting to note that nearly 20 yr of development were required before ammoniating liquids attained the rapidly accelerated growth of the past decade (Figure 14.1).

From the processing standpoint, it was no doubt fortunate that adaptation of the new liquid nitrogen carriers could be made in then existing plants with few changes and little cost. The installed fertilizer mixer was made into an ammoniator, and the principal changes required were piping from the supply source (tank car furnished by the manufacturer) and a measuring boot for controlling the addition of the ammoniating liquid. As time went by, some plants installed storage for the ammoniating liquids but it is still common practice to draw these materials directly from tank cars.

Better ammoniating equipment was also developed. Coolers and dryers, practically nonexistent in fertilizer plants in the 1930's, came into the picture with higher analysis fertilizers having less filler and greater hygroscopicity.

Concurrent with the introduction of liquid nitrogen sources having 37 per cent or more nitrogen content were the improved superphosphates that were developed. These have better physical characteristics and a greatly enhanced ability to absorb and react with ammonia. Gradually the P_2O_5 content of ordinary superphosphate was increased from the 16 to 18 per cent range to the present 20 per cent or above. Triple superphosphate likewise was improved, and phosphoric acid became available in the late 1950's in increased quantities; all of this contributed to the fertilizer industry's ability to make higher plant food grades. In the case of potassium chloride the K₂O content was raised first to 50 per cent, and today the 60 to 62 per cent K_2O grade is the most common material. Potassium sulfate became an increasingly important source of K_2O for special fertilizer grades and for the holding down of the total chloride content. By the early 1960's, all of the factors relating to the three principal plant foods (NPK) had led to a total nutrient content above 30 per cent.

In summary the major impacts of anhydrous ammonia and ammoniacal salt solutions on the mixed fertilizer industry have been

(1) The provision of nitrogen materials in liquid form, requiring the development of a considerably modified fertilizer technology;

(2) The availability of lower cost nitrogen as compared with the major solid products;

(3) The use of high concentrations of the essential plant food element nitrogen, which has made possible higher analysis fertilizer grades, particularly those of the 1:1:1 and 2:1:1 grades;

(4) The utilization of new combinations of nitrogen materials including ammonium nitrate, urea, and formaldehyde in readily handled and transported forms;

(5) The holding down or actually reducing of capital and operating costs per unit of production, an important factor in the relatively minor increase in mixed fertilizer prices in the past 20 yr;

(6) The improvement in quality of mixed fertilizers, particularly less dustiness and better uniformity; and

(7) The provision of a sound basis for manufacturing granular mixed fertilizers through developed control of liquid phase.

Looking ahead, one may anticipate that ammonia and ammoniacal salt solutions will continue to be the major source of nitrogen in mixed fertilizers. Although larger percentages of the total nitrogen going to agriculture will be used in direct application, solid mixed fertilizers will continue to be important sources of plant foods for many years.

Moreover, new ammoniating solutions should become available to meet special manufacturing and agronomic conditions. At present, many known nitrogen materials have not as yet attained the economic status needed to make them competitive. In time, some of these will no doubt appear in solutions, although of course some of the present solutions will disappear from the market and others become less popular. The large expansion in wet-process phosphoric acid production is causing changes in mixed fertilizer formulation, and has been responsible for bringing the newer solid ammonium-phosphate products on the market. Bulk blending of solids should grow and have an effect on ammoniated fertilizers. The basic economics, however, are such that ammoniated phosphates will continue to be large tonnage products in the foreseeable future.

REFERENCES

1. Adams, J. R., Anderson, M. S., and Hulburt, W. C., "Liquid Nitrogen Fertilizers for Direct Application," Agriculture Handbook 198, Agriculture Research Service, U. S. Dept. Agr., 1961.
2. Adams, J. R., "Physical and Chemical Characteristics of Commercial Nitrogen Solutions for Fertilizer Use," *Official Publication Assoc. Amer. Feed Control Off.*, **11** 66 H (1957).
3. Adams, J. R., "Review of Fertilizer Solutions for 1960 Shows Increased Facilities and Wider Use," *Crop Life*, **8** (5) 1, 22, 29 (1961); **8** (6) 24 (1961).
4. Adams, J. R., and Scholl, W., "Materials Used in the Manufacture of Mixed Fertilizer in the Continental United States Assoc. Amer. Fert. Control Off.," *Off. Publ.*, **12** 63 (1958).
5. Agel, F. O., "The Nitrogen Industry Chemical Growth Potentials Climbing in Central USA," *Chem. Eng. Progress*, **56** (2) 41 (1960).
6. Allied Chemical Corporation, "Nitrogen Fertilizer Solutions for Fertilizer Manufacture," 48 pp., New York, 1956.
7. Allingham, U.S. Patent 2,122,551 (1938).
8. Anonymous, "Solution Coding System Voted by Industry Group," *Farm Chem.*, **121** (10) 51 (1958).
9. Beekhuis, H. A., U.S. Patent 2,135,160 (1938).
10. Beekhuis, H. A., and Lawrence, C. K., U.S. Patent 2,220,059 (1940).
11. Beekhuis, H. A., and Macomber, W. D., U.S. Patents 2,198,151 (1940); 2,215,077 (1940); 2,215,092 (1940).
12. Boller, U.S. Patent 1,875,982 (1938).
13. Brill, J. L., U.S. Patent 2,102,830 (1937) and 2,102,831 (1937).
14. Calcott, W. S., U.S. Patent 1,961,194 (1934).
15. Chucka, J. A., "Problems in Mixed Fertilizer Production," in "Fertilizer Technology and Resources in the United States Agronomy," 3, Ed. K. D. Jacob, pp. 375–391, New York, Academic Press, 1953.
16. Sax, N. I., "Dangerous Properties of Industrial Materials," p. 838, New York, Reinhold Pub. Corp., 1963.
17. Crittenden, E. D., "Petrochemicals in Agriculture," Proceedings 34th Annual Convention Natural Gasoline Assoc. of America Dallas (1955).
18. Crittenden, E. D., "Chemical and Physical Properties of Nitrogen Materials and Their Sphere of Usefulness," in "Fertilizer Technology and Resources in the United States Agronomy," 3, Ed. K. D. Jacob, pp. 85–115, New York, Academic Press, 1953.
19. Fazel, C. S., U.S. Patent 2,077,469 (1937).
20. Franklin, E. C., "The Nitrogen System of Compounds," in ACS Monograph, 68, New York, Reinhold, 1935.
21. Greene, P. A., "Sampling of Pressure Fertilizer Solutions," *J. Assoc. Official Agr. Chemists*, **40** (1) 305 (1957).
22. Hagens, J. F. C., Rosenstein, L., Hirschkind, U.S. Patent 1,699,393 (1929) and U.S. Patent 1,967,205 (1934).
23. Hardesty, J. O., and Ross, W. H., "Heat Developed in the Ammoniation of Superphosphates with Ammonia," *Ind. Eng. Chem.*, **29** 1283 (1937).

24. Hardesty, J. O., "Principles of Fertilizer Agglomeration," Paper at 47th National Meeting Am. Inst. Chem. Engs., Baltimore, Md., May, 1962.
25. Harvey, E. W., U.S. Patent 1,894,767 (1933); U.S. Patent 1,948,520 (1934); U.S. Patent 1,981,729 (1934); U.S. Patent 2,023,199 (1935); U.S. Patent 2,036,870 (1936); U.S. Patent 2,053,432 (1936); U.S. Patent 2,060,310 (1936).
26. Harvey, E. W., and Jones, R. M., U.S. Patent 2,077,171 (1937).
27. Harvey, E. W., and Rohner, L. V., "Chemical Properties of Various Commercial Superphosphates Before and After Ammoniation," *Am. Fertilizer*, **97** (8) 5, 24, 26 (1942).
28. Hignett, T. P., "General Considerations on Operating Techniques, Equipment, and Practices on Manufacture of Granular Mixed Fertilizers," in "Chemistry and Technology of Fertilizers," Ed. V. Sauchelli, Chap. 9, New York, Reinhold, 1960.
29. Jones, R. M., U.S. Patent 1,966,820 (1934).
30. Keenen, F. G., "Reactions Occurring During the Ammoniation of Superphosphate," *Ind. Eng. Chem.*, **22**, 1378 (1930).
31. Keenen, F. G., "Available Phosphoric Acid Content of Ammoniated Superphosphate," *Ind. Eng. Chem.*, **24**, 44 (1932).
32. Keenen, F. G., *Fertilizer Greenbook*, **12**, 16 (1931).
33. Keenen, F. G., U.S. Patent 2,238,651 (1941).
34. Kniskern, W. H., U.S. Patents 2,007,251 (1935) and 2,018,857 (1935).
35. Kniskern, W. H., and Lawrence, C. K., U.S. Patents 2,022,672 (1935); 2,022,673 (1935); 2,022,674 (1935); 2,022,675 (1935); 2,022,676 (1935); 2,035,484 (1936); 2,067,931 (1937); 2,081,401 (1937); 2,116,866 (1938).
36. Kniskern, W. H., and Klingelhoefer, W., U.S. Patent 2,022,677 (1935).
37. Kniskern, W. H., and Rohner, L. V., U.S. Patents 2,036,481 (1936); 2,149,966 (1939).
38. Kolterman, D. W., and Rennie, W. W., "Conversion of Ammonia to Urea and Ureaforms," in "Chemistry and Technology of Fertilizers," Ed. V. Sauchelli, pp. 37–54, New York, Reinhold, 1960.
39. Lawrence, C. K., and Engle, R. F., U.S. Patent 2,366,796 (1945) and U.S. Patent 2,377,792 (1945).
40. Lawrence, C. K., and Harvey, E. W., U.S. Patent 2,050,493 (1936).
41. Lockwood, M. H., "High Analysis Mixed Fertilizers," in "Fertilizer Technology and Resources in United States Agronomy," 3, Ed. K. D. Jacob, pp. 393–412, New York, Academic Press, 1953.
42. MacDowell, C. H., U.S. Patent 1,889,125 (1932).
43. Marburger, G. C., "Ammoniating Solutions," *Agr. Chem.*, **14** (8) 37 (1959).
44. Mehring, A. L., and Bennett, G. A., *Agr. Chem.*, **6** (2) 47 (1951); **6** (3) 49 (1951).
45. Moore, H. C., U.S. Patent 1,931,768 (1933); Moore, H. C., and White, R., U.S. Patent 1,778,427 (1930).
46. Nelson, E. L., "Determination of Total Nitrogen in Materials Containing Nitrate —Reduction by Chromous Ion," *J. Assoc. Off. Agr. Chemists*, **43** (3) 468 (1960).
47. Nelson, L. B., "New Fertilizers—Present and Future," *Ag. Chem.*, **17**, 39, 105 (1962).
48. National Plant Food Institute, "Fertilizer Safety Guide," Washington, D. C. (1961).
49. "Official Methods of Analysis," 8th ed., Washington, D. C., Association of Official Agricultural Chemists (1955).
50. Schreiber, H., "Cooling Fertilizers During Manufacture," *Ag. Chem.*, **17** (6) 32, 98 (1962).

51. Shultz, J. F. and Elmore, G. V., "The System Ammonium Nitrate—Ammonia-Water Partial Vapor Pressures and Solution Densities, *Ind. Eng. Chem.*, **38,** 296 (1946).

52. Smith, R. C., "Plant Practices in the Manufacture of Non-Granulated Mixed Fertilizers," in "Chemistry and Technology of Fertilizers," Ed. V. Sauchelli, pp. 403–433, New York, Reinhold, 1960.

53. Tinsley, R. S., and Gilliam, G. R., "A Method of Predicting the Effect of Various Factors on the Liquid Phase of Granular Mixed Fertilizers," American Chemical Society Meeting, New York, Sept. 1957.

54. Tyler, Chaplin and Parker, F. W., U. S. Patent 1,894,136 (1933).

55. Vreeland, D. C., and Kahn, S. H., "Corrosion of Metals by Liquid Fertilizer Solutions," *Corrosion,* **12** (11) 569t (1956).

56. Waters, C. E., Arnold, W. W., and Payne, W. H., "Effect of Particle Size Upon the Ammoniation of Superphosphate," *J. Agr. Food Chem.,* **3** 218 (1955).

57. Waters, C. E., Smith, J. A., and Novotny, J., "Thermal Decomposition of High Analysis Fertilizers," *J. Agr. Food Chem.,* **8** 475 (1960).

58. White, L. M., Hardesty, J. O., and Ross, W. H., "Ammoniation of Double Superphosphate," *Ind. Eng. Chem.,* **27** 562 (1935).

59. Worthington, E. A., Datin, R. C., and Schutz, D. P., "Physical Properties of Ammonia Solutions," *Ind. Eng. Chem.,* **44** 1910 (1952).

60. Zoellner, J. H., and Heck, R. R., "Formulation Non-Granular Fertilizers," *Crop Life,* **9** 3 (1962).

15

Natural Chilean Nitrate of Soda

Production and Use in Agriculture

H. L. Tower, Jr.

Anglo-Lautaro Nitrate Corporation

AND

Herbert C. Brewer

Chilean Nitrate Educational Bureau, Inc.

While natural nitrate deposits of sodium and potassium have been reported in many widely scattered locations such as Egypt, South Africa, Mexico, and the United States, the only natural nitrate resources of real commercial significance occur in the northern part of Chile in a narrow strip ranging from 10 to 50 miles in width and some 450 miles in length located between latitudes 19° and 26° south. The typical deposits found on the comparatively level slopes on the easterly part of the Chilean coastal range vary in elevation from 3500 to 7500 feet above sea level and range in thickness from a few inches to depths of 10 or 15 ft. The nitrate ore body is usually covered with a similar thickness of overburden which may vary in composition from loose sand and dust to a firm and hard packed conglomerate of rock fragments and salts of little or no commercial value.

GENESIS

A number of theories as to the probable origin of Chile's natural nitrate deposits have been advanced through the years, but no single theory would seem to offer a thoroughly satisfactory explanation of all of their unique geological features. It seems more probable that a combination of the various agencies suggested by the different authorities has been responsible in varying degree for their origin.

According to Dr. Bruggen of the University of Chile, it would appear that parts of northern Chile were once at the bottom of the Pacific Ocean. This seems fairly well established by the occurrence of cetaceous limestone beds and the appearance of fossils in certain sections of the nitrate pampa, particularly in the northerly region of Iquique. A study of the Rio Loa's banks in the more southerly Tocopilla district also seems to indicate that the wide longitudinal tectonic valley of the area was originally an inland sea and this degrading river, which still is cutting its channel today, is gradually exposing loose sedimentary rocks.

With the raising of the coastal range through tectonic movements, the climate of the area was caused to change from a moist to a semi-moist, and finally to its present arid nature. As evaporation took place in this arid climate, the water probably became too alkaline to support vegetable life with the result that oxidation of the vegetable matter, kelp, and seaweed took place, giving rise to the formation of these nitrate deposits. While this is a prominent theory of genesis, it leaves numerous questions unanswered.

A more modern theory and one that seems more tenable because of the lack of negative evidence rather than the presence of confirmatory proof postulates that the nitrate deposits were of fumarolic origin. It assumes that contemporaneous with and immediately following the elevation of the coastal range the more volatile constituents of the magma together with the magmatic water were segregated at irregular intervals along the general axis of the mountain range but at great depth. Constant pressure slowly forced the solutions which were in excess of the requirements of the magma proper through the molten rock at its points of weakness. In the ascending solutions, the acids corresponding to the various high oxygen salts were generated by the extreme pressures and temperatures acting in the presence of a catalyst.

The acidic solutions formed as described above would have leached the overlying magma with the metallic elements of the semimolten rock, replacing the hydrogen of the acids. The soluble salts thus formed would have been forced to the surface through the vents if pressure conditions were favorable. The subsequent drainage was developed by the solutions, and the deposition of the salts took place along this system due to the rapid rate of evaporation of the solvent. Gravity undoubtedly influenced the general trend of the salt deposition but capillarity was also a prominent factor.

The assumption of a fumarolic origin of the deposits explains the source of the solutions which have weathered the igneous rock. The presence of nitrate and chlorine would hasten weathering and would more completely account for the development of large amounts of clay that has for its source the rhyolites of the coastal range.

Caliche is found on the slopes because there has been insufficient solvent to carry it to the lower ground and not because the nitrate creeps out of solution. Where water has been present in relative abundance, the nitrate is found in "salar" areas. Where water has been very scarce, practically all deposition has been restricted to slopes and high ground. Any graduation between the two is possible, dependent upon the relation between the amount of solvent and the rate of evaporation.

All elements found in a caliche deposit are or have been of igneous origin, so that it is not unreasonable to assume that in this particular case the compounds of sodium and potassium were derived directly from the original magma. The presence of iodine in no way detracts from this statement. The presence of perchlorate points to the direct pyrochemical derivation, as it is impossible to conceive of this compound as a secondary or an organic product. If these assumptions are tenable, they definitely establish the relationship between the igneous flows and caliche deposition.

CALICHE COMPOSITION

Considering the number of geological factors that may have contributed to the genesis of caliche, it is not strange that its chemical composition is extremely variable as are its physical characteristics. In nitrate content, caliches can range from practically zero to as high as 80 per cent, although grades of this high order of magnitude are now almost entirely exhausted.

In color, caliche varies from pure white to tan, brown, and red with occasional samples of blue and black, depending on the presence of iron, chrome, iodine, and other elements. While the hardness of caliche usually averages about 4 on the Mohs scale, this too can vary considerably, depending on the nature of the insolubles making up the conglomerate.

In view of the wide range of chemical and physical variables, it is almost impossible to cite any detailed analysis which might be termed "typical" of the caliche, but the following may be considered to be quite representative of the nitrate ores being treated today in the larger processing plants which employ mechanical mining methods:

Constituents	Per Cent
$NaNO_3$	7.0 to 10.0
NaCl	4.5 to 9.5

Na_2SO_4	10.0	to 30.0
Mg	0.2	to 1.3
Ca	1.0	to 2.7
K	0.5	to 1.6
$Na_2B_4O_7$	0.5	to 0.8
I_2	0.03	to 0.05
H_2O	1.0	to 2.0

Some of the simple salts reported in the above table actually do not occur as such in caliche but are found to exist in the form of rather complex double salts as indicated below:

Darapskite	$NaNO_3 \cdot Na_2SO_4 \cdot H_2O$
Glauberite	$CaSO_4 \cdot Na_2SO_4$
Bloedite	$MgSO_4 \cdot Na_2SO_4 \cdot 4H_2O$
Syngenite	$K_2SO_4 \cdot Na_2SO_4 \cdot H_2O$
Polyhalite	$K_2SO_4 \cdot CaSO_4 \cdot 2 Na_2SO_4$

PROSPECTING AND MINING PRACTICES

Inasmuch as the Chilean nitrate deposits are usually found quite close to the surface and in relatively shallow beds, prospecting and exploration are rather simple. In early prospecting, sample pits about 1 m in diameter were sunk by pick and shovel through the top layer of overburden and then through the ore body itself. Sample channels were cut vertically down the face of the pit and the cuttings collected and analyzed for nitrate content. For the preliminary exploration of promising localities, these test pits were sunk at fairly wide intervals ranging from 100 to 500 m between pits. When promising localities were thus located, the sample pits were more closely spaced to pinpoint the actual location of the deposits. In modern practice, mechanical wagon drills are replacing these earlier hand prospecting methods.

The first actual mining of the Chilean nitrate deposits is believed to have been done by the Spaniards in the early 19th century. In this period, only the very richest ores, usually those running as high as 60 to 80 per cent in nitrate content, were hand picked from the deposits for processing. Leaching was carried out in open pans heated by direct fire, the ore being leached with a combination of fresh water and mother liquor resulting from previous extractions. When saturation at the boiling point was reached, the solution was run off into smaller settling pans, and the rather impure crystals produced during atmospheric cooling were collected and harvested.

SHANKS PROCESS

Toward the latter part of the nineteenth century an improved process of nitrate extraction and recovery known as the "Shanks" process was introduced into Chile by J. D. Humberstone. Viewed from present-day standards, this process was quite primitive. It was characterized by hand mining, high temperature leaching, low extractions, and generally high operating costs. However, with little or no competition, a brisk product demand, and exceptionally high returns on a relatively low capital investment, there was no real incentive for process modernization. As late as 1926 there were 100 such plants in existence. Now only two Shanks process plants remain in operation.

GUGGENHEIM PROCESS

About 1916, engineers of the large American mining firm of Guggenheim Bros. engaged in the development of a Chile Copper Company property at Chuquicamata in the Province of Antofagasta, Chile, became convinced that the adjacent nitrate properties then employing the Shanks Process could be greatly improved by the mechanization and modernization of mine and plant equipment along the lines employed in large scale metallurgical leaching plants in this country where low grade ores were being cheaply processed.

In the latter part of 1918, a research group was organized to explore these possibilities more fully and to study the basic chemistry involved in leaching nitrate ores with a view to improving the Shanks Process. After successful investigations in their New York laboratories, research activities were transferred to Chile and a pilot plant of 20 tons/day ore capacity was erected and put into operation in October 1922. Operations of this pilot plant over a 2 yr period served to confirm the merits of the new process and construction of the first really modern nitrate plant, having a capacity of 500,000 metric tons of nitrate per year, was started in November 1924 and put into operation in December 1926. Construction of a second nearby plant having a rated capacity of 600,000 tons of nitrate per year began in January 1930, and in May 1931 the first nitrate was produced.

The new "Guggenheim" nitrate process employing the latest technological advances was developed basically to permit the treatment of low grade caliche ores, making it possible to mine by mechanical methods. Furthermore, this lower grade ore could be leached with only slightly warm solutions as opposed to the boiling solutions required for high grade ore, and the nitrate was precipitated by refrigeration replacing the process of evaporation and cooling in open tanks. In order to provide low cost heat to warm the leach solutions and make subsequent mechanical refrigeration economical, a carefully balanced system of power-plant heat recovery was put into operation. This new process soon demonstrated that caliche ores as low as 7 per cent in nitrate content could be economically processed, which greatly increased the life of Chile's nitrate deposits.

MINING–CRUSHING

In the Guggenheim Process, the overburden covering the nitrate deposits is first loosened by drilling and blasting and the barren material then removed or stripped by mechanical draglines to expose the actual ore body. After further drilling and blasting, the broken ore is loaded by shovel, dragline, or both into cars of 30 to 35 tons capacity which are hauled to the plant by electric- or diesel-powered locomotives. A loop system of electric haulage is laid out for each mining section in which the main lines are electrified. The frequently shifting mining lines are serviced by trolley-battery-type haulage units. A mining section generally includes about 2000-m distance between the empty line and the load line, and the area is laid out to give a favorable grade for the loaded ore trains wherever possible (Figure 15.1).

At the plant the ore cars pass through a rotary-car dumper, and the ore is dumped into the primary crushing units which are of the jaw or gyratory type. The feed to the crushers ranges in size from fragments up to pieces weighing 3 to 5 tons. Crushing is carried out in three stages with smaller gyratories serving as secondary and cone crushers as the tertiary units. The ore is screened following each crushing stage, and the clean crushed product constituting about 80 per cent of the input tonnage ranges between ⅜ and ¾ in. in size. Since the coarse ore fraction is to be treated in leaching vats and the nitrate extracted by downward percolation of the leach liquors, the removal of the fine undersize by screening is essential to permit the free

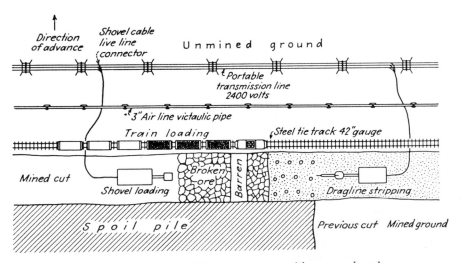

Figure 15.1. Plan for mining nitrate ores with power shovels.

flow of solutions and to give reasonably fast percolation rates. The fine ore removed in screening operations is processed by filtration on units of the Moore vacuum leaf type. Units permitting continuous filtration are now under active investigation.

LEACHING

The leaching vats, usually ten in number arranged in series, are built of reinforced concrete erected in blocks of two so that each pair of vats is structurally independent of the others. Vats are about 160 ft in length, 110 ft in width and 20 ft in height. These vats each have an ore capacity of about 10,000 metric tons of crushed caliche. The vat bottoms are provided with a filter bed of crushed stone and coco matting to insure the discharge of a clear solution.

The vat leaching cycle consists in the downward percolation of solutions successively advanced through a series of four vats. Mother liquor applied to the surface of the first vat percolates downward by gravity through the ore charge and the vat underflow is pumped on top of the second vat in the series. The leach solutions are thus advanced through the four vats in series successively increasing in concentration as they advance from vat to vat. The dissolving action of nitrate causes a cooling effect and the leach solutions are passed through heat interchangers between stages to maintain a fairly constant leaching temperature.

The average leaching temperature in the Guggenheim Process is about 40°C and the nitrate pick up from mother liquor to final strong solution stage is from an initial 350 to a final 450 gm/l nitrate concentration. The cycle time is about 10 hr, a newly charged vat entering the cycle every 10 hr and a leached vat dropping out.

After a vat has been in the four-stage leaching cycle for a total of about 40 hr, it is removed from the series and allowed to drain. The vat tailings are next washed with a series of graduated washes and finally with water. The residue which may contain from .75 to 1.5 per cent nitrate is then unloaded from the vat with 5-ton clam-shell grab buckets suspended from a movable gantry crane structure which serves all ten vats and is dumped into 16-cu yd cars which are hauled to the tailings disposal area (Figure 15.2).

FILTRATION OF FINES

As pointed out previously, the fines produced during the crushing operation are screened out to assure a clean feed to the main leaching plant. These fines are collected and processed separately in a Moore-type filter plant, the ore to the plant consisting of material about −20 mesh in size.

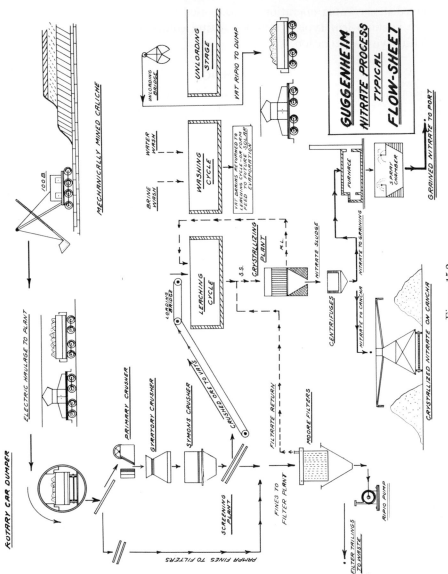

Figure 15.2

Fines are transferred from the screening plant to a large storage bin and are discharged through adjustable gates into ribbon-type screw conveyors which serve also as mixers. The fines are pulped with hot mother liquor to produce a homogeneous slurry having a density of about 1.90. After the mixing operation, the hot pulp flows through canals to distributing tanks which in turn feed the actual filter tanks. Each filter section consists of 9 tanks in series, the tanks being approximately 11 by 24 by 19 ft in depth. Volumetric capacity of the filter tanks is about 90 cu m each. Of the nine tanks in series, two serve as pulp tanks where the cake is formed, followed by three wash tanks, two drying tanks, and two cake discharge tanks. Solids are kept in suspension in the pulp tank by means of air-lift agitation.

The filter baskets which are advanced through the filter cycle by means of a 55-ton overhead travelling crane each contain about 40 canvas-covered filter leaves measuring 9 ft in width and 7 ft in depth. This provides a total filter area of 6000 sq ft per basket. All leaves are connected to a 4-in.-diameter vacuum header to which suction is applied. The concentrated solutions pass through the canvas covering into the interior of the leaf, the solids building up on the outside of the leaf to form a filter cake of about 1½ in. in thickness. After the cake is formed in the pulp tanks, the basket is transferred to a wash tank containing brine of low nitrate concentration. This brine wash originated as vat drains collected in the main leaching plant and serves as a displacement wash for replacing the highly concentrated filtrate in the filter cake.

From the wash tank, the basket is transferred to a drying tank where suction is maintained and the cake is allowed to dry for a period of about 10 min. Then the basket moves on to an unloading tank where high pressure air sent through the leaves in a reverse direction serves to discharge the cake. The strong filtrate recovered in filter operations joins the concentration solution from the last vat in the main leaching cycle, and the combination of the two solutions is pumped to the crystallizing plant for recovery of their nitrate content.

CRYSTALLIZATION

In the crystallizing plant there are 20 shell- and tube-type crystallizing tanks arranged in series, each containing about 500 vertical tubes 3-in. in diameter and 16 ft in length. The strong nitrate solution to be cooled is circulated rapidly through the inside of the tubes, the cooling medium circulating through the shells. This results in a gradual cooling from 40°C inlet temperature to about 10°C. The first 14 tanks of the 20-tank series serve as heat recuperators where the cooling medium is the 10°C countercurrent returning mother liquor. The last six tanks are refrigerators, and the cooling medium is liquid ammonia.

While the mother liquor is heated in its return flow through the crystallizing plant and emerges at about 35°C, leaching temperatures in the vat cycle must be maintained at about 40°C. The heat required to achieve this rise in temperature as well as to overcome radiation heat losses from the large open vats is obtained in the form of "waste heat" from the diesel power plants and ammonia compressors.

The sludge of nitrate crystals produced in the crystallizing plant is dewatered and given a short water displacement wash in a battery of 48-in. diameter by 24-in. basket-type centrifuges. There are 24 centrifuges in operation, each having a capacity of about 0.5 tons of nitrate per basket charge. Cycle time between loading and discharge is 7 to 8 min. The centrifuge product is pure white, about 48 mesh in crystal size, is of 95 to 96 per cent nitrate purity, and contains between 3.0 and 3.5 per cent moisture.

NITRATE GRAINING

After centrifuging operations, the nitrate is carried by conveyor belt to the graining plant where it is charged into large oil-fired reverberatory-type furnaces. At a temperature of about 350°C, the nitrate changes from solid to liquid form. Molten nitrate withdrawn from the furnace flows by gravity through inclined canals into holding pots from which it is pumped by vertical submerged pumps to the top of a large spray chamber about 100 ft in height. The molten nitrate is pumped through spray nozzles ⅝ in. in diameter and the droplets produced solidify in their fall into small solid pellets.

The product from the spray chamber is carried by conveyor belt to a screening plant where the oversize and any undersize product is removed and returned to the furnaces for remelting. The screened product passes next by gravity through ten shell and tube-type coolers about 6 ft in diameter by 10 ft high. Mother liquor is circulated on the outside of the tubes through the shell jacket thus recuperating additional heat for the main leaching circuit. The grained product consists of pellets ranging from about 20 to 8 mesh and has a purity in excess of 98 per cent sodium nitrate. Moisture content is about 0.20 with valuable traces of magnesium, potassium, boron, and other elements which have proven beneficial to plant life. Grained Chilean Nitrate is guaranteed to contain 16 per cent nitrogen.

STORAGE AND SHIPMENT

The finished product is removed from the processing plants on the nitrate pampa in gondola-type care of approximately 22-tons capacity down grade to the port of embarkation where large storage facilities are provided. At port it is dumped from the cars by means of a revolving railroad-car dumper from which the nitrate moves on belt conveyors to the top of six storage silos, each having a storage capacity of 10,000 metric tons. The nitrate is distributed into the silos by means of a movable belt tripper.

Discharge from the silos is accomplished by a series of belt feeders operating underneath the bin discharge gates. These feeders discharge their load on to the main out-loading conveyor leading to a uniquely designed ship loader bridge. This bridge is mounted on a pivot pier and extends as a cantilever 225 ft from the center of the pier and serves to transport the nitrate to the several hatches of a ship moored in deep water off shore. Within the main bridge structure there is a shuttle conveyor which extends the discharge point of the loading tower and permits the bridge to reach and discharge through a vertical telescopic chute to all five hatches of the cargo vessel without the necessity for moving the ship from its moored position. An operator's cab mounted on the outboard end of the shuttle truss contains the controls for all conveyor movements from the silo-discharge feeders to the final shuttle conveyor on the loading bridge. The capacity of this modern shiploading installation is such that a vessel carrying 10,000 metric tons of nitrate can be loaded in less than 10 hr.

CHILEAN IODINE

While Chile's caliche deposits are the world's only commercial source of natural nitrate of soda, they also constitute the world's largest source of iodine. Iodine occurs in caliche in the form of iodates, principally the iodates of sodium, potassium, and calcium. The average iodine content of caliche is about .04 per cent, although in some instances samples of ore running as high as 1 per cent in iodine content have been reported.

Iodine builds up in the nitrate leach solutions to concentrations ranging from 3 to 10 gm/l in the form of iodate. In a two-stage continuous process, this iodate is reduced to iodide and subsequently to iodine which is recovered in its elemental form. Iodine purity of the commercial product is about 99.5 per cent. Chile's iodine production is now in excess of 2100 metric tons per year and can readily be increased to meet the steadily increasing world demand.

BY-PRODUCT RECOVERY BY SOLAR EVAPORATION

Brief mention should be made of a recent and very significant development which permits the economic recovery of many other valuable chemicals present in caliche ores besides sodium nitrate which for years have been discarded to waste in the leaching vat residues.

After the normal nitrate leaching operation described on page 321, vat residues are now being given a secondary leach with raw water which serves not only to dissolve additional sodium nitrate but also extracts potassium nitrate and the sulfates, chlorides, borates, and iodates which are insoluble in the main-plant leach solutions. The weak brine containing these added chemical values is now collected and pumped to ten evaporating ponds arranged in series having a total area of approximately 100 acres. Under the hot desert sun these values concentrate to form a strong solution. Refrigeration of this strong pond solution produces potash nitrate of 14 per cent K_2O grade as well as substantial quantities of additional sodium nitrate not recovered in the main plant extraction operations. From this same solution, boric acid and additional quantities of iodine are likewise being recovered.

During this process, substantial tonnages of sodium chloride together with a mixture of sodium sulfate and magnesium sulfate in the form of the double-salt "astrakanite" precipitate in the ponds, and these values are continuously harvested by means of floating suction dredges. These salts are presently being stockpiled for future processing and refining.

NATURAL NITRATE OF SODA IN AGRICULTURE

Little is known of the circumstances attending the discovery of the fertilizing value of Chilean nitrate except what has come down to us in the form of Indian legend and folklore. Until the middle of the 19th century it was believed that the soil itself would supply all of the elements necessary to plant growth except phosphorus and potassium. It has now been demonstrated that nitrogen is actually the most important factor in crop growth. Chilean nitrate is the only natural source of nitrate nitrogen and aside from stable manure, it is the oldest source of fixed nitrogen.

Reduction of Nutrient Elements by Crop Growth

The process of growing and harvesting crops produces a steady drain on all of the nutrient elements in the soil. Unless their supply is maintained, yields and nutritional quality must suffer. This is generally recognized in respect to nitrogen, phosphorus, potassium, calcium, and to lesser extent in the case of magnesium. The importance of sodium, manganese, iron, zinc, copper, sulfur, boron, iodine, chlorine, cobalt, lithium, and other elements is, however, much better understood now than it used to be, and a deficiency of any one may adversely influence growth, yield, and quality.

Plants get carbon, hydrogen, and oxygen from the air and water. The other elements are obtained from the soil. Of these, nitrogen, phosphorus, potassium, and calcium are required in the largest amounts. Other elements usually are needed in small quantities and, therefore, are variously referred to as minor, trace, or micronutrients. Their importance and their roles in plant growth are readily discernible in the symptoms which develop when they are in deficient supply.

Nitrogen as a Limiting Factor in Crop Production

Generally, it may be said that lack of nitrogen is the first limiting factor in the growth of crops. Although necessary for the development of all parts of the plant, it functions primarily to promote root, stem, leaf, and fruit growth. The effect of nitrogen applications usually is more striking than that of other plant-food elements. This is especially true of the nitrate form of nitrogen, partly because of the ease with which plants are able to assimilate it.

Although it may not be said that one element is more essential to plants than another, the need for nitrogen usually is acute. This may be explained by the fact that protoplasm, the living substance of the cells of all living things, contains proteins as its principal dry-matter constituent. The proteins are organic nitrogen compounds resulting from the chemical condensation of carbohydrates and inorganic nitrogen. The manner in which the carbohydrates are utilized by the plant depends largely upon the carbohydrate-nitrogen assimilation balance. If the supply of carbohydrates is too high or too low, adverse results are certain to follow.

Nitrate Nitrogen

Ready Utilization by Plants.   Although nitrogen makes up about four-fifths of the volume of ordinary air, nonlegume plants cannot use it in that form. Nature converts limited amounts of nitrogen into forms which can be utilized as plant food through the action of soil bacteria. Some of these live by themselves in the soil, while other form colonies in small nodules on the roots of leguminous plants. In any extensive system of agriculture that permits the growing of clover or other legumes to be plowed under for soil improvement, the problem of the nitrogen supply may not be acute. When land must be used intensively, however, and at a high degree of efficiency for crop production, nitrogen fertilization is essential.

Unlike other plant food elements, nitrogen is not firmly held in the soil except in combination with organic matter. As the organic matter is decomposed by soil microbes, its nitrogen is changed to soluble forms and finally to nitrate. In sandy soils, if not taken up by the plants or by the soil microbes, the nitrate may be carried down by rain below the level of root development. In this event, the supply must be renewed for the next crop.

Thus, timing is an important factor in the efficient use of nitrogen fertilizers which contain essentially nitrate nitrogen.

The free movement of nitrate nitrogen in the soil moisture makes it particularly desirable for use whenever immediate action is required. Nitrogen characteristically produces a healthy, dark-green color in the vegetative parts of the plant. It increases leaf, stem, and fruit growth; adds crispness and quality to leafy vegetable crops; and increases the protein content of grains and grasses. It promotes rapid, early growth and aids in the production of increased yields. It feeds soil microorganisms during their decomposition of low nitrogen organic material. Nitrate nitrogen is non-acid forming whereas ammonia nitrogen has an acid reaction usually requiring substantial corrective applications of lime to maintain soil productivity.

Effectiveness with Varying Soil and Seasonal Conditions. All of the simple nitrates are highly soluble in water. Because of this, nitrate nitrogen is immediately available to plants once it has been applied to the soil. If a heavy rain comes before it has been taken up by the plant roots, the nitrate may be carried down into the soil profile and under extreme conditions may even be lost in the drainage water. This is one reason why farmers generally prefer to use nitrate of soda as a side dressing or top dressing for growing crops with well-developed root systems. At that stage, the plants pump large amounts of water from the soil and discharge it into the air from their leaves. Thus the soil has more storage space for rain when it comes again.

A considerable part of the fertilizer nitrogen that is applied to well-managed land is first consumed by microbes which are decomposing the soil organic matter. This is especially true when large quantities of crude plant residues have been ploughed under or worked into the soil. The nitrogen content of such materials is relatively low and the consuming microbes require more of it than is supplied by the organic matter. Consequently, a soluble mineral form of nitrogen, like nitrate of soda, is avidly consumed by them. Once the supply of crude, organic material has been used up by the soil microorgansms, many of them die for lack of food. Their bodies are consumed by other organisms and gradually the nitrogen in them is released in nitrate form for crop use. In this manner, nitrate nitrogen is changed to bacterial protein in the soil and later released in nitrate form to supply the needs of the growing crop.

Soil Reaction and Productivity

Soil reaction is one of the most important factors in soil productivity. It has a direct influence on the efficiency of nitrogen fertilizers. In large measure, it determines how much of the plant food in them will be maintained in available form for use by the plant and how much of it will be lost to the crop through conversion into forms that cannot readily be used by it. The total result of an application of a nitrogen fertilizer to a crop, therefore, is the direct effect of the nitrogen plus the side effects of the other elements associated with it. The side effects, if any, of nitrogen fertilizers may be immediately apparent in the crop, or they may become apparent later by way of soil.

Natural nitrate of soda possesses a series of valuable side effects, rising largely from the sodium and minor elements which it contains in natural combination with nitrate nitrogen. According to experimental evidence, when ammonia forms of nitrogen were substituted for nitrate of soda in commercially mixed fertilizers, it was found necesary to add more potash to them. It was also shown that the availability of soil phosphate was higher after the use of nitrate of soda than when other sources of nitrogen were employed. Other studies revealed that for some crops sodium had value in the presence of optimum supplies of available phosphate and potash. In other words, sodium in itself has value as a fertilizer element. Long-time comparisons of nitrate of soda with ammonia forms of nitrogen afforded striking demonstrations of their respective influences on soil reaction.

Ammonia forms of nitrogen have an acidulating effect on the soil. Thus, it would require 5.2 lb of limestone to neutralize the acidity produced by each pound of nitrogen applied to the soil in the form of sulfate of ammonia. On the other hand, each pound of nitrogen applied in the form of nitrate of soda has an alkaline value equivalent to 1.8 lb of limestone. It is this alkaline effect that explains the tendency of nitrate of soda to increase the availability of soil phosphate. In naturally alkaline soils or in those that have been adequately limed, no such increase in phosphate availability is likely to occur. In acid soils, however, this effect becomes important and it is particularly impressive in reports of the results of long-time comparison between nitrate of soda and sulfate of ammonia.

Sodium will Substitute for Potash when Necessary

The ability of sodium to substitute in part for potassium in plants is a matter of economic as well as of agronomic importance. In this process 23 lb of sodium will replace 39 lb of potassium. Each ton of nitrate of soda contains about 540 lb of sodium. This could replace 915 lb of potassium equivalent to approximately 1100 lb of potash (K_2O). This is as much potash as is contained in 1830 lb of a 60 per cent grade of muriate of potash. Thus sodium has value in itself as a partial substitute for potassium, as an agent for liberating soil phosphate, and as a corrector for soil acidity.

Important Difference Between Nitrogen Fertilizers is Nitrate Nitrogen

The principal difference between nitrogen fertilizers, however, is the form of nitrogen which they contain. A few of them contain nitrate nitrogen; others do not. All of the nitrogen in nitrate of soda is nitrate nitrogen. Nitrogen in the form of nitrate is more quickly available to crops than in the form of ammonia. Nitrate nitrogen applied to the surface of dry soil will dissolve in the moisture it attracts from the air. It will move downward to the root zone when it rains again. Ammonia, on the other hand, is fixed at the point of contact with the soil, and it stays there until the soil becomes moistened and the soil microbes have had time to change it to nitrate. Only then does it become mobile. This factor of delay is so well recognized that, in practice, ammonium salts and anhydrous ammonia are generally applied before planting. Because of the availability and mobility of its nitrogen content, nitrate of soda finds its largest usefulness in top dressing and side dressing growing crops.

There are many cases where not enough potash has been used, where phosphate availability is low, where the soil is too acid, and where availability and fast action are needed. Because of its unique ability to meet the requirements of these and other potentially adverse conditions, natural nitrate of soda is favored over other sources of nitrate quite generally by farmers, especially where top dressing and side dressing are so widely practiced.

16

Synthetic Sodium Nitrate— Production and Use

E. D. CRITTENDEN

Allied Chemical Corporation

The story of synthetic sodium nitrate is largely a chronicle of a nitrogen material which had humble beginnings early in the 20th Century, grew to a position of world prominence in the middle 1930's, and since that time has declined to a very minor role in the nitrogen industry in the United States and abroad. In the early years of the 20th Century sodium nitrate was a prime source of nitrogen for agriculture[8, 15, 24] as well as the basic raw material for nitric acid manufacture needed in explosives and for other purposes. Figure 13.1 in Chapter 13 shows the position of sodium nitrate in U. S. agriculture for the years 1930 through 1961. World War I brought home the great dependence of the world on sodium nitrate from Chile and the vulnerability of the supply.

Several factors have played an important part in the rise and decline of synthetic sodium nitrate, undoubtedly the most important being economics to be discussed in a later section. It must be recognized that the development of the synthetic material came at a time when total nitrogen supply, particularly for the United States was short. Initial production also coincided with the beginnings of the synthetic ammonia industry and with the ample supply of relatively cheap soda ash; both necessary basic raw materials for synthetic $NaNO_3$. It is thus evident that the market situation was favorable and prices attractive.

Synthetic sodium nitrate is a white salt offered for sale in three crystal sizes and in pelleted form. The material is odorless, saline in taste, is quite soluble in water, ammonia, and glycerine, but only slightly soluble in alcohol. Physical properties are given in Table 16.1, while typical chemical and screen analyses are given in Table 16.2. The guaranteed nitrogen and sodium contents are 16.0 per cent and 26 per cent respectively. Impurities are low and are of the type not objectionable in agricultural and industrial

TABLE 16.1. PROPERTIES OF SYNTHETIC SODIUM NITRATE

Formula...	$NaNO_3$
Molecular weight.....................................	85.01
Appearance..	White crystals or pellet
Melting point..	308°C (586°F)
Specific gravity......................................	2.267
Bulk density:	
Coarse (1 C)..	80 lb/cu ft
Medium (2 B).......................................	82 lb/cu ft
Fine (3 A)..	85 lb/cu ft
Pellets...	75 lb/cu ft
Solubility in 100 gm water:	
0°C...	73 gms
10°C..	96 gms
30°C..	176 gms

outlets. The outstanding chemical property is oxidizing ability. Thermal stability is high; decomposition to sodium nitrite and oxygen starting only at temperatures (450°C) well above the melting point.

PROCESSES AND CHEMISTRY

Five processes are in use or have been utilized in the world for making synthetic sodium nitrate. In order of importance these are as follows:

(1) Reaction of nitrogen oxides from ammonia oxidation with a sodium alkali, usually sodium carbonate.[23, 29]

(2) Reaction of sodium chloride with nitric acid giving chlorine, nitrosyl chloride, and nitrogen tetroxide as coproducts, the salt process.

(3) Neutralization of nitric acid with a sodium alkali, either sodium carbonate or sodium hydroxide.

(4) From sodium chloride in sea water by ion exchange, the so-called zeolite process.

(5) From ammonium nitrate by reaction with caustic soda, whereby sodium nitrate is formed and ammonia volatilized for recovery.

In all of these processes an aqueous solution of sodium nitrate is obtained from which the product is recovered finally by evaporation and crystallization. In some plants, the sodium nitrate crystals are melted and pelletized. The principal quality controls are on moisture, particle-size distribution, nitrite content, total impurity content, and a guaranteed 16 per cent N content.

TABLE 16.2. ANALYSES OF SYNTHETIC SODIUM NITRATE

	Typical Analysis	
	Crystal Product, (parts by wt.)	Pelleted Product, (parts by wt.)
Total nitrogen.................	16.3	16.39
Moisture......................	0.35	0.04
Sodium nitrate, dry basis.......	99.5	99.5
Insolubles.....................	0.005	0.014
Sodium chloride...............	0.20	0.15
Sodium nitrite................	0.007	0.016
Total alkalinity as Na_2O.......	0.006	0.043
NH_3, free and combined........	0.0048	0.0017
Sulfates as Na_2SO_4.............	0.11	0.28

TYPICAL SCREEN ANALYSIS (U. S. STANDARD SCREENS)

Grades	Crystal Product			Pelleted Product
	1 C (Coarse)	2 B (Medium)	3 A (Fine)	
On 10 mesh....................	10.6	5.8	Trace	32.4
On 14 mesh....................	36.0	14.5	Trace	63.4
On 20 mesh....................	77.9	47.2	Trace	87.6
On 28 mesh....................	96.5	65.1	22.0	94.8
On 35 mesh....................	99.7	86.0	73.4	97.5
On 48 mesh....................	99.7	97.4	93.7	98.4
On 100 mesh...................	100	100	99.7	99.4
Through 100 mesh.............	Trace	Trace	0.3	0.6

Nitrogen Oxides Process[1, 3, 7, 10, 12, 14, 18, 19, 27, 31]

One of the principal processes is the reaction of nitrogen oxides from oxidizing ammonia with air with circulating soda ash solution in large packed reaction towers.

$$4NH_3 + 5O_2 \rightarrow 4NO + 6H_2O \tag{16.1}$$

This reaction is highly exothermic and conversion is complete with respect to the ammonia. The gases leaving the ammonia oxidizer at a high temperature have relatively small concentrations of oxides of nitrogen other than NO. On lowering the temperature, oxidation of the NO takes place by reaction with the excess oxygen present. Molecular species besides NO are NO_2, N_2O_4, possibly N_2O_3, and some nitric acid, since water is a major component in the gases. The net result of these various reactions when an alkali is present is to produce a solution containing sodium nitrate and sodium nitrite. The nitrite is converted by reaction with nitric acid or nitrogen dioxide to sodium nitrate with liberation of nitric oixde which is cycled back through the process. In over-all, an equation can be written thus

$$12NH_3 + 21O_2 + 4Na_2CO_3 \rightarrow$$
$$8NaNO_3 + 4NO + 4CO_2 + 18H_2O$$
(16.2)

In the ultimate process, the tail gases from the last absorption towers of the sodium nitrate plant contain a relatively low concentration of nitrogen oxides, mostly in the NO form, together with larger quantities of CO_2, water vapor, N_2, and residual O_2. Figure 16.1 shows a flow diagram of this process and of the salt process.

Sodium nitrate was the sole product from oxidized ammonia at the start of the first American plant in the late 1920's. As the markets for ammonium nitrate grew while those for sodium nitrate declined, a larger and larger proportion of the oxidized ammonia was converted to nitric acid and in turn to ammonium nitrate. Thus, more and more sodium nitrate came from what essentially is a clean-up operation for nitrogen oxides, since these in dilute concentration are much more readily absorbed by an alkali like soda ash than by water. This minor role of sodium nitrate prevails today in most of the synthetic sodium nitrate plants in the world.

Salt Process[4, 9, 11, 13, 17, 21, 26, 28, 30]

A distinctly novel process for sodium nitrate involving the so-called aqua regia reaction was developed and put into operation at Hopewell, Virginia in 1936. The basis for such a process dates back into the middle 1800's, and the literature records several unsuccessful attempts to commercialize the reaction. The plant at Hopewell is not now operating. It is believed to be the only plant of this kind in the world for sodium nitrate. Figure 16.2.

This process utilizes sodium chloride (salt) and nitric acid to produce sodium nitrate and chlorine as coproducts; obviously a way to obtain chlorine without the more common product, caustic soda (NaOH).

$$3NaCl + 4HNO_3 \rightarrow 3NaNO_3 + Cl_2 + NOCl + 2H_2O \quad (16.3)$$

The process is operated to convert substantially all of the sodium chloride, and it will be noted that not all of the chloride is obtained as elemental chlorine. The other major product is nitrosyl chloride which can be re-

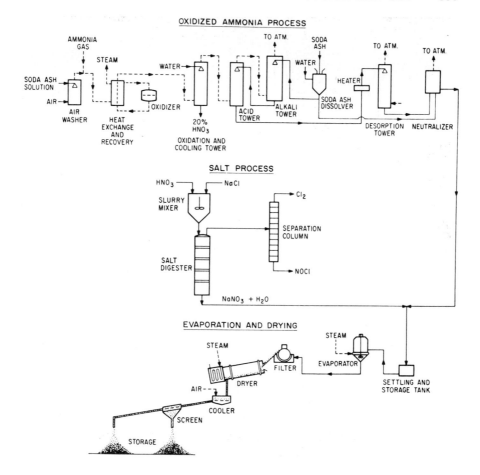

Figure 16.1. Synthetic sodium nitrate processes.

covered as such or converted by either of the two following methods to useful materials.

(1) NOCl is reacted with an alkali such as soda ash.

$$3NOCl + 2Na_2CO_3 \rightarrow NaNO_3 + 3NaCl + 2CO_2 + 2NO \quad (16.4)$$

The mixture of sodium chloride and sodium nitrate is recovered and returned to the digester of the main process, while the NO is returned to nitric acid or sodium nitrate production. This reaction was utilized in the early days of the U. S. commercial operation but has been superseded by the second method.

(2) NOCl undergoes oxidation with oxygen.

Figure 16.2. Synthetic sodium nitrate at Hopewell, Virginia. (*Courtesy Allied Chemical Corp.*)

$$2NOCl + O_2 \rightarrow N_2O_4 + Cl_2 \qquad (16.5)$$

The chlorine is recovered as product and the nitrogen tetroxide is obtained as product if desired or returned to nitric acid production. The over-all reaction may be written thus:

$$6NaCl + 8HNO_3 + O_2 \rightarrow$$
$$6NaNO_3 + 3Cl_2 + N_2O_4 + 4H_2O \qquad (16.6)$$

The key to successful operation lay in the development of materials and methods for handling exceedingly corrosive reactants and products in properly sized vessels which are both fluid tight and corrosion resistant. This process represents an outstanding achievement in chemical engineering. The first detailed description of the process has been published recently.[13]

While used on sodium chloride at present, the process is applicable to other chlorides such as potassium or calcium chlorides. In fact, a rather similar process with potassium nitrate as product has been brought into operation recently by Southwest Potash Corporation at Vicksburg, Mississippi.

Nitric Acid Process

The simplest and most direct process for synthetic sodium nitrate is the neutralization of dilute nitric acid with soda ash or caustic soda solutions:

$$2HNO_3 + Na_2CO_3 \rightarrow 2NaNO_3 + H_2O + CO_2 \qquad (16.7)$$

$$HNO_3 + NaOH \rightarrow NaNO_3 + H_2O \qquad (16.8)$$

Such a process is used in special situations only and a relatively small percentage of the total synthetic $NaNO_3$ has ever been produced in this way.

Zeolite Process[2]

The ability of certain complex silicates known as zeolites to exchange calcium ions for sodium ions has been known for many years and is utilized in water softening for industrial and home use. Adaptation of this reaction to convert calcium nitrate made from nitric acid and limestone to sodium nitrate was made by Norsk-Hydro in Norway. The reactions involved are

$$2HNO_3 + CaCO_3 \rightarrow Ca(NO_3)_2 + H_2O + CO_2 \qquad (16.9)$$

$$Ca(NO_3)_2 + \text{sodium zeolite} \rightarrow NaNO_3 + \text{calcium zeolite} \quad (16.10)$$

Calcium zeolite + NaCl (sea water) $\rightarrow$

$$\text{Na zeolite} + CaCl_2 \qquad (16.11)$$

As much as 20,000 tons/yr were reported to be made by this process at one time. The possibility for utilizing a similar process in the United States has been investigated but as far as can be determined no plant was ever installed. Obviously, such a process to be successful would have to be competitive with the synthetic methods utilizing soda ash made likewise from sodium chloride.

By-Product Sodium Nitrate

Minor quantities of sodium nitrate are recovered by reacting ammonium nitrate solution with caustic soda to evolve ammonia and form sodium nitrate. The sodium nitrate is recovered as a crystallized product and is sold into agricultural outlets.

Minor attention has been given to double decomposition reactions,[16] say between NH_4NO_3 and NaCl, as a means for securing $NaNO_3$, but no plant has ever been built.

PRODUCTION AND MARKETING

Plants

Large tonnage production of synthetic sodium nitrate in the United States began at Hopewell, Virginia late in 1928. This plant was based on oxidized ammonia using a process developed by Allied Chemical Corporation and included many innovations in processing and in large scale equipment. The product was known as the American Nitrate of Soda and is still being made although in much reduced quantity compared to the peak years. In the early 1930's production of some synthetic sodium nitrate was begun at Hopewell, Virginia by a second process, the so-called salt process, which involved reaction of sodium chloride with nitric acid with chlorine as a coproduct. Figure 16.3. Material from this process was finished to crystal products in the same manner as those coming from oxidized ammonia.

In the early 1950's another plant for synthetic sodium nitrate based on oxidized ammonia was installed at Lake Charles, Louisiana by the Olin-Mathieson Corporation. The product of this plant is finished as a pelletized material. Small tonnages of synthetic sodium nitrate are made from ammonium nitrate and caustic soda at one of the Government Ordnance Plants.

Historically, a small plant made sodium nitrate at Niagara Falls, New

Figure 16.3. Nitrogen products plant including synthetic sodium nitrate. (*Allied Chemical Corp., Hopewell, Va.*)

York for a short time in connection with an arc process installation for nitrogen fixation.

In Europe, the principal plants producing synthetic sodium nitrate during the 1930's were located in Germany, France, Belgium, Great Britain, Poland, and Italy. In Scandanavia, Norway produced $NaNO_3$ in connection with its nitrogen fixation operations. The material was also produced at one time from the sodium chloride in sea water by an ion exchange process involving calcium nitrate. This process was investigated elsewhere but no plants were ever built. As of 1962, plants for synthetic sodium nitrate are believed to be in existence in West Germany, France, and Italy and behind the Iron Curtain in Bulgaria and Poland. The best information available indicates that production has been quite small in recent years.

Production and Capacity

U.S. production of synthetic sodium nitrate was relatively small in 1929 but increased to a peak of about 500,000 tons/yr in the middle 1930's and continued at this rate well into the 1940's. European production was greater than 300,000 tons/yr in 1932, went through a low point of around 200,000 tons/yr in 1936, and came back to around 330,000 tons/yr in 1939. Indicated world capacity for the synthetic product in the years just prior to World War II was thus around 800,000 tons/yr, equivalent to about 128,000 tons of nitrogen.

Production continued to be relatively high through the early 1950's but declined steadily since that time as other nitrogen products became available in increasing tonnages throughout the world. By 1962 world production is estimated to have been no more than 20 per cent of that in the peak year.

Consumption[22]

Synthetic sodium nitrate has been and still is consumed in two major outlets, namely agriculture and industry. Peak world consumption of this material was around 800,000 tons/yr but has declined in recent years to 200,000 tons/yr or less. Producing countries at one time exported relatively large tonnages, amounting to as much as 25 per cent of the total annual production for the peak years, which went to nitrogen-short countries such as Egypt. At one time as much as one third of the domestic production was exported, but only small amounts now find a market outside the United States.

Domestic consumption until the late 1950's was chiefly in the agricultural field, but the proportion has been steadily declining and is now roughly equal in industry and in agriculture. At the peak in the late

1930's, upwards of 400,000 tons of synthetic $NaNO_3$ was consumed in the domestic market, although today's consumption is under 150,000 tons. From about 12% of the total nitrogen consumed in the United States in 1946, consumption has declined to well under one-half per cent of the total in 1962. No factors are evident to indicate any major recovery to the prominent position once held by sodium nitrate in the world nitrogen picture.

Shipment, Handling, and Storage

Synthetic sodium nitrate is shipped in bulk in box cars or hopper cars, and in trucks. The bagged product is packaged in 100-lb multi-wall asphalt-lined, moisture-resistant paper bags. For export trade, it was formerly packaged in 200-lb burlap bags. Yellow label is required under ICC regulations for both bag and bulk shipments.

In general this nitrate can be handled without special precautions. It is moderately hygroscopic and should be stored in a dry place to prevent excessive caking. Payloaders for handling bulk product and forklift trucks for bagged material are safe. This product should be stored away from organic and other flammable materials. Wood and empty bags saturated with sodium nitrate are fire hazards and should be treated accordingly.

Uses

Sodium nitrate was a well-established material both in agriculture and industry before the advent of the synthetic product. The use pattern has changed materially over the years, influenced largely by the increasing availability of other nitrogen products.

In agriculture, sodium nitrate furnishes the essential plant-food element nitrogen—all in nitrate form. Synthetic $NaNO_3$ has been used largely as a top and side dressing material in the southeastern United States and Egypt. It is considered a very good nitrogen source for cotton, tobacco, and vegetable crops. Certain crops such as cotton and beets require sodium for best results, and for these crops $NaNO_3$ is still an important fertilizer. In the early 1930's as much as 40,000 tons/yr were used in making mixed fertilizers but today practically no $NaNO_3$ is used in mixed goods. For a few years in the early 1930's an ammoniating solution containing sodium nitrate, ammonia, and water was marketed for fertilizer manufacture but was replaced by the type containing ammonium nitrate.

In industry, synthetic $NaNO_3$ has been and is utilized in a half dozen important outlets. Historically it was the raw material for nitric acid and explosives production before synthetic ammonia became plentiful for oxidation, and into the 1940's synthetic $NaNO_3$ was employed extensively in these outlets. Today, minor tonnages go into the manufacture of black powder and permissibles. Some potassium nitrate and other nitrates are made from sodium nitrate.

Sodium nitrate is used as a fluxing and oxidizing ingredient in the manufacture of glass, enamels and porcelain and to a limited extent in the manufacture of certain dyes. It is employed in the nutrient medium in which certain antibiotics and vitamins are produced. In curing corned beef, hams, and bacon sodium nitrate is utilized as a preservative and for fixing a desirable bright pink color.

Heat treatment baths for metals and alloys utilize NaNO$_3$ alone or in admixture with other salts. Such baths add a black or blue color to finished

TABLE 16.3. AVERAGE WHOLESALE PRICES OF VARIOUS NITROGEN CARRIERS

Calendar Year	Ammonium sulfate, $	Anhydrous ammonia, $	Calcium cyanamide, $	Sodium nitrate, $	Ammoniating Solutions, $	Urea	Natural organics, $
1900	2.79	—	—	2.37	—	—	2.57
1905	3.01	—	—	2.97	—	—	2.88
1910	2.64	—	3.43	2.76	—	—	3.63
1915	3.09	—	2.54	3.04	—	—	3.54
1920	4.08	—	3.40	4.44	—	—	8.71
1925	2.65	—	2.20	3.28	—	—	4.88
1926	2.52	1.75	2.19	3.27	—	—	4.62
1928	2.27	1.54	2.01	2.88	—	—	6.13
1930	1.79	1.40	1.65	2.49	—	—	4.50
1932	1.02	1.34	1.00	1.86	—	—	1.83
1935	1.13	1.09	1.20	1.47	1.07	—	3.38
1937	1.32	1.09	1.26	1.64	1.17	1.52	4.49
1940	1.37	1.09	1.20	1.68	1.22	1.32	3.55
1945	1.42	.72	1.44	1.75	1.07	1.37	4.85
1947	1.60	.72	1.98	2.50	1.03	1.39	9.71
1949	2.29	.94	2.82	3.15	1.23	—	8.45
1950	1.95	.91	2.26	3.00	1.20	2.02	8.66
1952	2.09	.97	3.11	3.34	1.20	3.03	9.23
1957	1.75	.99	2.62	2.75	1.21	2.43	8.15
1959	1.67	1.06	2.71	2.66	1.21	2.30	8.15
1960	1.67	1.07	2.71	2.75	1.27	2.28	6.80
1961	1.67	1.10	2.71	2.75	1.31	1.89	7.22

Basis: Prices for 20 lb N (one unit) at producing points or ports in bulk car lots.

Computed largely from published quotations in the *Oil, Paint and Drug Reporter*. The earlier quotations for cyanamid, ammonia, solutions, and urea were supplied by the producers. These prices are for spot purchases. Contract prices are usually lower than those given here.

Mehring, A. L., and Bennett, G. A., *Ag. Chem.*, 6 (2) 47 (1951).
Mehring, A. L., Adams, J. Richard, and Jacob, K. D., Statistical Bulletin 191, Agricultural Research Service, U.S. Department Agr. 1957.
Adams, J. Richard, Unpublished figures for 1957-1961.

steel products, and in heat treating aluminum alloys an increase in tensile strength is obtained.

In the petroleum industry, molten sodium nitrate is employed as a heat exchange medium in catalytic refining processes. Sodium nitrate aids in the decomposition of organic wastes and helps prevent pollution from industrial wastes.

This salt serves also as a fluxing agent in ore separation processes and is used as an agent in the alkaline nitrate process for recovery of tin from scrap.

Competitive Market Situation[6]

The competitive situation faced by synthetic sodium nitrate in the United States can best be understood by tracing its price relationship to the other principal nitrogen carriers. Generally speaking, synthetic $NaNO_3$ and imported material have been priced on an equal basis with the exception of a few years in the 1950's. A price relation study covering 1880 through 1952 has been published,[20] and significant data are given in Table 16.3 together with unpublished data for 1957–1961.

REFERENCES

1. Agel, F. O., U. S. Patent 2,148,793 (1939).
2. Bardwell, D. C., U. S. Patent 2,344,929 (1944).
3. Beekhuis, H. A., Sodium Nitrate, U. S. Patent 1,994,239 (1935); U. S. Patent 2,019,112 (1935); U. S. Patent 2,124,536 (1938); U. S. Patent 2,138,016 (1938); U. S. Patent 2,347,073 (1944). Beekhuis, H. A. and Gaskins, E., U. S. Patent 2,287,856 (1942).
4. Beekhuis, H. A., Salt Process, U. S. Patent 2,148,429 (1939); U. S. Patent 2,181,559 (1939); U. S. Patent 2,201,423 (1940); U. S. Patent 2,208,112 (1940); U. S. Patent 2,215,450 (1940); U. S. Patent 2,215,451 (1940); U. S. Patent 2,268,999 (1942); U. S. Patent 2,269,000 (1942); U. S. Patent 2,296,762 (1942); U. S. Patent 2,296,763 (1942).
5. Brink, J. A., Jr., "Sodium Compounds," in "Encyclopedia of Chemical Technology," Vol. 12, New York, Interscience Publishers, 1955.
6. Chemical Economics Handbook Sheet 706–5060, Stanford Research Institute, July 1961.
7. Crittenden, E. D., "Nitric Acid In The Fertilizer Industry," Paper given at Soil Science Society Annual Meeting at Pennsylvania State College, 1951.
8. Curtis, H. A., Ed. "Fixed Nitrogen," Am. Chem. Soc. Monog. 59, New York, Chemical Catalog Company, 1932.
9. DeJahn, F. W., *Chem. Met. Eng.* **42**, 537 (1935).
10. Denny, A. S., U. S. Patent 2,106,168 (1938).
11. Dominik, V., *Chem. Ind.*, **18**, 24 (1927).
12. Fogler, M. F., U. S. Patent 1,949,462 (1934).
13. Fogler, M. F., in "Chlorine Its Manufacture Properties and Uses," Ed. J. S. Sconce, Chap. 8, New York, Reinhold, 1962.

14. Fogler, M. F., and Rogers, D. A., U. S. Patent 2,072,947 (1937).
15. German Patent 220,539 (1909).
16. German Patent 476,254 (1924).
17. German Patents 630,652 (1936) and 636,981 (1936).
18. Keane, A. F., U. S. Patent 2,212,835 (1940).
19. McCann, W. R., U. S. Patent 2,024,830 (1935).
20. Mehring, A. L., and Bennett, G. A., *Ag. Chem.*, **6** (2) 47 (1951).
21. Mellor, J. M., Modern Inorganic Chemistry, 8th ed., 2nd imp., p. 623, 1934.
22. Merz, A. R., and Fletcher, C. C., U. S. Department Agr. Circ. 346 (revised) 1940 Production and Agricultural Use of Sodium Nitrate.
23. Miles, F. D., "Nitric Acid—Manufacture and Uses," Chap. 6, Auspices of Imperial Chemicals Inds., Ltd., London, Oxford University Press, 1961.
24. Norwegian Patent 20,907 (1910).
25. *Oil, Paint, and Drug Reporter*, Oct. 1, 1962.
26. Pauling, H., U. S. Patent 2,147,988 (1939).
27. Rowland, W., U. S. Patent 2,043,710 (1936).
28. Shreve, R. M., "Chemical Process Industries," McGraw-Hill, New York, 1945.
29. Stengel, L. A., U. S. Patent 2,535,990 (1951).
30. Vasilev, B. B., and Ravdin, Y. A., *J. Chem. Ind.* (*USSR*) **14** 1136 (1937).
31. Weston, C. F., U. S. Patents 2,041,504 (1936); 2,106,196, and 2,139,142 (1938).

17

Nitrogen Solutions for Direct Application

J. Richard Adams

U. S. Fertilizer Laboratory, Soil and Water Conservation Research Division, Agricultural Research Service, U. S. Department of Agriculture

The quantity of fertilizer nitrogen consumed in the form of nitrogen solutions in the United States is second only to that supplied by anhydrous ammonia. Nitrogen solutions are employed in the manufacture of mixed fertilizers and as separate materials to be applied directly to the soil. Wide-spread use of nitrogen solutions for direct application has developed in recent years, although the possibility was recognized more than a century ago.

The discussion here will be confined to direct-application solutions containing only one plant nutrient, nitrogen. These solutions are generally classified in two categories as nonpressure and pressure solutions. The nonpressure solutions are aqueous solutions of nitrogen compounds such as ammonium nitrate, urea, etc. The pressure solutions are aqua ammonia (ammonia liquor) and a few of the ammoniating solutions that contain neutralizing ammonia in addition to other nitrogen materials. Materials most commonly utilized with aqua ammonia are ammonium bisulfite, ammonium nitrate, calcium nitrate, and urea.

This chapter considers early developments, domestic consumption, characteristics of liquid nitrogen fertilizers for direct application, production and handling of these solutions, and their potential use.

EARLY DEVELOPMENTS

According to Boussingault,[22] the feasibility of applying aqueous solutions of nitrogen fertilizers was demonstrated by Davy when he showed that water solutions of ammonium carbonate increased the growth of

344

wheat. The solubility of nitrogen fertilizers and the fact that nitrogen was found to be equally effective in either solution or solid form favored the development of solution application. Commercial domestic utilization of nonpressure nitrogen solutions was first reported in California in 1944 when 422 tons of ammonium nitrate solution were used.[4] This service had increased to 34,904 tons by 1960.[14]

Interest in the utilization of ammoniacal liquor as a source of fertilizer nitrogen has appeared periodically in Europe for more than a century. In 1843 Bishop[21] in Scotland found that ammoniacal water produced a 25 per cent greater grass yield than either potassium nitrate or rape-dust, although initially the ammonia caused some scorching of the grass.

This work was followed by limited employment of ammonia liquor on grassland[40] and in 1852 Johnston[37] wrote "To grassland this ammoniacal liquor may be applied with great advantage, by means of a water-cart—being previously diluted with from three to five times its bulk of water. If too strong it will burn up the grass at first, especially if the weather be dry; but, on the return of rain, the herbage will again spring up with increased luxuriance. On arable land it may be applied with profit to the young wheat or other corn by the water-cart...." The use of ammoniacal liquor continued to develop in England[40, 43] and the British Government recognized it as a nitrogenous fertilizer in 1952 and granted a subsidy for its utilization.

Considerable interest was aroused by the fertilizer use of aqua ammonia subsequent to World War I, and among the countries in which its value has been demonstrated are Czechoslovakia,[39] Germany,[19, 25, 46] Italy,[30] Japan,[36] Poland,[26] and the USSR.[38] Early work in the United States by Tiedjens and Robbins[49] showed aqua ammonia to be a better source of nitrogen than either ammonium sulfate or calcium nitrate for tomatoes and soybeans. MacIntire and coworkers[41] later found that aqua ammonia up to rates of 50 lb of nitrogen per acre was as effective as equivalent quantities of ammonium nitrate and ammonium sulfate in promoting the growth of sudan grass.

Solutions of ammonium nitrate and/or urea in aqua ammonia, usually called ammoniating solutions, are being applied now in irrigation water or injected beneath the surface of the soil. Shipments of this type of solution are known to have been made to Arizona and California in about 1947 for use as direct application material.

DOMESTIC CONSUMPTION

Little information is available on the consumption of solutions of fertilizer nitrogen previous to the year which ended on June 30, 1947. Annual

TABLE 17.1. CONSUMPTION OF DIRECT-APPLICATION NITROGEN IN THE UNITED
STATES AND TERRITORIES AND THE PORTION APPLIED IN SOLUTION FORM

Year Ending June 30	Total Nitrogen[a] (tons N)	Nitrogen in Solution Form			
		Aqua Ammonia[b] (tons N)	Other Solutions[b] (tons N)	Total (tons N)	Portion of Total Nitrogen (per cent)
1947	315,685	78	2815	2893	0.9
1948	363,438	1067	4716	5783	1.6
1949	407,472	1175	3072	4247	1.0
1950	510,164	2192	5305	7497	1.5
1951	653,018	3804	6705	10,509	1.6
1952	773,937	4235	10,044	14,279	1.8
1953	908,961	6365	14,955	21,320	2.3
1954	1,069,317	22,588	28,816	51,404	4.8
1955	1,156,995	46,612	38,367	84,979	7.3
1956	1,136,669	62,510	34,493	97,003	8.5
1957	1,291,661	76,844	75,241	152,085	11.8
1958	1,429,155	73,342	99,897	173,239	12.1
1959	1,671,695	96,940	159,024	255,964	15.3
1960	1,720,632	85,380	194,740	280,120	16.3
1961[c]	1,955,421	84,364	281,452	365,816	18.7

[a] 1947–54, Mehring, Adams and Jacob[44]; 1955–61, based on U. S. Fertilizer Laboratory surveys.

[b] 1947–53, based on U. S. Fertilizer Laboratory surveys; 1954–60, Adams[17]—adjusted to include consumption in Hawaii and Puerto Rico; 1961, Scholl, Schmidt, and Wilker.[47]

[c] Preliminary.

consumption data for that year and each year up to June 30, 1961 are given in Table 17.1. The practice of applying liquid nitrogen fertilizers developed in the western states, and the only report of their application east of the Mississippi River in 1946–7 was from Mississippi. This situation remained static, except for the use of token quantities, until 1950–51 when 354 tons of liquid nitrogen found application in Florida. The practice spread rapidly and the utilization of liquid nitrogen fertilizers had been reported for every State except Rhode Island by 1956–57. Small quantities were employed in Rhode Island in 1960–61.

Nitrogen solutions, other than aqua ammonia, were the major source of liquid nitrogen fertilizer until 1954–55 when they were superseded by aqua ammonia. Large shipments of aqua ammonia to Hawaii had been initiated the previous year and by 1955–56 this material supplied more than half the liquid nitrogen utilized for direct application in the United States and Territories. However, other nitrogen solutions rapidly regained favor, and by 1960–61 they supplied more than three-quarters of the direct-application liquid nitrogen.

CHARACTERISTICS OF NITROGEN SOLUTIONS

A nitrogen-solution survey and an addendum[16] showed that 99 nitrogen solutions, other than aqua ammonia, were available to the fertilizer trade as of July 1960. These were produced by 24 domestic and three Canadian companies. Many solutions are produced by several companies, and each company will generally produce various solutions. Twenty-one of the listed solutions are nonpressure ones produced for direct application. Several of the pressure solutions have found use as direct-application materials. Additional companies have started to manufacture direct-application nitrogen solutions since this survey, and new solutions have appeared on the market.

Nomenclature

A system for characterizing the nitrogen solutions[11, 42] has been rather generally accepted by the fertilizer industry. In this system the per cent of total nitrogen is given with the decimal point omitted, followed, in parentheses, by the percentage composition of ammonia, ammonium nitrate, urea, and a fourth figure representing any other significant source of nitrogen, if present—all rounded to the nearest whole number and in the order given. The company name, a trade mark, or trade name will often precede the total nitrogen per cent. For example, a solution labeled 206 (25-0-0) would be an ammonia solution containing 20.6 per cent total nitrogen and 25 per cent ammonia. A 414 (19-66-6) solution would contain 41.4 per cent total nitrogen and 19, 66, and 6 per cent, respectively of ammonia, ammonium nitrate, and urea.

Composition

The composition, salting-out temperature, specific gravity, the weight of a gallon of solution, and the weight of nitrogen contained therein are given in Table 17.2 for the nonpressure solutions. The temperature at which crystals begin to appear in the solution is the salting-out temperature and is one of the critical properties. When the ambient temperature falls below the salting-out temperature, crystals begin to form in the solution, causing equipment failure and uneven distribution.

Table 17.3 gives the properties of the pressure solutions that are used most often as direct-application materials and the proportion of the various forms of nitrogen that occur in these solutions. The positive vapor pressures are due to the neutralizing ammonia and are equally as important as the salting-out temperature in the utilization of these solutions for direct application.

TABLE 17.2. COMPOSITION AND PROPERTIES OF NONPRESSURE NITROGEN SOLUTIONS[a]

Solution Nomenclature	Forms of Nitrogen			Salting-out Temperature (°F)	Specific Gravity at 60°F	Weight of solution per gal at 60°F (lb)	Weight of Nitrogen per gal of Solution at 60°F (lb)
	Combined ammonia (% N)	Nitrate (% N)	Urea (% N)				
160 (0-46-0)	8.0	8.0	—	11	1.207	10.07	1.61
170 (0-31-0-36)[b]	5.4	11.6	—	32	1.499[c]	12.50[d]	2.13[d]
170 (0-49-0)	8.5	8.5	—	16	1.222	10.19	1.73
175 (0-50-0)	8.8	8.8	—	22	1.231	10.27	1.81
180 (0-51-0)	9.0	9.0	—	23	1.235	10.30	1.85
190 (0-54-0)	9.5	9.5	—	33	1.253	10.45	1.99
200 (0-57-0)	10.0	10.0	—	41	1.264	10.54	2.11
200 (0-0-44)[e]	—	—	20.3	41	1.124	9.36	1.87
210 (0-60-0)	10.5	10.5	—	49	1.286	10.73	2.25
228 (0-65-0)	11.4	11.4	—	65	1.307	10.90	2.49
230 (0-0-50)[e]	—	—	28.0	63	1.152	9.60	2.21
245 (0-70-0)	12.3	12.3	—	86	1.346[f]	11.23[f]	2.76[f]
280 (0-39-31)	6.9	6.9	14.3	−1	1.279	10.67	3.00
280 (0-40-30)	7.0	7.0	14.0	−1	1.283	10.70	3.00
280 (0-80-0)	14.0	14.0	—	136	1.360[g]	11.34[h]	3.18[h]
290 (0-83-0)	14.5	14.5	—	154	1.380[g]	11.51[h]	3.34[h]
300 (0-42-33)	7.4	7.4	15.3	15	1.301	10.85	3.27
315 (0-0-68)[i]	—	—	31.5	135	1.170[j]	9.76[j]	3.07[j]
320 (0-44-35)	7.8	7.8	16.5	32	1.327	11.07	3.55
320 (0-45-35)	7.9	7.9	16.3	32	1.325	11.05	3.55
338 (0-0-72)[i]	—	—	33.8	155	1.18[k]	9.84[k]	3.33[k]
376 (0-0-80)[i]	—	—	37.6	190	1.19[l]	9.92[l]	3.73[l]

[a] Each product represents one or more similar commercial products; slight variations occur in the published data for similar solutions.
[b] Contains 36.2 per cent calcium nitrate.
[c] At 68°F/60°F.
[d] At 68°F.
[e] Represents two solutions; one standard and the other with a low biuret content.
[f] At 70°F.
[g] At 68°F/60°F.
[h] At 158°F.
[i] Contains 3.0 per cent biuret.
[j] At 140°F.
[k] At 160°F.
[l] At 194°F.

Chemical Properties

Nitrogen solutions are corrosive. Aqua ammonia reacts with copper, brass, zinc (galvanized equipment), and many alloys,[2] and should never be handled in equipment made with these metals. It can be safely stored in steel or iron equipment. Essentially copper-free aluminum alloys or certain stainless steels are recommended[7] for the storage of the other direct-application nitrogen solutions. Ordinary steel can also be used but cor-

TABLE 17.3. COMPOSITION AND PROPERTIES OF PRESSURE NITROGEN SOLUTIONS USED AS DIRECT APPLICATION MATERIALS[a]

Solution Nomenclature	Forms of Nitrogen				Vapor Pressure (gage) at			Salting-out Temperature (°F)	Specific Gravity	Weight of Solution per gal at 60°F (lb)	Weight of Nitrogen per gal of Solution at 60°F (lb)
	Ammonia		Nitrate (% N)	Urea (% N)	90°F (psi)	104°F (psi)	120°F (psi)				
	Neutralizing (% N)	Combined (% N)									
201 (24-0-0)	20.1	—	—	—	0	0	7	−62	0.913	7.61	1.53
247 (30-0-0)	24.7	—	—	—	4	11	20	−112	0.896	7.47	1.85
370 (17-67-0)	13.7	11.7	11.7	—	−3	1	7	50	1.184	9.87	3.65
410 (19-58-11)	15.6	10.2	10.2	5.1	4	10	18	7	1.162	9.69	3.97
410 (22-65-0)	18.3	11.4	11.4	—	5	10	19	21	1.138	9.49	3.89
410 (26-56-0)	21.6	9.7	9.7	—	—	16	—	−23	1.077	8.98	3.68
411 (50-0-0)	41.1	—	—	—	55	74	103	Below −100	0.832	6.93	2.85

[a] Each product represents one or more similar commercial products; slight variations occur in the published data for similar solutions.

rosion occurs and will shorten the life of the equipment.[27] Small amounts of ammonium thiocyanate alone or with sodium arsenite are used as rust inhibitors in the ammoniacal solutions of solid materials.

Equipment coatings of natural or synthetic rubber, glass, plastics, and corrosion-resistant metals have been used to minimize corrosion. Rubber containers of 15,000-gal capacity or less are also available.

The fire and explosion hazards[1, 3, 5, 7, 8, 12, 28] presented by the ammonia vapor from the pressure solutions are small. Ammonia-air mixtures containing 16 to 25 per cent ammonia by volume and ammonia-oxygen mixtures containing 15 to 79 per cent ammonia will explode upon ignition; however, concentrations of this magnitude are not normally encountered.

Ammonium nitrate in the solutions presents potential hazards. It is safe so long as it stays in solution, but precautions should be taken to prevent the deposition of solid ammonium nitrate. The salt is a powerful oxidizing agent and presents serious fire hazards, especially in contact with combustible materials. Decomposition at high temperatures may proceed at an explosive rate.

Neutralization of the acid residue left in the soil from the use of liquid nitrogen fertilizers requires the addition of 180 lb of calcium carbonate per 100 lb of nitrogen applied.

Physical Properties

The gage pressures of the nitrogen solutions range from 0 for the non-pressure solutions to a maximum of 74 lb at 104°F for the pressure solutions most often used for direct application. This factor must be carefully considered in selecting a solution for direct application. The nonpressure solutions can be handled in open containers and spread on the surface of the soil. Solutions with positive vapor pressures must be handled in closed containers and to prevent nitrogen losses should be injected below the surface of the soil.

The vapor pressures of the more concentrated solutions can be lowered by dilution, thereby eliminating the need for high pressure equipment. Advantage is taken of this fact by shipping the more concentrated solutions from the producer to a bulk distribution station where they are diluted. This practice reduces the unit shipping costs of the nitrogen. Solutions 201 (24-0-0) and 247 (30-0-0) in Table 17.3 are diluted solutions of 411 (50-0-0). Table 17.4 gives an example of the effect of dilution on an ammonia-ammonium nitrate-water solution.

The addition of water also decreases the salting-out temperatures of the nitrogen solutions and the decrease is continuous with dilution. Excessively high salting-out temperatures can be reduced to temperatures compatible with the conditions under which the solution is to be applied. This is shown in Table 17.2 where dilution has changed solution 290 (0-83-0) to solution 160 (0-46-0) and has lowered the salting-out temperature from 154°F to 11°F. Intermediate values are given in Table 17.2. Another example of the effects of dilution is given in Table 17.4.

Physiological Properties

The physiological properties of nitrogen solutions are a combination of the properties of water solutions of ammonia and the solid nitrogen prod-

TABLE 17.4. EFFECTS OF DILUTION ON THE PROPERTIES OF SOLUTION 410 (22-65-0)[13]

Quantity of Water Added to 100 gals of Solution		Nitrogen Content (% N)	Vapor Pressure (gage) at 104°F	Salting-out Temperature[a] (°F)	Weight of solution per gal at 60°F (lb)	Weight of Nitrogen per gal of Solution at 60°F (lb)
(lb)	(gal)					
0	0	41.0	10	10	9.49	3.89
2	2.28	40.2	8	11	9.46	3.80
5	5.70	39.0	6	10	9.44	3.68
10	11.4	37.3	4	8	9.37	3.50
15	17.1	35.7	2	7	9.33	3.33
20	22.8	34.2	1	5	9.29	3.18
30	34.2	31.5	0	0	9.22	2.90
40	45.6	29.3	0	−5	9.16	2.68
50	57.0	27.3	0	−11	9.09	2.48

[a] Salting-out temperatures vary because of fractional differences in the constituent contents and because either the temperature of formation or dissolution of the crystal may be used.

ucts. The characteristics and precautions given for these materials should be observed in handling the solutions.

The ammonia vaporized from the ammoniacal solutions is a health hazard and in heavy concentrations is lethal to man. Physiological effects and remedial treatments are discussed in publications from the Manufacturing Chemists' Association, Inc.[1, 3] and various ammonia producers.[6, 8, 9, 10, 15]

Exposure to ammonia may produce nausea, vomiting, pain in the throat and abdomen, weak and rapid pulse, convulsions, and collapse. Fortunately, the sharp pungent odor of ammonia is a warning of its presence even in very small concentrations. The effects of various concentrations of gaseous ammonia on unprotected workers and the permissible exposure periods are given in Table 17.5.

The major exposure danger from nitrogen solutions comes from splashing them on the skin or in the eyes. The ammonia vapor is soluble and will dissolve in the perspiration of the body. The skin cannot tolerate ammonia concentrations greater than 2 per cent for more than a few seconds. Caustic burns will result and the severity of the burn will vary with the ammonia concentration and the exposure time.

Personnel subject to ammonia exposure should be impressed with the potential danger it represents. They should be provided with approved masks, eye goggles, rubber gloves, aprons, and an easily accessible supply of water.

Skin burns should be flooded with water, followed by 2 per cent acetic acid or vinegar, and then washed again with water. When eyes are affected,

TABLE 17.5. CRITICAL GASEOUS AMMONIA CONCENTRATIONS[a]

Concentration (parts per million)	Effects on Unprotected Worker	Exposure Period
50	least detectable odor	permissible for 8-hr working exposure
100	no adverse effects for average unprotected worker	
400	causes irritation of throat	ordinarily no serious results following infrequent short exposures (less than 1 hr)
700	causes irritation of eyes	
1720	causes convulsive coughing	no exposure permissible (may be fatal after short exposure—less than half an hour)
5000–10,000	causes respiratory spasm, strangulation, asphyxia	no exposure permissible, rapidly fatal

[a] Data from Manufacturing Chemists' Association, Inc.[1]

they should be washed with generous amounts of water, 5 per cent boric acid, or 1 per cent acetic acid. This should be continued for at least 15 min. When throat and internal exposure occurs, the victim should drink large quantities of water, followed by harmless weak acid solutions such as lemonade or dilute vinegar. A person subject to severe vapor exposure should be placed on his back and kept warm until a physician arrives. If the victim is unconscious, artificial respiration should be applied, and if his breathing is weak, oxygen should be administered.

The ammonium nitrate in nitrogen solutions presents an additional hazard to humans. It may cause death within 20 min to 5 hr after being swallowed.[50] Copious quantities of water should be taken to wash out ingested nitrate; starch, flour water, milk, and egg white may be swallowed to absorb the free nitrate ions.

Livestock should not have access to nitrogen solutions, as they are toxic. The solutions are palatable and any spilled solution should be cleaned up to avoid ingestion of the solution and salts left after evaporation. Poisoning of animals has been attributed to ammonia,[24] ammonium nitrate,[20] and urea.[45]

PRODUCTION FACILITIES

Figure 17.1 and Table 17.6 show the location of the 27 domestic producers of nitrogen solutions other than aqua ammonia. There is no clear-cut distinction between plants producing direct-application solutions and those producing only ammoniating solutions. However, since ammoniating solutions can be converted to direct-application solutions by dilution, plants producing either type of solution are listed. Aqua ammonia is produced by many of these companies, and any of the ammonia producers (page 355) are potential sources of this material.

The domestic producers of aqueous or ammoniacal solutions of solid nitrogen materials have productive facilities at 33 locations. These are rather evenly distributed with 16 east of the Missisippi River and 17 west of the River. The great majority lie between the Appalachian Mountains and the Great Plains. All but one of the productive facilities are located on the sites of synthetic ammonia plants.

SAFETY RECOMMENDATIONS

There are no general regulations governing the handling of nitrogen solutions. Recommended safety precautions are based on the constituents of the solutions being handled. Adams and others[18] list the State agencies having jurisdiction over the storage and handling of nitrogen solutions.

Figure 17.1. Domestic producers of nitrogen solutions other than aqua ammonia, July 1, 1962. Numbers in the illustration are keyed in Table 17.6.

Brochures containing information on handling the nitrogen solutions have been published by some of the producers.[6, 7, 8, 10, 13]

Aqua ammonia is usually shipped in tank cars complying with ICC specifications 103 or 103A and steel drums with ICC specifications 5 or 5A. The other pressure solutions are shipped in low-pressure tank cars equipped with spring-loaded or equivalent type safety relief valves. Nonpressure solutions do not require pressure equipment for shipping.

Containers for the pressure solutions should be constructed of corrosion-resistant materials and should be designed for a working pressure of not less than the vapor pressure of the contained solution at 115°F. Nonpressure solutions can be stored in open containers. When pressure is used to transfer a solution, the container should be designed for a working pressure of 30 to 35 lb/sq in., in accordance with the code for unfired pressure vessels. Closed containers should be equipped with safety valves connected directly to the vapor space of the container and vented to the open air. Excess flow and backflow check valves are recommended for loading and unloading operations. All valves and accessory equipment must be approved for the material to be handled.

Nitrogen solution equipment should never be repaired until it is thoroughly cleaned.[31] Welding or cutting may ignite flammable air-ammonia

TABLE 17.6. DOMESTIC PRODUCERS OF NITROGEN SOLUTIONS OTHER THAN
AQUA AMMONIA, JULY 1, 1962

1. Allied Chemical Corp., Hopewell, Va.	17. Hercules Powder Co., Hercules, Calif.
2. Allied Chemical Corp., La Platte, Neb.	18. Hercules Powder Co., Louisiana, Mo.
3. Allied Chemical Corp., South Point, Ohio	19. Ketona Chemical Corp., Ketona, Ala.
4. Apache Powder Co., Benson, Ariz.	20. Mississippi Chemical Corp., Yazoo City, Miss.
5. Armour Agricultural Chemical Co., Cherokee, Ala.	21. Monsanto Chemical Co., El Dorado, Ark.
6. Armour Agricultural Chemical Co., Crystal City, Mo.	22. Monsanto Chemical Co., Luling, La.
7. California Chemical Co., Richmond, Calif.	23. Northern Chemical Industries, Inc., Searsport, Me.
8. Calumet Nitrogen Products Co., Hammond, Ind.	24. Phillips Chemical Co., Etter, Texas.
9. Collier Carbon & Chemical Corp., Brea, Calif.	25. St. Paul Ammonia Products, Inc., Pine Bend, Minn.
10. Commercial Solvents Corp., Sterlington, La.	26. Shell Chemical Co., Ventura, Calif.
11. Cooperative Farm Chemicals Assn., Lawrence, Kans.	27. Solar Nitrogen Chemicals, Inc., Lima, Ohio
12. Deere & Co., Pryor, Okla.	28. Southern Nitrogen Co., Inc., Savannah, Ga.
13. E. I. du Pont de Nemours & Co., Inc., Belle, W. Va.	29. Southwestern Nitrochemical Corp., Chandler, Ariz.
14. Escambia Chemical Corp., Pensacola, Fla.	30. Spencer Chemical Co., W. Henderson, Ky.
15. Florida Nitrogen Co., Tampa, Fla.	31. Spencer Chemical Co., Pittsburg, Kans.
16. W. R. Grace & Co., Memphis, Tenn.	32. Texaco, Inc., Lockport, Ill.
	33. U. S. Industrial Chemicals Co., Tuscola, Ill

mixtures and decompose any residual ammonium nitrate. The decomposition reaction is exothermic and potentially explosive.

Areas contaminated with ammonium nitrate solutions should be thoroughly cleaned to avoid accumulation of the ammonium nitrate left after evaporation of the solution. Davis[29] has pointed out that ammonium nitrate offers a fire hazard. Violent combustion occurs where organic or other easily oxidizable substances impregnated or in contact with ammonium nitrate are ignited. The oxygen released by decomposition of the nitrate will add to the intensity of the fire and will support combustion. Authoritative information on the hazardous properties of nitrogen compounds may be found in "Dangerous Properties of Industrial Materials" by N. I. Sax, Second Edition, 1963 (Reinhold).

MARKETING AND DISTRIBUTION

The primary producers of nitrogen solutions may sell to fertilizer manufacturers, bulk distributors, or to the ultimate consumer. Purchasers are generally equipped with storage facilities capable of handling at least a tank car of solution. Thus a farmer or group of farmers can purchase nitrogen solutions directly from the producer. In some cases, tank cars have been spotted on railroad sidings to serve as storage tanks.

Aqua ammonia is shipped in tank cars with capacities of 6000 to 30,000 gal, in truck tanks with 1000 to 3000-gal capacities, and in water-borne barges with capacities ranging from 5000 to 42,000 gal. Bulk distributors

TABLE 17.7. ANHYDROUS AMMONIA PLANTS, JANUARY 1, 1962

Name of Company	Plant Location	NH₃ Capacity (thousand tons/yr)[a]
1. Allied Chemical Corporation*	Hopewell, Virginia	400
2. Allied Chemical Corporation	LaPlatte, Nebraska	76
3. Allied Chemical Corporation*	South Point, Ohio	320
4. American Cyanamid Company	Fortier, Louisiana	53
5. Apache Powder Company	Benson, Arizona	11
6. Armour Agricultural Chemical Company	Crystal City, Missouri	86
7. Armour Agricultural Chemical Compnay	Cherokee, Alabama	126
8. Atlantic Refining Company	Philadelphia, Pennsylvania	60
9. California Ammonia Company	Lathrop, California	45
10. California Chemical Company	Richmond, California	115
11. California Chemical Company	Fort Madison, Iowa	105
12. Calumet Nitrogen Products Company	Hammond, Indiana	108
13. Coastal Chemical Corporation	Pascagoula, Mississippi	70
14. Collier Carbon and Chemical Corporation	Brea, California	115
15. Commercial Solvents Corporation*	Sterlington, Louisiana	144
16. Consumers Cooperative Association	Hastings, Nebraska	70
17. Cooperative Farm Chemicals Association	Lawrence, Kansas	147
18. John Deere Chemical Company	Pryor, Oklahoma	72
19. Diamond Alkali Company	Deer Park, Texas	40
20. Dow Chemical Company	Freeport, Texas	115
21. Dow Chemical Company*	Midland, Michigan	36
22. Dow Chemical Company*	Pittsburg, California	11
23. E. I. du Pont de Nemours and Company*	Belle, West Virginia	250
24. E. I. du Pont de Nemours and Company	Gibbstown, New Jersey	75
25. E. I. du Pont de Nemours and Company*	Niagara Falls, New York	11
26. Escambia Chemical Corporation	Pensacola, Florida	81
27. FMC Corporation	Charleston, West Virginia	24
28. Grace Chemical Corporation	Memphis, Tennessee	160
29. Hercules Powder Company*	Hercules, California	55
30. Hercules Powder Company*	Louisiana, Missouri	43
31. Hooker Electrochemical Corporation	Tacoma, Washington	22
32. Ketona Chemical Co rporation	Ketona, Alabama	45
33. Mississippi Chemical Corporation	Yazoo City, Mississippi	117
34. Monsanto Chemical Company*	El Dorado, Arkansas	224
35. Monsanto Chemical Company	Luling, Louisiana	184
36. Northern Chemical Industries	Searsport, Maine	45
37. Olin Mathieson Chemical Corporation	Lake Charles, Louisiana	131
38. Olin Mathieson Chemical Corporation*	Niagara Falls, New York	6
39. Pennsalt Chemicals Corporation	Portland, Oregon	15
40. Pennsalt Chemicals Corporation*	Wyandotte, Michigan	34
41. Petroleum Chemicals, Incorporated	Lake Charles, Louisiana	100
42. Phillips Chemical Company	Etter, Texas	208
43. Phillips Chemical Company	Pasadena, Texas	219
44. Phillips Pacific Chemical Company	Kennewick, Washington	73
45. Pittsburgh Plate Glass Company, Chemical Div.	Natrium, West Virginia	27
46. Rohm and Haas Company	Deer Park, Texas	50
47. St. Paul Ammonia Products Company	Pine Bend, Minnesota	110
48. San Jacinto Chemical Div., Smith-Douglass Co.	Houston, Texas	40
49. Shell Chemical Corporation*	Pittsburg, California	110
50. Shell Chemical Corporation	Ventura, California	73
51. Solar Nitrogen Chemicals, Incorporated	Lima, Ohio	133
52. Solar Nitrogen Chemicals, Incorporated	Joplin, Missouri	108
53. Southern Nitrogen Company	Savannah, Georgia	150
54. Southwestern Nitrochemical Corporation	Chandler, Arizona	28
55. Spencer Chemical Company*	Henderson, Kentucky	76
56. Spencer Chemical Company*	Pittsburg, Kansas	184
57. Spencer Chemical Company	Vicksburg, Mississippi	74
58. Sun Oil Company	Marcus Hook, Pennsylvania	108
59. Tennessee Corporation	Tampa, Florida	123
60. Tennessee Valley Authority*	Wilson Dam, Alabama	90
61. The Texas Company	Lockport, Illinois	65
62. U. S. Steel Corporation	Geneva, Utah	72
63. U. S. Industrial Chemicals Division, National Distillers Corporation	Tuscola, Illinois	70
64. Valley Nitrogen Producers	Fresno, California	65
Total Capacity..		6203

TABLE 17.7.—*Continued*

Name of Company	Plant Location	NH₃ Expansion (thousand tons/yr)ᵃ

ANHYDROUS AMMONIA PLANTS UNDER EXPANSION

1. American Cyanamid Company	Fortier, Louisiana	25
2. Coastal Chemical Company	Pascagoula, Mississippi	70
3. Hercules Powder Company	Louisiana, Missouri	—
4. St. Paul Ammonia Products	Pine Bend, Minnesota	110
Total Capacity Under Expansion..		205

ANHYDROUS AMMONIA PLANTS PROPOSED OR UNDER CONSTRUCTION

1. Amoco (American Oil Company)	Texas City, Texas	165
2. Central Nitrogen, Inc.	Near Terre Haute, Indiana	115
3. Dow Chemical Company	Plaquemine, Louisiana	50
4. E. I. du Pont de Nemours Company	Victoria, Texas	—
5. Farmers Chemical Association	Chattanooga, Tennessee	60
6. Grace Chemical Company	Big Spring, Texas	60
7. Hawkeye Chemical Company	Clinton, Iowa	105
8. Monsanto Chemical Company	Muscatine, Iowa	70
9. Pure Oil Company	Worland, Wyoming	11
10. Shamrock Gas and Oil Company	Dumas, Texas	53
11. Tenneco Chemical Company	Houston, Texas	53
Total Known Reported Capacity of Plants Proposed and Under Construction.............		742

ᵃ These data pertaining to capacities have been extracted from various published sources and may be subject to error.

* Plants operating in 1943. In addition, the Morgantown Ordnance Works, Morgantown, West Virginia, which was operating in 1943, discontinued operations in 1959.

Note: Present plant capacities for some of the listed companies are slightly higher than the capacities given in published sources.

with ammonia convertors may purchase anhydrous ammonia and convert it to aqua ammonia as it moves from the tank car into storage.

Producers commonly use insulated 10,000-gal tank cars to move nitrogen solutions containing dissolved salts from the plant. Short hauls may be handled in transport trucks. Low pressure equipment is suitable for the commercial direct-application nitrogen solutions.

Nitrogen solutions are sold to the farmer at either a delivered-to-the-farm or an applied-to-the-soil price. The farmer, who has application equipment, will have solution delivered to farm-storage facilities or in small, distributor-owned "nurse" tanks, which are left on the farm until empty. Custom application is supplied by an operator who provides over-the-road transportation, field tanks, and application equipment. The bulk distributor supplies this service. The cost of application depends on the texture of the soil and methods of application—whether the solution is applied on or beneath the surface of the soil or in irrigation water. This cost is sometimes included in the price of the solution.

Solutions move from the bulk distributor to the farm in mobile supply trucks or portable tanks of 500- to 1000-gal capacity. The portable tanks serve as nurse tanks and, when empty, are picked up, serviced, and refilled by the bulk distributor.

Methods for transferring the various types of nitrogen solutions are given in commercial brochures.[6, 7, 13] The pressure solutions should be transferred in closed systems to prevent vaporization losses of nitrogen. This precaution is unnecessary in the transfer of nonpressure solutions.

Compressed air is generally used to transfer solutions at the bulk distribution centers despite the hazard of forming explosive air-ammonia mixtures. Nonpressure solutions are often moved by solution pumps. The same type of pump can be used for the pressure solutions with negligible loss of nitrogen and elimination of the formation of the air-ammonia mixtures. Gravity transfer from bottom outlets is also employed, but sludge and crystal formation at the outlet may make this difficult.

Hand pumps, power takeoff pumps, gravity, and the vapor pressure of the solution may be utilized to transfer solutions to applicator tanks in the field. The vent valve of the applicator tank is held open to prevent a build-up of back pressure. The tank is 85 to 90 per cent full of pressure solution when a white fume appears at the vent. Nonpressure solutions in the tank must be measured by a sight gage or measuring stick.

APPLICATION METHODS AND EQUIPMENT

Pressure solutions are applied beneath the surface of the soil and by ditch or flood irrigation. Nitrogen losses are minimized by the soil cover in the first case and by dilution of the solutions in the second. Subsurface applications are used for preplant applications of nitrogen solutions and to supply supplemental nitrogen to row crops.

Nonpressure solutions can be applied by the same methods employed for pressure solutions. Nonpressure solutions can also be applied by spraying or dribbling directly onto the soil or by introduction into the water of sprinkler irrigation systems. Surface application makes it possible to apply nitrogen solutions on stony soils where subsurface application would be impractical and on fields where it would severely damage the roots of plants.

Subsurface Application

Subsurface application units consist essentially of a solution tank, metering system, and injection blades or application knives. The assembly

Figure 17.2. Subsurface application of aqua ammonia.

may be a trailer unit (Figure 17.2), be tractor mounted, or supported by both the tractor and a trailing unit. Air compressors or solution pumps are used to force the solution into a manifold equipped with orifices to apportion the solution into small metal pipes through which the liquid discharges into the soil. The metal pipes are welded to the back of the application knives, and the solution passes through exit ports usually located on the side of the pipes near the bottom of the knife.

The air compressors and solution pumps are driven by a power takeoff or are geared to the drive wheel of the tractor. A uniform discharge rate will be obtained with an air compressor if a constant pressure is maintained by a pressure-regulating valve between the solution tank and the compressor.

Centrifugal, diaphragm, gear, piston, and roller pumps are among the various types of pumps for moving pressure solutions. Solution discharge will continue after most of these pumps stop, and a manually operated valve is needed to stop the flow. Uniform discharge rates can be maintained by these pumps, but uniform application rates also require uniform rates of travel over the field.

A variable stroke piston pump driven by a chain from the tractor axle will give a uniform rate of application regardless of throttle or gear changes of the prime mover, but its utilization is handicapped by the higher initial cost and greater corrosion hazards.

Horton[35] has suggested the use of a high pressure (400 lb/sq in.) jet for injecting nitrogen solutions into the soil. The experimental model consists of a coulter for cutting a small furrow in the ground. The solution is injected into the furrow and sealed in by packer wheels that press the soil back in place.

Surface Application

Surface application of nitrogen solutions can be accomplished by means of surface irrigation water, spray and sprinkler systems, and spray booms fed by gravity or by metering systems. Many of the metering systems are employed for either surface or subsurface application.

Both the pressure and nonpressure solutions are applied to the soil in flood and ditch irrigation water. The solutions are taken to the field in tanks set up on adjustable legs adjacent to irrigation water (Figure 17.3). The solution, regulated by a manually operated control valve, flows through a hose into the water. Atmospheric pressure is maintained in the tank by an open vent. Any ammonia-gas losses that might occur, when pressure solutions are applied in this manner, are minimized by a flow of air into the tank as the solution level drops. Excessive quantities of nitrogen may be taken up near the water inlet by soils with high infiltration rates.

Nonpressure nitrogen solutions are added to the water of sprinkler systems by either a gravity or differential-pressure method.[7] In the gravity method the supply tank is connected to a valve on the suction side of the

Figure 17.3. Gravity application of nitrogen solution to irrigation water.

water pump. The valve is opened after irrigation begins, and the solution is sucked into the system.

In the differential-pressure method, a valve is placed on each side of an orifice in the water line. The valves on the entrance and exit sides of the orifice are connected, respectively, to the vent and discharge valves of the solution container. A flow of water builds up a differential pressure that draws the solution into the water stream. The rate at which solution is added to the water is governed by regulation of the valves.

The nonpressure solutions can be applied directly to the soil by gravity. Relatively uniform liquid pressure will be maintained in an open-gravity system if the bottom of the container is at least 4 ft above the discharge nozzles or orifices. A uniform pressure can be maintained by inserting a float chamber between the container and the discharge orifices. The rate of application will depend on the liquid pressure, the size of the discharge orifices, and the tractor speed.

Uniform liquid pressure can be maintained at the discharge valve or orifice of a closed-gravity system by having an air-intake pipe open to the air at the top of the container and extending down to a point near the bottom. The hydrostatic pressure at the discharge valve is the pressure exerted by the height of the liquid from the valve to the bottom of the in-take pipe. A cutoff valve should be in line ahead of the valve. Such a system has been described by Futral and others.[32]

A metering hose pump has been developed for farm use by Gantt and others[33] by modifying an earlier liquid fertilizer distributor.[48] The pump (Figure 17.4) consists of 1 to 12 flexible hoses stretched over a 4-bar reel in the form of an inverted U. Each bar, as it comes in contact with the hoses, closes each hose, and pockets containing solution are formed between the contact points. As the reel turns, the solution is forced forward and discharged through the open ends of the hoses. In another commercial pump of this type, revolving reel bars form the solution pockets by pressing the hoses against a rigid backing.

The rate of application of metering hose pumps is governed by the reel speed in relation to ground speed and is uniform regardless of ground speed. As the machine slows or stops, the solution flow slows or stops automatically. These pumps can be employed also with low pressure solutions and for subsurface applications.

POTENTIAL FOR DIRECT-APPLICATION NITROGEN SOLUTIONS

Nitrogen solutions have met general acceptance as a satisfactory fertilizer. Nitrogen, when properly applied to the soil in either solution or solid

Figure 17.4. A metering hose pump.

form, is equally efficient in promoting plant growth. The solutions are attractive to the farmer because of the ease of handling—it is easier to turn a valve than lift a bag. They can be applied rapidly and uniformly to the soil at accurately metered rates of application.

Certain disadvantages are also attached to the utilization of nitrogen solutions. They are single nutrient solutions and a field must be covered a second time if other nutrients are required. Special storage facilities and application equipment are necessary. The solutions are corrosive. Spilled solutions generally result in the total loss of contained nitrogen.

The ultimate market for direct-application nitrogen solutions will depend to a large extent on the economics involved. Based on applications of 60 lb of nitrogen per acre with nitrogen at 11 cents/lb in solution form and 15 cents/lb in solid form, Bowen and others in North Carolina[23] found that

(1) it is cheaper to have nitrogen solutions custom applied than for the farmer to apply dry materials;

(2) the cost of custom application of nitrogen solutions will be smaller than the cost of farmer application with $100 equip-

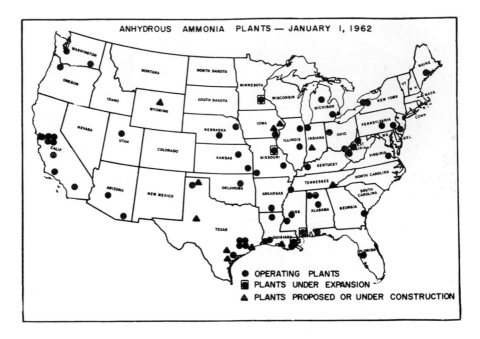

Figure 17.5. Anhydrous ammonia plants in U.S.A. January 1, 1962 (From TVA).

ment on less than 17 acres and will be greater if this acreage is exceeded; and

(3) the break-even acreage for $200 equipment is 31 acres.

Heady and Baum[34] studied this problem as related to Northern Iowa with nitrogen at 13.3 cents/lb for dry fertilizer and 11.3 cents/lb for solutions. A farmer with a 5-row applicator could apply 50 lb of nitrogen per acre, utilizing nonpressure and low pressure solutions on approximately 185 acres, as economically as the same amount of nitrogen could be applied in a solid form with a 12-ft distributor. The use of solutions on larger acreages would be more economical. The break-even acreage would be 260 acres if the farmer invested in a 550-gal storage tank for his solutions.

REFERENCES

1. Anonymous, "Aqua Ammonia," Washington, Manufacturing Chemists' Association, Inc., 1947.
2. ——, "Standards for the Storage and Handling of Anhydrous Ammonia and Ammonia Solutions," New York, Compressed Gas Association, Inc., 1950.
3. ——, "Anhydrous Ammonia," Washington, Manufacturing Chemists' Association, Inc., 1952.

4. ——, "Fertilizing Materials," Sp. Publ. 255, p. 10, Sacramento, California Department of Agriculture, 1954.
5. ——, "Anhydrous Ammonia," Chicago, National Safety Council, 1954.
6. ——, "Ammonia," Kansas City, Missouri, Spencer Chemical Co., 1956.
7. ——, "Nitrogen Fertilizer Solutions for Direct Application," New York, Nitrogen Division, Allied Chemical and Dye Corp., 1956.
8. ——, "Ammonia," New York, Nitrogen Division, Allied Chemical and Dye Corp., 1957.
9. ——, "Ammonia," Midland, Michigan, The Dow Chemical Co., 1957.
10. ——, "Ammonia," Philadelphia, Pennsalt Chemicals Corp., 1958.
11. ——, *Farm Chemicals* **121** (10), 51 (1958).
12. ——, "Sohiogen Nitrogen Solutions for Liquid Fertilizer Manufacture," Lima, Ohio, Sohio Chemical Co., 1958.
13. ——, "Ammonia and Nitrogen Solutions for Farm and Industry," p. 28, Chicago, Texaco Petrochemical Sales, 1961.
14. ——, "Fertilizing Materials, 1960," p. 9, Sacramento, California Department of Agriculture, 1961.
15. ——, "NH$_3$—Its Uses and Properties," New York, Commercial Solvents Corp., [n.d.].
16. Adams, J. R., *Croplife*, **8** (5), 1 (1961); ibid. **8** (6), 24 (1961).
17. ——, *Fertilizer Solutions*, **4** (2), 8 (1962).
18. ——, Anderson, M. S., and Hulburt, W. C., "United States Department of Agriculture Handbook," 198, p. 44, Washington, U. S. Government Printing Office, 1961.
19. Bimschas, *Gas u. Wasserfach*, **74**, 13 (1931).
20. Binns, W., "United States Department of Agriculture Yearbook," p. 113, Washington, U. S. Government Printing Office, 1956.
21. Bishop, T., *Highland and Agr. Soc. Trans., N. S.*, **8**, 357 (1843).
22. Boussingault, J. B. "Rural Economy," p. 255, New York, D. Appleton & Co., 1845.
23. Bowen, H. D., Ferguson, J. C., and Pierce, W. H., *Agr. Food Chem.*, **4** (4), 316 (1956).
24. Boyd, E. M., MacLachlan, M. L., and Perry, W. F., *J. Ind. Hyg. Toxicol.*, **26**, 29 (1944).
25. Brücker, H., *Gas u. Wasserfach*, **90**, 378 (1949).
26. Byczkowski, A., and Batalin, M., *Roczniki Nauk Rolniczych i Leśnych.*, **A69** (1), 65 (1954).
27. Chronister, B. S., *Com. Fertilizer*, **88** (4), 34 (1954).
28. Crittenden, E. D., "Fertilizer Technology and Resources in the United States," Ed. K. D. Jacob, p. 85, New York, Academic Press, Inc., 1953.
29. Davis, R. O. E., United States Department of Agriculture Circular 719, Washington, U. S. Government Printing Office, 1945.
30. Doldi, S., *Ann. Tech. Agr. (Italy)*, **6** (1), 146 (1933).
31. Franklin, C. E., *Com. Fertilizer*, **94** (4), 46 (1957).
32. Futral, J. G., Butler, J. L., Ford, J. H., and Savage, E. F., Georgia Agricultural Experiment Station, Agricultural Mimeograph Series (N.S.) 35, Experiment, Georgia Agricultural Experimental Station, 1957.
33. Gantt, C. W., Jr., Hulburt, W. C., and Bowen, H. D., United States Department of Agriculture Bulletin 2128, Washington, U. S. Government Printing Office, 1959.

34. Heady, E. O., Baum, E. L., Pesek, J. T., and Hildreth, C. G., "Economic and Technical Analysis of Fertilizer Innovations and Resource Use," 89, Ames, The Iowa State College Press, 1956.
35. Horton, D. B., *Agr. Ammonia News,* **12** (4), 16 (1962).
36. Ishizuka, Y., and Fukai, T., *J. Sci. Soil Manure Nippon,* **21,** 99 (1950).
37. Johnston, J. F. W., "Elements of Agricultural Chemistry and Geology," 6th ed., p. 248, Edinburgh and London, Blackwood & Sons, 1852.
38. Kachaev, A. P., and Sinel'shchikov, V. V., *Lenin Acad. Agr. Sci. USSR, Gedroiz Inst. Fertilizers and Agro-Soil Sci.,* **3,** 166 (1934).
39. Kunz, E., and Sladovnik, K., *Sbornik Akad. Zemedel. Ved. Rostlinna Vyroba,* **3,** 353 (1957).
40. Laurence, H. M., *Gas World,* **142,** 1671 (1955).
41. MacIntire, W. H., Winterberg, W. H., Dunham, S. H., and Clements, L. B., *Soil Sci. Soc. Am. Proc.,* **8,** 205 (1944).
42. Marburger, G. C., *Agr. Chemicals,* **14** (8), 37 (1950).
43. Marsden, A., *Gas World,* **139,** 126 (1954).
44. Mehring, A. L., Adams, J. R., and Jacob, K. D., United States Department of Agriculture Statistical Bulletin 191, p. 15, Washington, U. S. Government Printing Office, 1957.
45. Osebold, J. W., *North Am. Veterinarian,* **28,** 89 (1947).
46. Raupp, K. H., *Gas u. Wasserfach,* **73,** 230 (1930).
47. Scholl, W., Schmidt, G. W., and Wilker, C. A., *Agr. Chemicals,* **17** (4), 34 (1962).
48. Sharp, M. A., Tennessee Agricultural Experiment Station Circular 87, Knoxville, Tennessee, Agricultural Experiment Station, 1944.
49. Tiedjens, V. A., and Robbins, W. R., New Jersey Agricultural Experiment Station Bulletin 526, New Brunswick, New Jersey Agricultural Experiment Station, 1931.
50. Van Arsdell, P. M., *Chem. Eng. News,* **26,** 304 (1948).

18

Comparing Efficiency of Nitrogen Fertilizers*

John T. Pesek, Jr.

Iowa State University of Science and Technology, Ames, Iowa

There are many potentially important and desirable nitrogen compounds for agricultural purposes. However, some compounds that are major sources of nitrogen for crop fertilization today, as measured by tonnage consumed, were relatively insignificant twenty years ago (ten years in some areas), while others, once utilized in large quantities at least in certain areas, now make up a small part of the three million tons of nitrogen applied each year. Moreover, some compounds not in use at present may become valuable for agriculture in the future and others now being utilized in great quantities may assume relative unimportance. This seems inevitable as more is learned about the specific crop requirements for nitrogen and as nitrogen compound–soil reactions become better understood.

Thus the nitrogen in fertilizers presently employed in quantity may appear in completely reduced form, as in ammonia or in ammonium ions, or may be completely oxidized, as in the nitrate form. Nitrogen may also be available in the amine form, as in urea, and this may be accessible in a resin, as in the gamut of urea-formaldehyde formulations.

Physically, nitrogen fertilizer may be a liquefied gas, a solution of solids in water, an aqueous solution of gas, a solution of solids and gas in water, and finally it may be a solid. The solutions may vary from those made containing only one solid compound or only ammonia in water to those with more than one nitrogenous compound with or without the ammonia added. Hence these solutions may have low or relatively high vapor pressures of ammonia. They vary in concentration of nitrogen from below 20 per cent to about 45 per cent, as well as in density and in salting-out temperatures.

* Journal Paper No. J-4541 of the Iowa Agricultural and Home Economics Experiment Station, Ames, Iowa. Project No. 1530.

Important solid nitrogen fertilizers today may contain only ammonium, only nitrate, both ammonium and nitrate, or only amine nitrogen. They may be pulverulent, granular, or prilled, varying in bulk density and specific gravity.

This wide range of nitrogen fertilizer materials has required the development of highly specialized machinery for application. This machinery differs in design as well as in materials utilized in its construction. A new concept of merchandizing nitrogen (and other) fertilizers, i.e., custom application or bulk spreading, has developed as a result, in part, of the diversity of nitrogen materials for fertilizers.

The many forms of nitrogen fertilizers raise the question of their agronomic differences. Moreover, there are a very large number of combinations of climate, soils, crops, and management systems where supplemental nitrogen may be desirable for crop production. It is the purpose of this chapter to examine some of the properties of important nitrogen fertilizers as they relate to soil reactions and crop production through soil applications, to detail some of the results reported in the literature, and to develop and illustrate a concept for comparing sources of nitrogen for plant growth. Because most of our crops are grown in the field and the nitrogen fertilizers are applied there, this presentation will tend to be field-oriented.

REACTION OF NITROGEN COMPOUNDS WITH SOILS

With some exceptions involving a relatively small proportion of nitrogen for crop production, the nitrogen compounds employed as fertilizers must be applied to soil where the nitrogen is held temporarily until utilized by the crop. Therefore, the reactions of nitrogen compounds with soils play an important role in first retaining and then releasing the applied fertilizer nitrogen for plant absorption.

Arable soils usually contain one or more of the following in significant quantities: relatively stable organic matter, crystalline clay minerals or amorphous oxides, and hydroxides of iron and aluminum. All of these groups of substances exhibit cation exchange capacity, a property which dominates the soil's chemical reactions and, to a somewhat lesser extent, its biological reactions as well. Hence, soils exhibit strong attraction for positively charged ions like ammonium. On the other hand, soils do not attract and hold monovalent anions such as nitrate. This behavior of soils toward the two types of nitrogen-containing ions is a major factor in determining fertilization practices.

While there is a large variety of nitrogen compounds which may be used as fertilizer, the bulk of the nitrogenous fertilizers supply combined nitrogen as un-ionized amine and/or ammonia or as ammonium and nitrate ions. Hence, relatively few chemical and biochemical reactions are needed to describe the fertilizer nitrogen-soil interactions.

Reaction of Ammonia with Soils

Jackson and Chang[28] concluded that there are several ways in which ammonia might be retained in soils. First it may react with hydrogen-saturated colloids (organic matter, clay minerals, and amorphous oxides and hydroxides) or with partially hydrogen-saturated colloids to form ammonium colloids or colloids partially saturated with ammonium. Ammonia also reacts with soil moisture to form ammonium hydroxide. The ammonium may then react with the colloidal complex through a neutralizing reaction with the hydrogen in the system or by displacing other cations into the soil solution. This action results in some shifting of the equilibrium of cation distribution between solution and adsorbed phases. Mortland[42] found that the amount of ammonia adsorbed by different colloidal materials was in the decreasing order of muck (organic matter) > hydrogen bentonite > calcium bentonite > sodium bentonite > kaolinite. Burns[12] reported that magnesium saturated colloids are almost as efficient in adsorbing ammonia as hydrogen-saturated systems and that calcium, potassium, or sodium systems adsorb relatively less ammonia.

The reactions just described are thought to dominate the process of application of anhydrous ammonia in agriculture; however, Jackson and Chang[28] indicated that ammonia might also be adsorbed to soil particles physically in nonexchangeable positions. Burns[12] found that this could account for only a small amount of ammonia retention in soils, as the relationship between ammonia sorbed in nonexchangeable positions and the amount of water present could be measured only at high moisture levels not usually encountered in soils. In addition, he found that the ammonia held in this way was volatilized at room temperature as the system dried.

Finally, Sohn and Peech[55] suggested a reaction of ammonia with soil organic matter to account for at least one half of the ammonia applied to soils being held against acidified sodium chloride leaching. Up to 28 per cent of the ammonia applied was found to resist this treatment. Shoji[52] reported that fixation of ammonia by organic matter increased with ammonia concentration and pH.

Behavior of Urea and Ammonium in Soil

Volk and Sweat[65] concluded that soils exhibit some weak but unspecified attractive forces for urea, causing it to move through a soil column more slowly than the water in which it becomes dissolved. However, these workers, Broadbent,[11] and others before them have reported that urea does not persist long in warm moist soils. It is rapidly hydrolyzed to ammonium by urease which seems to be universally present in soils as a result of metabolic activities of both higher and lower plants. Volk and Sweat[65] found that, on some soils, 60 ppm of nitrogen applied as urea was essentially all hydrolyzed within a one-day period and within three days on all soils where urease activity had not been inhibited by excessive concentrations of copper in solution. The process is temperature dependent.[21, 32, 68]

Ammonium from ammonium salts and aqua ammonia employed as fertilizer or from hydrolysis of urea and the reaction of ammonia with soil water reacts with soil colloids to establish a new equilibrium and suite of cations on the exchange complex as described previously. Part of the ammonium may be held in interlayer positions of the expanding lattice types of soil colloids. Allison, *et al.*,[2] found that up to 4 m.e. of ammonium per 100 gm were so held by illite and vermiculite. Previous work[1, 25, 55] indicates that this is a common reaction in laboratory studies and that it probably occurs in the field. The concentrations of ammonium in the vicinity of dissolving solid materials and saturated solutions or anhydrous ammonia bands are higher than those used in much laboratory research and they persist for extended periods in many cases.

Many, if not all, common crops can utilize ammonium for growth. Some crops may actually absorb almost all their nitrogen in ammonium form. But nitrogen in ammonium is in reduced form and, therefore, substantial amounts of energy can be released if it is oxidized. Oxidation of ammonium to nitrite and nitrate is accomplished by *Nitrosomonas* and *Nitrobacter* species in the soil. Like other biological processes, it will proceed at temperatures above freezing and increase in rate with temperatures within the range usually found in field soils. Sabey, *et al.*[50] showed that ammonium from ammonium sulfate broadcast in the field was oxidized within a period of a few weeks even when applied in the fall in Iowa when soil temperatures are relatively low and decreasing. McIntosh and Frederick[37] found that this was the case with applied anhydrous ammonia and that during the summer the disappearance of ammonia and appearance of nitrate was extremely rapid.

Besides favorable temperature and the presence of the organisms previously mentioned, moisture and oxygen are needed for nitrification to take place. Dry soils do not nitrify because of lack of water, and nitrification is restricted in saturated soils because of a lack of oxygen. The ammonium levels present in well-drained soils during the growing season are usually low. The rapid formation of nitrates from ammonium is an advantage in the sense that plants can absorb nitrates from soil more efficiently than they can absorb the ammonia because nitrates diffuse readily toward zones of low concentration near roots and move with the water toward the water-absorbing roots. However, it is also a disadvantage because the formation of nitrate opens the way for some of the most serious potential nitrogen losses from soils.

Nitrate in Soils and Nitrogen Immobilization

Negatively-charged nitrate is not held in the soil. Hence, it is free to move with soil water and may travel downward and out of the profile as shown by Bates and Tisdale,[4] as well as by Raney[40] who related the importance of nitrate losses from soils through leaching to the loss of bases—especially calcium, magnesium, and potassium. Nitrate may move laterally or even upward, as shown by Krantz, *et al.*,[31] as a result of water movement in response to evapo-transpiration effects. Leaching is a major means of potential nitrogen loss from soils.

Nitrate is a source of nitrogen for protein formation in the metabolism of microorganisms. Jansson, *et al.*,[29] showed that ammonium is used preferentially to nitrate by organisms during the decay of carbonaceous materials. However, Munson and Pesek[43] found that large quantities of nitrate are immobilized in the decomposition of corn residues but in their study nitrogen again started to appear as nitrate within three weeks after the beginning of incubation.

Mineral nitrogen applied to the majority of arable soils, when they are warm, aerated, and moist, is soon transformed into nitrate. The completely oxidized nitrogen in nitrate is of value to both the lower and higher plants as a source of nitrogen for protein synthesis and to some lower forms as a source of oxygen for respiration. However, respiration involves another potential loss of nitrogen from soil.

LOSSES OF NITROGEN FROM SOIL

The geologic materials from which soils are formed do not contain nitrogen, for, as has been previously noted, nitrogen is a constituent of the atmosphere rather than of the earth's crust. Hence the nitrogen in soils is there by virtue of chemical and biological reactions involving atmospheric nitrogen. Furthermore, nitrogen is generally found in compounds with reduced carbon. Like reduced nitrogen, reduced carbon is a source of both energy and matter for metabolism of soil organisms and, therefore, nitrogen becomes directly or indirectly involved in frequent biological and chemical transformations, some of which permit escape of gaseous nitrogen or nitrogenous compounds into the atmosphere.

Nitrate Losses

Mention has already been made of nitrate movement in soils as a function of water movement. Nitrate leaching may be high[35, 49] or low,[19, 26] depending upon the conditions of soil, plant cover, precipitation, and time as well as the time, method, and rate of nitrogen application. Among others, Kilmer, *et al.*,[30] pointed out that activities which promote percolation of water will also promote nitrate loss through leaching. The most serious losses are likely to be encountered in areas and periods of high precipitation and on light textured soils without an actively growing plant cover. It must be remembered that our best agricultural soils will retain three or more surface inches of water per foot of soil profile against drainage under the force of gravity; that most of our acreage is planted in crops able to exploit the moisture and nutrient supplies of soils to depths greater than 4 ft; that crops are ordinarily growing during the annual high precipitation periods; and that, over a large area, the annual precipitation does not exceed the annual evaporation and transpiration losses or exceeds them to a small degree, part of this excess being lost through surface runoff rather than percolation. Calvert[16] found that corn utilizes nitrate deep in the soil profile if moisture is available, and White and Pesek[71] reported that even oats can utilize nitrate present below the plow layer. Nitrate is not lost until it leaves the root zone or perhaps until it enters the groundwater.

A second avenue of potential nitrate loss is denitrification. By denitrification is meant the reduction by microbiological processes of nitrate to gaseous products, such as free nitrogen or nitrous oxide, with a decrease in the general nitrogen level in the immediate environment of the organism. According to Verhoeven,[62] this is a result of nitrate acting as a nonessential or incidental hydrogen acceptor or as an essential hydrogen acceptor. Denitrification does not include nitrate reduced and assimilated in organism protein. Nason and Takahashi[45] described denitrification similarly.

Cady[15] showed that gaseous nitrogen losses from nitrate could occur even though the oxygen concentration of the medium was not zero, perhaps a consequence of nitrate acting as an essential hydrogen acceptor. Broadbent[11] as well as Wagner and Smith[66] found evidence of gaseous nitrogen losses in soils apparently under aerobic conditions. This may be explained on the basis that oxygen diffusion in water is slow and that an active microbial population located on soil particle surfaces under a film of water may be operating in an oxygen-deficient environment. Nevertheless, experimental denitrification is usually conducted under conditions which tend to exclude oxygen.

Soil reaction and temperature must be favorable before denitrification occurs. According to Nommik[46] denitrification is greatly reduced below pH

5, increases in rate as pH increases, and reaches its maximum between pH 7 and 8. Nitrate can be lost through denitrification even at 10°C, but the rate increases with temperature, changing relatively little, however, between 25° and 60°C.[10] Nommik[46] reported that the maximum rate of denitrification occurred at 65°C.

Since all nitrogen carriers add or eventually produce nitrate in soils, the nitrogen which they supply is subject to potential loss through denitrification or leaching. The main difference between the nitrate fertilizers and the ammonia, ammonium, or urea fertilizers is the time before the nitrogen in the latter group is nitrified and becomes subject to denitrification. This period may be long or short,[37, 50] depending on the soil conditions and to some extent the actual source. Hence, there may be differences between nitrogen fertilizers due to the differential nitrate losses from nitrate and the other sources.

Ammonia and Ammonium Losses

Ammonia is a gas at normal temperatures and atmospheric pressure, and solutions of ammonia in water have significant ammonia vapor pressure. Salts containing ammonium can react with salts in soils to form less stable ammonium salts which can decompose. Urea is hydrolyzed to form ammonium. Hence there are conditions under which nitrogen applied to soil in these nitrogen carriers can be lost. Under specific conditions these reactions may be a source of difference in effectiveness among different nitrogen fertilizers.

Losses Related to Ammonia Application. When liquid ammonia is released under atmospheric conditions, it becomes gaseous almost instantaneously and hence occupies a far greater volume than before. If reactive materials, such as hydrogen colloids or water, are present, ammonia will react to form ammonium as discussed previously. Ammonium in turn is held on the exchange complex of the soil and becomes nitrified. Since direct losses of ammonia during application or immediately thereafter could result in inportant losses of fertilizer nitrogen, the problem is to inject the material deeply enough into the soil to prevent the expanded volume of the ammonia from intersecting the soil surface.

Successful anhydrous ammonia application first of all requires that the crumbling soil fills the opening made by the ammonia injector tool.[9, 38, 56] Placement must be deepest in sandy soils having relatively low ammonium holding capacity and need not be as deep on heavier textured soils high in cation exchange capacity. Moisture content of the soil is important first from the standpoint of the soil condition permitting sealing of the injection furrow and secondly for solution and temporary holding of the ammonia until other reactions can be completed. Significant ammonia losses accompanying application can result because (1) soils are too wet, (2) soils are too dry, (3) application is too shallow, (4) application furrow is not closed, and (5) applications are spaced too far apart, causing the amount of ammonia applied to be in excess of the retaining capacity of the soil at a given rate per acre.

Losses from Surface Application of Urea. The presence of urease in almost all soils assures that any urea applied to the soil will be hydrolyzed rather quickly. This hydrolysis results in formation of ammonium and an elevation of pH in the volume of soil containing the particle of urea, and subsequent reactions lead to the attachment of the ammonium to the exchange complex or the formation of ammonium-carbonate or ammonium-bicarbonate. Both are unstable and will decompose readily, with free ammonia as one product, especially if drying occurs.

The loss of ammonia from surface application was studied extensively by Volk.[63] He concluded that losses were potentially greatest for surface-applied urea in conjunction with the following: (1) low-exchange capacity of soils, (2) high rates of urea application, (3) high temperatures, (4) high pH, (5) application to a moist surface which then dries out, and (6) the presence of a grass sod. Although the conclusion of Volk relating to the effect of sod is corroborated in some studies[27, 53] but not in others,[32] some or all of the other conclusions of Volk have been verified.[21, 36, 39, 44, 68]

Just as gaseous loss of anhydrous ammonia during application is a unique behavior of this material, the loss of ammonia from surface-applied urea containing fertilizers under the range of conditions shown by the various investigators is unique to urea and a possible reason for its ineffectiveness as compared to other carriers. Jackson and Burton[27] have shown almost certainly that ammonia loss from urea is the main cause of relatively poorer performance of coastal bermuda grass when fertilized with this material.

Reaction of Ammonium Salts with Salts in Soils. Soils above neutrality in reaction frequently contain significant levels of salts, and all soils above pH 8 contain carbonates and bicarbonates of calcium, potassium, and/or sodium. These react with ammonium salts to form ammonium-carbonate or ammonium-bicarbonate which are unstable and decompose readily as evaporation takes place. Martin and Chapman[36] pointed out that this is not a serious consequence if the ammonium salt is initially incorporated with the soil but it may be if it is surface applied. Results of Kresge and Satchell[32] and of Wahhab, et al.,[69] as well as others investigating this general problem, support these views. While most of the research was directed toward investigation of ammonium sulfate, the effect would apply to all ammonium salts, but perhaps not to as great a degree.[39, 64]

Ammonia Loss from Aqueous Solutions with High Ammonia Vapor Pressures. Aqua ammonia and certain nitrogen fertilizer solutions contain ammonia in aqueous solution and, therefore, have a significant vapor pressure of ammonia. When such solutions are applied to the soil surface and dry, they may lose significant portions of their "free" ammonia as shown by Kresge and Satchell[32]. This ammonia loss may account in part, for the relatively poor results Nowakowski[47] obtained when he applied aqua ammonia at a concentration of 5 per cent nitrogen to a seedbed for grass or to established grass stands. Mikkelsen[40] reported inferior results with aqua ammonia applied to rice in California.

The potential ammonia loss situation for nitrogen fertilizer solutions containing urea or ammonium salts or both is aggravated by the urea hydrolysis process and the reaction of ammonium salts with carbonates in the soil. These have been discussed before. Efficient use of these solutions as fertilizers probably requires as much or more care than the utilization of any of the other carriers of nitrogen. The possible effect of the complex physical and chemical properties of these solutions on relative efficiency is obvious.

Loss of Nitrogen During the Nitrification Sequence. Oxidation of ammonia to nitrate takes place in at least two steps, and each step involves different organisms. One step ends with the formation of nitrite and the subsequent step further oxidizes the nitrite to nitrate, thus completing the sequence. Nitrogen losses during nitrification of applied ammonium have been reported.[17, 18, 23, 24] These losses, which were not in the form of ammonia, were as high as one-third of the ammonium added, in some cases, and occurred as oxides of nitrogen or as free nitrogen. They are thought to occur as a result of nitrite accumulation caused by an interference with the oxidation of nitrite to nitrate. Under some conditions the nitrite is unstable and decomposes to gaseous products, or it may react with other soil constituents with the same result. This pathway of nitrogen disappearance is limited to sources which supply ammonium to soils.

MEASURING RELATIVE EFFECTIVENESS OF FERTILIZERS

Fertilizers are basically inorganic materials applied to soil for the purpose of influencing the behavior of rooted green plants. In a restricted sense, this biological effect is achieved directly through the supplying of essential elements for plant growth and development, although indirect effects frequently are important. Since the desirable effects of fertilizers are expressed through biological reactions to them, their value or effect needs to be evaluated with plants in the usual environment for production. In general agriculture, this means in soil in the open field.

Finney[22] has summarized various biological assay methods which have been employed for comparing the biological activity of unknown dilutions of an active ingredient in an inert medium with a known standard or with other preparations of the same ingredients. He has also elaborated the fundamental assumptions and conditions underlying biological assay and developed and presented the numerous statistical tests needed to interpret data generated by experiments designed to compare preparations of biologically active substances. His work deals mostly with the effect of complex substances such as vitamins, antibiotics, insecticides, poisons, etc., rather than with fertilizers.

Black and Scott[7] have considered and presented the underlying principles of comparing fertilizers which supply the same essential plant nutrient. In fact, one of the conditions for comparing fertilizers is that the essential element under study be the only one supplied or that it be the only biologically effective one in limiting concentration in the unfertilized growth medium. They also pointed out that, unlike classical biological assay problems, fertilizer evaluation seldom is concerned with dilutions of the same chemicals, but does compare preparations containing the essential element in different forms. To compare two sources of an essential element without bias it is necessary that the concentration of the element or its total content in the plant or plant parts must have equivalent effect on the biological response, e.g., yield of dry matter or grain. According to Black and Scott[7] the relative effectiveness of two different sources of an element is measured by the ratio of the respective availability coefficients, which cannot be determined directly but whose ratio is given by

$$\gamma_t/\gamma_s = x_s/x_t \qquad (18.1)$$

where γ_t and γ_s are the availability coefficients of the test, t, and standard, s, fertilizers and x_s and x_t are the quantities of the fertilizer element in the two fertilizers having identical availability or effective quantities as shown by biological test.

Black and his coworkers[8, 70] developed the concepts further and applied them to problems dealing with availability of phosphorus in acidulated phosphatic fertilizers. Illustrative examples were concerned with the total phosphorus in the aerial portions of oats, the plant phosphorus in oats derived from fertilizer, and the yield of corn as a function of the water-soluble portion of citric acid-soluble phosphorus in several fertilizers. Effectiveness of fertilizers as measured by effect on yields is usually of primary practical interest when fertilizers are compared, so the last of the previous examples is pertinent to further development in this paper.

Properties of Curvilinear Fertilizer Evaluation Models

The evidence indicates that unlike different phosphorus fertilizers which may vary in citrate-solubility, water-solubility, etc., as well as in the initial properties which may sometimes persist in soils for extended periods of time, all commonly used inorganic nitrogen fertilizers either are, or are converted to, nitrate rapidly during the growing season. (A major exception would be ammonium or ammonium-forming fertilizers applied to flooded rice.) As nitrate, the fertilizers would have equal availability coefficients; their effectiveness is a function of the quantity of nitrate produced and maintained in the root zone by a given application of a particular carrier. Similarly, when ammonium is not readily oxidized as in flooded rice culture, the availability coefficients for all ammonium and ammonium-forming fertilizers should be equal, the effectiveness is a function of the ammonium concentration in the root zone and of the initial spatial distribution in the soil volume because ammonium diffuses very slowly in most soils.

Since regardless of carrier the bulk of the nitrogen utilized by a given crop will be either nitrate or ammonium, the availability coefficient concept of Black and Scott[7] does not seem to be applicable or necessary in comparing nitrogen sources. Amer[3] ignored the availability coefficient when he compared the effect of subsurface placement of ammonium sulfate in a dry soil with placement of this fertilizer on the moist surface in a study involving rice production. On the basis of the ratio of the Mitscherlich-effect coefficients, c, Amer[3] concluded that application to the dry soil was more effective.

Assuming that the availability coefficient is not relevant for comparing nitrogen sources ignores the fact that, while eventually all nitrogen carriers supply nitrate, plants may derive significant portions of their current needs from the ammonium until complete nitrification has taken place. This, in turn, would affect early growth and subsequent uptake. The author has not found any conclusive evidence that there may not be some "carrier effect" of currently common fertilizers on the final yield of a crop due to the original species of ion. However, there is evidence which suggests that "nitrogen is nitrogen" as long as it gets into the corn plant, for example, by the time of inflorescence. Research[6, 20, 60, 61] indicates that there is a good relationship between the per cent nitrogen in a selected corn leaf and yield over a wide range of other environmental conditions. This satisfies one of the conditions of Black and Scott in dealing with the biological effectiveness of the element in the plant, i.e., a given concentration in the tissue has an equivalent effect independent of the initial source. This relationship would also support the idea that the potentially different availability coefficients soon after application of a soluble non-nitrate nitrogen compound are not very different from that for nitrate or that the soluble non-nitrate compound exists for such a short period that it does not have a major effect on the outcome. Practically, however, the differences in c constitute the important consideration, the reason for the divergences not being significant at this point.

Concerning cases where the biological response may be represented as a linear function of the rate of application and where the intercepts (yield at zero rate of all preparations) are the same, Finney[22] and White, *et al.*,[70] pointed out that the relative effectiveness of different preparations is given by the ratios of the slopes of these lines, i.e., the ratios of the first derivatives of these functions relating yield or yield response to the rate of application. This method of evaluation applies to linear relationships, and some biological responses to fertilizers do not deviate significantly from linearity and others may not do so within selected ranges of application. But yield of agricultural crops is a curvilinear function of rate of application over the relevant economic range of fertilizer application, i.e., the law of diminishing returns operates and the simple linear model is not adequate.

To use yield as the criterion for comparing fertilizer effectiveness, a curvilinear model must be used. White, *et al.*,[70] used the Mitscherlich equation to express yield as a function of phosphorus applied but defined the c in the equation as the product of an availability coefficient, γ, that is characteristic of the fertilizer and the general effect coefficient, c, which is the medium of operation of the element phosphorus. In this case c is assumed constant and the ratio of two products, $\gamma_1 c/\gamma_2 c$, depends upon the values of γ_i and represents the relative effectiveness of the two fertilizers. Without the redefinition of the Mitscherlich c, the relative effectiveness of the two fertilizers is given by the ratio of the two values for c. Amer[3] used the latter procedure as indicated before.

Development of the General Comparison

If the Mitscherlich equation

$$y = A[1 - 10^{-c(x+b)}] \tag{18.2}$$

is differentiated with respect to x the first derivative is

$$dy/dx = c(A - y) \tag{18.3}$$

where A is the maximum yield, y, attainable with increasing applications of the mineral element, x, c is the effect coefficient and b is a regression constant interpreted to be the quantity of the element, x, present in the soil measured in effect units of the fertilizer in which x occurs. Hence, when the ratio of c for two different fertilizers is taken as a measure of the relative effectiveness, the comparison is simply that of the first derivatives of two yield functions provided the difference, $A - y$, is identical in both cases. Both White, et al.,[70] and Amer[3] fitted all their functions with a common A, and through the same intercepts, so they did the equivalent of comparing first derivatives at the same level of y. Since the ratios of first derivatives of two functions are compared in each case, the comparison involving the straight-line model is equivalent in principle to that involving the Mitscherlich model. A unique property of the straight-line model is that the values of the first derivatives are independent of yield or yield response, so the yield level does not enter the comparison of fertilizers. The unique property of the Mitscherlich function is that with a common A the ratio of the first derivative of one function to that of another will always be the same as the ratio of the c values if the derivatives are evaluated at the same yield level, y.

Intuitively, two fertilizers might be compared by measuring the change in yield, Δy, due to identical increments of the nutrient element in them, Δx. The relative effectiveness, k, is given by

$$k = \frac{\Delta y_1/\Delta x_1}{\Delta y_2/\Delta x_2} \qquad (18.4)$$

where the subscripts refer to the fertilizers. As Δx approaches zero, k is given by the ratio

$$\frac{dy_1/dx_1}{dy_2/dx_2} \qquad (18.5)$$

which is equivalent to the relationships described previously, i.e., the ratio of two slopes.

If values for Δx are taken to be too small, the values of Δy will become so small that they will be within the experimental error and the test will fail to give a confident differentiation between fertilizers. Unless one fertilizer carries some detrimental factor for crop growth, it is obvious that the values for Δx can be taken large enough so that the corresponding values of Δy approach the maximum or limiting response, and under these conditions, all fertilizers will appear equal in value when experimental error is considered. Under these conditions the test will also be insensitive to differences between fertilizers.

Since the comparisons can be ineffective as a result of poor choices of Δx, it is concluded that simple single rate ("without" compared to "with") tests are not satisfactory for comparing fertilizers.

Multiple rate experiments permit the fitting of curvilinear regressions to the observed data (as was done by White, et al.,[70] and Amer[3]) as well as the evaluation of the first derivatives for the yield functions of the various fertilizers. When the relative efficiency of two fertilizers is viewed as the ratio of the first derivatives of the two yield functions relating yield to fertilizer nutrient quantity in each fertilizer at a given level of yield, the uniqueness of the straight-line and Mitscherlich models serves no special purpose for practical fertilizer evaluation.

The straight-line model has limitations because the yield response over the economic range simply is not a linear function and those attributes of a crop responding linearly may not predict yield very accurately, may have little or no economic value, and are usually more difficult and costly to determine. Difficulties with the Mitscherlich equation are mostly computational. The best fitting curve can be found only by a series of approximations. The restriction of a common value for A, the maximum attainable yield or response, is needed in subsequent computations but is a serious limitation because fixing its value will ordinarily have the effect of giving a poorer "fit" of the equation as measured by sum of squares due to regression, and will tend to make some fertilizers which could not cause a response of the magnitude of A to appear relatively better than they actually are. This together with the greater mean square for deviations from regression (error) will reduce the chances of observing differences which are real. While this test is not applicable (and not necessary) if there is a significant difference between values of A for two fertilizers, there are occasions when the yield level of A is reached only with inputs far beyond those in the test and this extrapolated value is measured with so little confidence that any two values for A within a wide range would not differ significantly. (In case of Eq. (18.2), $y = A$ is never reached.)

Some of the limitations just listed for the response models previously used to evaluate relative effectiveness of fertilizers can be overcome by use of polynomial functions or transformations of these functions. They have the advantage of being easy to fit by direct methods of least squares, and statistical tests for significance of coefficients and differences between coefficients are easy to apply.[54] In addition, the functions have simple first derivatives, are easy to plot, are fitted within the range of observations only and have the simple restriction of having the same intercept, i.e., yield at zero applied fertilizer is the same for all fertilizers. The general form of the quadratic polynomial equation is

$$y = a + b_1x_1 + b_{11}x_1^2 + b_2x_2 + b_{22}x_2^2 + \ldots + b_ix_i + b_{ii}x_i^2 \quad (18.6)$$

where a is the intercept; b_1, b_2, $\ldots$, b_i are the linear coefficients for the different fertilizers; b_{11}, b_{22}, $\ldots$, b_{ii} are the quadratic coefficients; the subscripts of x are different fertilizers; and x is the rate of the element supplied by the fertilizers.

Differentiating Eq. (18.6) with respect to x_1 and x_2, in order, leads to

$$dy/dx_1 = b_1 + 2b_{11}x_1 \qquad (18.7)$$

and

$$dy/dx_2 = b_2 + 2b_{22}x_2 . \qquad (18.8)$$

The relative effectiveness k is given by

$$k = \frac{dy/dx_1}{dy/dx_2} = \frac{b_1 + 2b_{11}x_1}{b_2 + 2b_{22}x_2} \qquad (18.9)$$

or simply

$$k = \frac{b_1}{b_2} \qquad (18.10)$$

when Eqs. (18.7) and (18.8) are evaluated at $x = 0$, that is, at $y = a$. Evaluation at this point has the advantage of simplicity; however, the standard error of the slope is usually greater at $y = a$ than it is in the vicinity of the mean observed y, $\bar{y}$. It can be shown that, if the second fertilizer is or behaves like a dilution of the first and application is made on the basis of the quantity of fertilizer rather than x, Eq. 18.9 has the same value at all values of y except at maximum yield (Eqs. (18.7) and (18.8) equal to zero) where it is indeterminate.

In practice, the maximum predicted yields for different sources of x in Eq. (18.6) will be or will appear to be different. Therefore, an evaluation of relative effectiveness at the maximum value of y of the function with the lowest maximum will be indeterminate, and the value of Eq. (18.9) will increase or decrease slowly as evaluation is made at successive points above $y = a$ depending upon whether the function with the lower maximum is in the denominator or the numerator of this equation. One could add the restriction that functions of all x's in Eq. (18.9) would go through the same maximum, but this restriction is not considered desirable or necessary.

Evaluation of relative fertilizer effectiveness is economic as well as agronomic. Thus far only the agronomic considerations have been given, and Wahhab and Ahmad[67] concluded that an agronomically inferior nitrogen fertilizer should be applied to cotton in Pakistan because it produced more response in cotton per rupee of nitrogen applied than the nitrogen source which was superior in producing cotton per pound of nitrogen applied.

The relative economic effectiveness, k_e, of two fertilizers may be derived from Eqs. (18.9) or (18.10) by multiplying the function by P_2/P_1 where P_1

is the price per unit of the element x in the first fertilizer and P_2 is the price of the element in the second fertilizer or

$$k_e = \frac{b_1 P_2}{b_2 P_1} \qquad\qquad (18.11)$$

Alternately, one could express Eq. (18.6) in monetary units instead of physical units, and Eqs. (18.9) and (18.10) would produce k_e instead of k.

Because different nitrogen fertilizers may add ions which do not contain nitrogen to the soil, the indirect effect on the soil or on plants may be different and a fertilizer will, therefore, affect yield response differently at very low rates (approaching $x = 0$) than it might at higher rates. Where these indirect effects are offset by additional treatments, Eqs. (18.10) or (18.11) provide valid comparisons between x_1 and x_2. However, additional treatments may not be possible, and the economic evaluation under such circumstances would be more complicated. Practically, nevertheless, one is interested in comparing the sources on the basis of their whole contribution (direct and indirect) to yield over some entire economic input increment. This is the equivalent of comparing two sources of x in Eq. (18.4), but the question of choice of Δx still remains.

To make a valid economic comparison according to Eq. (18.4) it is necessary to have Eq. (18.6) (or its equivalent). Equation (18.6) is differentiated with respect to the standard fertilizer, or an arbitrarily selected one, to obtain Eq. (18.7). This first derivative is then equated to the ratio, P_x/P_p, where P_x is the price per unit of the fertilizer and P_p the price per unit of product. Solving the equation

$$b_s + 2b_{ss} x_s = P_x/P_p \qquad\qquad (18.12)$$

for x_s (rate of nutrient in standard fertilizer) gives the optimum or most profitable rate, x_{os}, of the nutrient in the standard fertilizer. Inserting x_{os} into Eq. (18.6) in place of each x in succession, solving and subtracting the intercept, a, leads to a value of Δy for each fertilizer. Because now $\Delta x_1 = \Delta x_2 = \ldots \Delta x_i = x_{os}$, Eq. (18.4) becomes

$$k = \Delta y_1/\Delta y_2 \qquad\qquad (18.13)$$

where either Δy_1 or Δy_2 may be the response to x_{os}. If x_1 and x_2 have different costs, the economic efficiency k_e may be calculated as in Eq. (18.11) by multiplying Eq. (18.13) by the ratio, P_2/P_1, previously defined.

Now Eq. (18.13) makes a comparison of two yield responses at a common rate which is similar to comparisons in single rate experiments which were found objectionable earlier. The difference is that, in this case, the comparison is made over an economically or practically relevant increment which is determined by regression from responses to a series of rates covering at least most of the range over which the response is positive. On the basis of what has been said single rate experiments are not desirable for precise comparison of fertilizers because (1) the optimum rate of the standard fertilizer may not be known, (2) the optimum rate, if known for one condition, may be different under the conditions of the new test, and (3) the optimum rate will differ with changing prices and the appropriate Δx will therefore be different.

RELATIVE EFFECTIVENESS OF SOME NITROGEN FERTILIZERS

The material in this section consists of the application of the ideas and concepts just presented to some sets of data which have been published. These data are used because they are published and permit illustration of procedures. They are not necessarily generally representative of all such data, and the implied interpretation given here is not meant to supersede the interpretation given and conclusions drawn by the authors.

Effect of Nitrogen Sources on Yields of Corn in Nebraska

Olson, *et al.*,[48] published the average responses of corn to ammonium nitrate, anhydrous ammonia, and urea applied in the previous fall, in the spring before planting, and as a side-dressing after the corn was growing. The average represents five experiments conducted during the period of 1957–59 in irrigated corn fields. The levels of nitrogen supplied were 0, 80, or 160 lb/acre.

Because there were only three levels of nitrogen for each source, the data could be fitted without residual error, i.e., the response curves passed precisely through each observed yield. The yield function for fall, f, applied fertilizers is

$$y_f = 76 + 31.5N_1 - 6.5N_1^2 + 18.5N_2 - 1.5N_2^2 + 48.5N_3 - 13.5N_3^2 \quad (18.14)$$

where N is measured in units of 80 lb of nitrogen per acre; the subscripts 1, 2, and 3 refer to ammonium nitrate, urea, and anhydrous ammonia; and y is measured in bu/acre.

Differentiating Eq. (18.14) with respect to N_1, N_2, and N_3 leads to

$$\partial y_f / \partial N_1 = 31.5 - 13.0N_1 \quad (18.15)$$

$$\partial y_f / \partial N_2 = 18.5 - 3.0N_2 \quad (18.16)$$

and

$$\partial y_f / \partial N_3 = 48.5 - 27.0N_3 . \quad (18.17)$$

On the basis of the first partial derivatives evaluated at $N = 0$, the best source of nitrogen for fall application under the conditions of these experiments is anhydrous ammonia as its partial derivative is 48.5 bu/acre/unit of nitrogen while those for ammonium nitrate and urea are only 31.5 and 18.5 bu/acre/unit of nitrogen. Since anhydrous ammonia is usually less expensive than the other carriers, economic effectiveness makes it even more desirable under these conditions.

Observed responses to a fixed quantity of nitrogen applied (160 lb/acre or 2 units) were 37, 31, and 43 bu/acre for N_1, N_2, and N_3 fertilizers. On this basis N_3, anhydrous ammonia, would also be superior, but it appears a modest one-third better than urea. This compares with about one and a half times better (two and a half times as good) on the basis of the yield-function slope ratio at $N = 0$. This illustrates the problem of evaluating two sources at one arbitrary rate of application of each.

The yield functions for spring, s, applied nitrogen and side-dressed, d nitrogen are

$$y_s = 76 + 42.5N_1 - 11.5N_1^2 + 37.0N_2$$
$$- 8.0N_2^2 + 36.0N_3 - 8.0N_3^2 \tag{18.18}$$

and

$$y_d = 76 + 63.5N_1 - 20.5N_1^2 + 51.0N_2$$
$$- 14.0N_2^2 + 69.5N_3 - 23.0N_3^2. \tag{18.19}$$

Linear coefficients of N_1, N_2, and N_3 indicate that ammonium nitrate is only a little superior to the other two sources of nitrogen when spring applied and that urea and anhydrous ammonia are about equally effective under these conditions. As a side dressing, anhydrous ammonia is superior to ammonium nitrate and the two are superior to urea.

If one compares the first derivatives with respect to each source over the different times of application, it becomes obvious that both ammonium nitrate and urea become more effective as application is delayed until side-dressing in late spring or early summer. For example, the first derivatives with respect to rate of urea applied in the fall or spring or side-dressed, and evaluated at $N = 0$, are 18.5, 37, or 51 bu/acre/unit of nitrogen. For some reason, anhydrous ammonia is an exception in that its effectiveness when applied in spring is lower than when applied in the fall or as a side-dressing. Olson, *et al.*,[48] concluded that it is best to side-dress these nitrogen sources for corn under the conditions of the experiments. One would also conclude that anhydrous ammonia should be used if applications have to be made in the fall.

Because the side-dressed application was superior for all sources combined, consider the relative effectiveness of the three sources at this time with ammonium nitrate, N_1, as the standard.

Differentiating Eq. (18.19) with respect to N_1 produces

$$\partial y_d / \partial N_1 = 63.5 - 41.0N. \qquad (18.20)$$

Then assuming an 80-lb unit of nitrogen costs \$10 as ammonium nitrate and corn is priced at \$1 per bu, Eq. (18.20) is equated to the ratio of the price of nitrogen to the price of corn to give

$$-41.0N_1 + 63.5 = 10 \qquad (18.21)$$

Solving Eq. (18.21) for N_1 results in an estimate of 1.3 units or 104 lb of nitrogen per acre as the optimum rate. Placing this value into Eq. 18.19 in place of N_1, N_2, and N_3, in order, and subtracting the intercept predicts yield responses of 47.9, 42.6, and 51.5, respectively, for the three nitrogen sources.

Under these conditions, $\Delta y_1 / \Delta y_2$ is equal to 1.12 which means that at the optimum level of application for N_1, it is 12 per cent better than N_2. The ratio $\Delta y_1 / \Delta y_3$ is equal to 0.93 (or N_1 is only 93 per cent as effective as N_3 when both are applied at this rate). Consider that anhydrous ammonia, N_3, may cost only \$8 per 80-lb unit of nitrogen. Multiplying the ratio $\Delta y_1 / \Delta y_3$ by the rates P_3 / P_1 (\$8/\$10) gives 0.74 (or N_1 is only 74 per cent as effective as N_3 in producing corn per dollar invested at this level of application). Corn produced by N_1 is about 3.7 bu/acre/dollar at this level of fertilizer application, while N_3 produces about 5.0 bu/acre/dollar.

Effect of Nitrogen Sources on Yield of Bermuda Grass

Burton and De Vane[13] reported yields of Bermuda grass in Georgia when it was fertilized with nitrate of soda, ammonium nitrate, or uramon. The nitrogen was top-dressed on the sod in spring at levels of 0, 50, 100, 200, or 400 lb/acre. The yield function is

$$y = 0.95 + 1.44N_1 - 0.10N_1^2 + 1.15N_4$$
$$- 0.05N_4^2 + 1.06N_5 - 0.05N_5^2, \qquad (18.22)$$

where y is in tons of hay, N is measured in 50-lb units of nitrogen, and the subscripts 1, 4, and 5 refer to ammonium nitrate, sodium nitrate, and uramon.

The 6.1-ton response caused by 400 lb of nitrogen as sodium nitrate, N_4, was significantly greater than the 5.3-ton response due to the same quantity of nitrogen in the other two carriers. This would seem to clearly establish sodium nitrate as the superior material; however, a comparison of the linear coefficients of N_1, N_4, and N_5 indicates that the best response to the initial increment of nitrogen is to that of N_1. In fact, $b_1/b_4 = 1.25$ and $b_1/b_5 = 1.36$ so the initial increment of N_1 is about 25 and 36 per cent more effective, agronomically, than those of N_4 and N_5.

For purposes of illustration, assume that a 50-lb unit of N_1 can be purchased for $7.50 and that the hay is worth $25 per ton. Equating the first partial derivative of Eq. (18.22) with respect to N_1 to the nitrogen-hay price ratio gives

$$\partial y/\partial N_1 = -0.2N_1 + 1.44 = 0.3. \qquad (18.23)$$

Solving for N_1 gives the optimum rate of 5.7 units (285 lb) of nitrogen as ammonium nitrate. Substituting 5.7 for N_1, N_4, and N_5 in order into Eq. (18.22) and solving and subtracting the intercept gives yield responses of 5.0, 4.9, and 4.4 tons for the three sources. In this case, $\Delta y_1/\Delta y_4 = 1.02$ and $\Delta y_1/\Delta y_5 = 1.14$; ammonium nitrate and sodium nitrate are of about equal agronomic effectiveness, and the two are more effective than uramon. Suppose that a unit of sodium nitrate costs $9 instead of $7.50. Then the economic effectiveness of ammonium nitrate is given by $1.02 \times \$9.00/\$7.50$ or 1.22 and this source is 22 per cent more effective than sodium nitrate under these conditions.

This would complete the evaluation if all sources at the highest rate used would have given about the same maximum yield. But the sodium nitrate caused about 0.8 ton more response than the other sources, and this probably was a real difference on the basis of the statistical analysis reported. If one calculated the optimum rate of sodium nitrate at the cost of $7.50 per unit of nitrogen, he would find it to be 8.5 units of nitrogen (425 lb), costing $63.75 and causing a response in yield of 6.2 tons worth $155 and a profit of $91.25 per acre. The profit from the 5.7 units of ammonium nitrate would be only $82.25 on the basis of 5.0 tons of hay response worth $125 and a nitrogen cost of $42.75 per acre. If, however, the sodium nitrate did cost $9 per unit of nitrogen (20 per cent more than the ammonium nitrate), the optimum rate would have been 7.9 units of nitrogen costing $71.10 per acre and giving a response of 6.0 tons worth $150. The profit, in this case, would be $78.90 or less than for the optimum ammonium nitrate rate at the lower cost.

In practice, the agronomic effectiveness is only the first step in determining the relative value of different sources of fertilizer. Final decisions regarding the rate and source have to be based on the economics of input and response, which in turn are based on the agronomic yield function. In the illustration just presented, one may conclude that ammonium nitrate would have been superior agronomically if the comparison had been made only at 50 or 100 lb of nitrogen per acre in single rate experiments. If the comparison had been made at 200 lb/acre, the difference among sources would have been small but slightly in favor of sodium nitrate, while at 400 lb/acre, it was clear that nitrate of soda gave the highest response, and the other two sources were equal. It is obvious that an economic analysis of the agronomic production functions is needed to specify which source of nitrogen is most efficient from a production point of view.

CONCLUSIONS

Almost all the nitrogen absorbed from soil by rooted green plants is in the form of nitrate or ammonium ions. Generally, plants are capable of absorbing either of these ions and utilizing them in nitrogen metabolism. However, the form in which they absorb nitrogen depends upon the environment in which crop plants grow.

Common nitrogen compounds used as fertilizers supply nitrate or ammonium to soil directly or indirectly through hydration of ammonia and hydrolysis of urea. Ammonium is rapidly oxidized to nitrate through microbiological processes in warm, moist, and well aerated soils. In cold, dry, or unaerated soils ammonium will remain unoxidized.

Because of the facts just stated, it is not likely that the efficiency of different nitrogen sources will depend upon the relative availability of the ion species. Efficiencies of different nitrogen fertilizers can vary, however, because of their different physical properties and different chemical reactions with soil and soil microflora. These impose certain limitations on the methods employed to apply the fertilizers and on the place where the materials can be utilized most effectively.

Anhydrous ammonia is a gas at normal temperature and pressure and must be injected into soil for most effective use,[9, 38, 56] and the spacing of the injected bands is limited by the lateral spread of the roots of the fertilized crop. Commonly used injectors seriously disturb the soil surface at intervals, and this disturbance may be responsible for inefficiency.[14, 34] The mechanics of application require that anhydrous ammonia be applied when the soil is near field capacity in moisture content. Loss of ammonia directly to the atmosphere during application constitutes the most important and unique potential cause of inefficiency where soil disturbance is of no consequence to the growing crop.[58] Ammonia forms ammonium in moist soil and thus is retained on the exchange complex. In this condition ammonium is almost impossible to leach. Anhydrous ammonia is likely to be a superior source of nitrogen when used in areas where there is percolation of water through the soil and under conditions of poor aeration.

Urea hydrolyzes rapidly in soils and forms high local concentrations of ammonium carbonate accompanied by an increase in pH in the vicinity of the solid particle. Major inefficiencies in use of urea result from losses of ammonia which may occur as a result of hydrolysis on a moist soil surface which then dries out.[63] These potential losses are magnified by the presence of some plant material, high pH, especially calcareous conditions,[39, 59] and low base-exchange capacity. If urea is incorporated into the soil, it should be a superior source of nitrogen where water percolates through soils and where soils are water-logged after application.[5] The literature suggests that urea should not be surface applied especially on moist surfaces of calcareous or sandy soils and on the sods of at least some grasses.[27]

Ammonium sulfate, like anhydrous ammonia and urea, provides ammonium ions which are held against the action of percolating water. It is most effective under conditions where this property can be exploited and under conditions of water-logging of the soil after application of the fertilizer.[5, 40] Because it carries an acid radical, ammonium sulfate may be a superior source of nitrogen under conditions where lowering the pH even more than it is lowered by other acid nitrogen sources is desirable or where the sulfur is needed.[57] On the other hand, this extra acid-forming potential may be a serious cause of inefficiency over an extended period of usage. In calcareous soils it reacts with the calcium carbonate to form gypsum and ammonium carbonate. When this occurs on the soil surface, ammonia may be lost from the unstable carbonate and effectiveness thus reduced.[17, 36] Like urea, ammonium sulfate should be incorporated into soils which are calcareous.

Ammonium nitrate, unlike anhydrous ammonia and urea, is a neutral salt and does not cause a sharp increase in pH in the region of application. Unlike ammonium sulfate, ammonium nitrate does not react with calcareous soils to form a combination of ammonium carbonate and another salt of low solubility. Hence, large ammonia losses from ammonium nitrate application to soils have not been reported. The ammonium part of the fertilizer is retained on the colloidal complex of the soil, but the nitrate part will move with water. If aeration is poor, half of the nitrogen in this carrier is subject to denitrification.[51] This fertilizer should perform best in well-aerated soils where top-dressing is required[14, 33, 58] and precipitation not excessive. With high water percolation and normally water-logged conditions such as those encountered in rice culture, ammonium nitrate tends to be less effective than the ammonium sources that have been discussed.

Sodium nitrate and calcium nitrate are also neutral salts causing little disruption of soil reaction upon application. While the other sources mentioned have the long-term effect of lowering the pH of soils, sodium nitrate and calcium nitrate increase the pH. Since they supply nitrates, they must be employed with more care, where precipitation is high and soil textures light, than is required with some other sources. For the same reason, they have serious limitations for utilization where regular or continuous water-logging of soils is expected. Sodium ions have a dispersing effect on soil clay minerals, and the use of sodium nitrate is not desirable where alkali is, or may become, a problem. Sodium nitrate and calcium nitrate are likely to be superior in their direct, indirect, and long-term effects where their basicity or calcium or sodium content can be of added benefit.

Nitrogen solutions are subject to the limitations of the materials in solution, all of which have already been discussed. The restrictions on ammonium nitrate solutions are the same as those on ammonium nitrate, the potential hazards being from leaching and denitrification. Ammonium nitrate-urea solutions have the limitations just stated for ammonium nitrate solution plus the limitations to their use on the surface of calcareous soils and on the sods of some grasses. Except on bare acid soils, these solutions are probably most effective if incorporated into the soil during or soon after application. Solutions containing urea and ammonia; urea, ammonium nitrate, and ammonia; ammonium nitrate and ammonia; and ammonia (aqua ammonia) have to be injected into the soil for the most effective results.[58] In addition, those containing ammonium nitrate should be used in light of the restrictions stemming from the nitrate content.

Agronomic efficiency within and among sources of nitrogen varies with rate of application, time of application, placement, environment, and crop; and physical and chemical properties of the sources specify the conditions under which they may be employed and how they must be used for optimum effectiveness. Economic efficiency is the relevant criterion upon which utilization of nitrogen sources in production is based. This criterion depends upon agronomic efficiency, prices, and other conditions of the economic and decision-making environment of the user.

In conclusion it can be said that a method for comparing the relative agronomic efficiency of different nitrogen sources has been presented and applied to selected yield-response data from the literature. These relative agronomic efficiencies were transformed into the relative economic effectiveness of the nitrogen sources and some of the implications discussed.

REFERENCES

1. Allison, F. E., Doetsch, J. H., and Roller, E. M., "Ammonium Fixation and Availability in Harpster Clay Loam," *Soil Sci.*, **72**, 187–200 (1951).
2. Allison, F. E., Kefauver, M., and Roller, E. M., "Ammonia Fixation in Soils, *Soil Sci. Soc. Amer. Proc.*, **17**, 107–110 (1953).

3. Amer, Fathi, "Evaluation of Dry-Subsurface and Wet-Surface Ammonium Sulfate Application for Rice," *Plant and Soil*, 13, 47–54 (1960).

4. Bates, T. E., and Tisdale, S. L., "The Movement of Nitrate-Nitrogen Through Columns of Coarse Textured Soil Materials," *Soil Sci. Soc. Amer. Proc.*, 21, 525–528 (1957).

5. Beacher, R. L., and Wells, J. P., "Rice Fertilizer Studies 1952 to 1958," *Ark. Agri. Exp. Sta. Bul.* 620 (1960).

6. Bennett, W. F., Stanford, G., and Dumenil, L., "Nitrogen, Phosphorus, and Potassium Content of the Corn Leaf and Grain as Related to Nitrogen Fertilization and Yield," *Soil Sci. Soc. of Am. Proc.*, 17, 252–258 (1953).

7. Black, C. A., and Scott, C. O., "Fertilizer Evaluation: I. Fundamental principles," *Soil Sci. Soc. Amer. Proc.*, 20, 176–179 (1956).

8. Black, C. A., Webb, J. R., and Kempthorne, O., "Fertilizer Evaluation: III. Availability Coefficient of Water-Soluble and Citrate-Soluble Phosphorus in Acidulated Phosphate Fertilizers," *Soil Sci. Soc. Amer. Proc.*, 20, 186–189 (1956).

9. Blue, W. G. and Eno, C. F. "Distribution and Retention of Anhydrous Ammonia in Sandy Soils," *Soil Sci. Soc. of Am. Proc.*, 18, 420–424 (1954).

10. Bremner, J. M., and Shaw, K. "Denitrification in Soil I. Methods of Investigation," *J. Agr. Sci.*, 51, 22–39 (1958).

11. Broadbent, F. E., "Denitrification in Some California Soils," *Soil Sci.*, 72, 129–137 (1951).

12. Burns, G. R., "Factors Affecting the Retention of Gaseous Ammonia by Soil Exchange Materials," Unpublished M.S. Thesis, Raleigh, North Carolina State College Library, 1955.

13. Burton, G. W., and De Vane, E. H., "Effect of and Rate of Method of Applying Different Sources of Nitrogen upon Yield and Chemical Composition of Bermuda grass, *Cynondon dactylon* (L.) Pers., Hay," *Agron. J.*, 44, 128–132 (1952).

14. Burton, G. W. and Jackson, J. E., "Effect of Rate and Frequency of Applying Six Nitrogen Sources on Coastal Bermuda Grass," *Agron. J.*, 54, 40–43 (1962).

15. Cady, F. B., "Gaseous Nitrogen Products Resulting from Denitrification Reactions in Soil," Unpublished Ph.D. Dissertation, Raleigh, North Carolina State College Library, 1960.

16. Calvert, D. V., "Absorption of Nitrate by Corn as Related to Movement of Nitrate and Water in Soil," Unpublished Ph.D. Dissertation, Ames, Iowa State University Library, 1962.

17. Carter, J. N., and Allison, F. E., "The Effect of Rates of Application of Ammonium Sulfate on Gaseous Losses of Nitrogen from Soil," *Soil Sci. Soc. Amer. Proc.*, 25, 484–486 (1961).

18. Clark, F. E., Blard, W. E., and Smith, D. H., "Dissimilar Nitrifying Capacities of Soils in Relation to Losses of Applied Nitrogen," *Soil Sci. Soc. Amer. Proc.*, 24, 50–54 (1960).

19. Dreibelbis, F. R., "Soil Type and Land Use Effects on Percolation of Soil Water Through Monolith Lysimeters," *Soil Sci. Soc. of Am. Proc.*, 18, 358–362 (1954).

20. Dumenil, L., "Nitrogen and Phosphorus Composition of Corn Leaves and Yields Relative to Critical Levels and Nutrient Balance," *Soil Sci. Soc. of Am. Proc.*, 25, 295–298 (1961).

21. Ernst, J. W., and Massey, H. F., "The Effect of Several Factors on Volatilization of Ammonia Formed from Urea in the Soil," *Soil Sci. Soc. Amer. Proc.*, 24, 87–90 (1960).

22. Finney, D. J.,"Statistical Method in Biological Assay," New York, Hafner Publishing Company, 1952.

23. Gerretsen, F. C., "Microbiological Transformation of Nitrogen and Its Influence on Nitrogen Availability in the Soil," *Trans. Intern. Congr. Soil Sci., 4th Congr., Amsterdam.* **2**, 114–117 (1950).

24. Gerretsen, F. C., and de Hoop, H., "Nitrogen Losses During Nitrification in Solutions and in Acid Sandy Soils," *Can. J. Microbiology*, **3**, 359–380 (1957).

25. Hanway, J. J., and Scott, A. D., "Ammonium Fixation and Release in Certain Iowa Soils," *Soil Sci.*, **82**, 379–386 (1956).

26. Harrold, L. L., and Dreibelbis, F. R., "Agricultural Hydrology as Evaluated by Monolith Lysimeters," *U.S.D.A. Tech. Bull.*, **1050** (1951).

27. Jackson, J. E., and Burton, G. W., "Influence of Soil Treatment and Nitrogen Placement on the Utilization of Urea Nitrogen by Coastal Bermuda Grass. *Agron. J.*, **54**, 47–49 (1962).

28. Jackson, M. L., and Chang, S. C., "Anhydrous Ammonia Retention by Soils as Influenced by Depth of Application, Soil Texture, Moisture Content, pH Value and Tilth, *J. Amer. Soc. Agron.*, **34**, 623–633 (1947).

29. Jansson, S. L., Hallam, M. J., and Bartholomew, W. V., "Preferential Utilization of Ammonium over Nitrate by Microorganisms in the Decomposition of Oat Straw," *Plant and Soil*, **6**, 282–290 (1955).

30. Kilmer, V. J., Hays, O. E., and Muckenhirn, R. J., "Plant Nutrient and Water Losses from Fayette Silt Loam as Measured by Monolith Lysimeters," *J. Amer. Soc. Agron.*, **36**, 249–263 (1944).

31. Krantz, B. A., Ohlrogge, A. J., and Scarseth, G. D. "Movement of Nitrogen in Soils," *Soil Sci. Soc. of Am. Proc.*, **8**, 189–195 (1943).

32. Kresge, C. B., and Satchell, D. P., "Gaseous Loss of Ammonia from Nitrogen Fertilizers Applied to Soils, *Agron. J.*, **52**, 104–107 (1960).

33. Kresge, C. B., and Younts, S. E., "Effect of Nitrogen Source on Yield and Nitrogen Content of Bluegrass Forage," *Agron. J.*, **54**, 149–152 (1962).

34. Laughlin, W. M., "Fertilizer Practices for Bromegrass," *Alaska Agri. Exp. Sta. Bul.*, **32** (1962).

35. Mac Intire, W. H., Young, J. B., Shaw, W. M., and Robinson, B., "Nitrogen Recoveries from Applications of Ammonium Chloride, Phosphate and Sulfate and Outgo of Complimentary Ions in Rainwater Leaching Through a Six-Foot Soil-Subsoil Column," *Soil Sci. Soc. Amer. Proc.*, **16**, 301–306 (1952).

36. Martin, J. P., and Chapman, H. D., "Volatilization of Ammonia from Surface-Fertilized Soils," *Soil Sci.*, **71**, 25–34 (1951).

37. McIntosh, T. H., and Frederick, L. R., "Distribution and Nitrification of Anhydrous Ammonia in Nicollet Sandy Clay Loam," *Soil Sci. Soc. Amer. Proc.*, **22**, 402–405 (1958).

38. McDowell, L. L., and Smith, C. E., "The Retention and Reactions of Anhydrous Ammonia on Different Soil Types," *Soil Sci. Soc. of Am. Proc.*, **22**, 38–42 (1958).

39. Meyer, R. D., Olson, R. A., and Rhoades, H. F., "Ammonia Losses from Fertilized Nebraska Soils," *Agron. J.*, **53**, 241–244 (1961).

40. Mikkelsen, D. S., "Nitrogen Fertilization of Japonica Rice in California," *Rice J.*, **65**, 8–13 (1962).

41. Mitscherlich, E. A., "Das gesetz des minimums und das gesetz des abnehmenden bodenertrages," *Landw. Jahrb.*, **38**, 537–552 (1909).

42. Mortland, M. M., "Adsorption of Ammonia by Clays and Muck," *Soil Sci.*, **80**, 11–18 (1955).

43. Munson, R. D., and Pesek, J. T., "The Effects of Corn Residue, Nitrogen, and Incubation on Nitrogen Release and Subsequent Nitrogen Uptake by Oats: A Quantitative Evaluation," *Soil Sci. Soc. Amer. Proc.*, **22**, 543–547 (1958).

44. Murray, J. F., and Gausman, H. W., "Volatilization of Nitrogen from Maine Soils," Maine Farm Research, **8**, (4), 27–28 (1961).

45. Nason, A. and Takahashi, H., "Inorganic Nitrogen Metabolism," *Annual Review of Microbiology*, **12**, 203–246 (1958).

46. Nommik, H., "Investigations on Denitrification in Soil, *Acta Agr. Scand.*, **6**, 195–228 (1956).

47. Nowakowski, T. Z., "The Effect of Different Nitrogenous Fertilizers, Applied as Solids and Solutions, on the Yield and Nitrate-N Content of Established Grass and Newly Sown Ryegrass," *J. Agr. Sci.*, **56**, 287–292 (1961).

48. Olson, R. A., Lambke, W. E., and Rhoades, H. F., "Time of Nitrogen Fertilization is Important," *Neb. Agri. Exp. Sta. Quarterly*, **7**, 10–11 (1960).

49. Raney, W. A., "The Dominant Role of Nitrogen in Leaching Losses from Soil in Humid Regions," *Agron. J.*, **52**, 563–566 (1960).

50. Sabey, B. R., Bartholomew, W. V., Shaw, R. and Pesek, J., "Influence of Temperature on Nitrification in Soils," *Soil Sci. Soc. Amer. Proc.*, **20**, 357–360 (1956).

51. Schwartzbeck, R. A., MacGregor, J. M., and Schmidt, E. L., "Gaseous Nitrogen Losses from Nitrogen Fertilized Soils Measured with Infrared and Mass Spectroscopy," *Soil Sci. Soc. Amer. Proc.*, **25**, 186–189 (1961).

52. Shoji, S., "The Fixation of Ammonia and Nitrate by Organic Materials," Unpublished M.S. Thesis, East Lansing, Michigan State University Library, 1958.

53. Simpson, D. M. H., and Melsted, S. W., "Gaseous Ammonia Losses from Urea Solutions Applied as a Foliar Spray to Various Grass Sods," *Soil Sci. Soc. Amer. Proc.*, **26**, 186–189 (1962).

54. Snedecor, G. W., "Statistical Methods, 5th ed.," Ames, Iowa State University Press, 1956.

55. Sohn, J. B., and Peech, M., "Retention and Fixation of Ammonia by Soils," *Soil Sci.*, **85**, 1–9 (1958).

56. Stanley, F. A., and Smith, G. E., "Effect of Soil Moisture and Depth of Application on Retention of Anhydrous Ammonia," *Soil Sci. Soc. of Am. Proc.*, **20**, 557–561 (1956).

57. Stephens, D., "Fertilizer Experiments with Phosphorus, Nitrogen, and Sulfur in Ghana," *Emp. J. Exp. Agr.*, **28**, 151–164 (1960).

58. Trickey, N. G., and Smith, G. E., "Losses of Nitrogen from Solution Materials," *Soil Sci. Soc. Amer. Proc.*, **19**, 222–224 (1955).

59. Tyler, K. B., Lorenz, O. A., Takatori, F. H., and Bishop, J. C., "Urea Nitrogen for Potatoes," *Amer. Potato J.*, **39**, 89–99 (1962).

60. Tyner, E. H., "The Relation of Corn Yields to Leaf Nitrogen, Phosphorus and Potassium Content," *Soil Sci. Soc. Amer. Proc.*, **11**, 317–323 (1947).

61. Tyner, E. H., and Webb, J. R., "The Relation of Corn Yields to Nutrient Balance as Revealed by Leaf Analysis," *J. Amer. Soc. Agron.*, **38**, 173–185 (1946).

62. Verhoeven, W., "Some Remarks on Nitrate Metabolism in Microorganisms," in "A Symposium on Inorganic Nitrogen Metabolism," Eds. W. D. McElroy and B. Glass, pp. 61–86, Baltimore, The Johns Hopkins Press, 1956.

63. Volk, G. M., "Volatile Loss of Ammonia Following Surface Application of Urea to Turf or Bare Soils," *Agron. J.*, **51**, 746–749 (1959).

64. Volk, G. M., "Gaseous Loss of Ammonia from Surface-Applied Nitrogenous Fertilizers," *J. Agr. Food Chem.*, **9**, 280–283 (1961).
65. Volk, G. M., and Sweat, A. W., "Mobility of Urea Nitrogen Applied to Florida Soils," *Proc. Soil Sci. Soc. of Florida*, **15**, 117–123 (1955).
66. Wagner, G. H., and Smith, G. E., "Nitrogen Losses from Soils Fertilized with Different Nitrogen Carriers," *Soil Sci.*, **85**, 125–129 (1958).
67. Wahhab, A., and Ahmad, R., "Manuring Cotton in West Pakistan," *Emp. J. of Exp. Agr.*, **28**, 145–150 (1960).
68. Wahhab, A., Khan, M., and Ishaq, M., "Nitrification of Urea and its Loss through Volatilization of Ammonia under Different Soil Conditions," *J. Agr. Sci.*, **55**, 47–51 (1960).
69. Wahhab, A., Randhawa, M. S., and Alam, S. Q., "Loss of Ammonia from Ammonium Sulfate under Different Conditions when Applied to Soils," *Soil Sci.*, **84**, 249–255 (1957).
70. White, R. F., Kempthorne, O., Black, C. A., and Webb, J. R., "Fertilizer Evaluation: I. Estimation of Availability Coefficients," *Soil Sci. Soc. Amer. Proc.*, **20**, 179–186 (1956).
71. White, W. C., and Pesek, J., "Nature of Residual Nitrogen in Iowa Soils," *Soil Sci. Soc. of Am. Proc.*, **23**, 39–42 (1959).

Plant Tests

The growing of nonleguminous plants in the field and the determination of their yield and amounts of nitrogen removed from the soil is perhaps the most reliable method for assessing the content of available soil nitrogen. This method takes into account the effect of weather and cultural practices on the release of nitrogen from both the plow layer and subsoil. To be most effective, test plots of the crop in question should be placed in each field where the soil or previous cultural practices are or have been appreciably different. Although this method is too slow and expensive by itself, data is provided on which less expensive methods may be based.

Because of the difficulties encountered in carrying on a large number of field tests, suitable samples of soil are frequently potted and crops grown on them in the greenhouse to determine the amounts of nitrogen released. This method makes possible the testing of many different soil types and of the effect of different cultural practices. Although temperature, moisture, and aeration are usually more favorable for release of nitrogen in the greenhouse than in the field, the data obtained in the greenhouse make possible a relative evaluation of a large number of soils. In most cases the values obtained are much higher than those found in the field and may be misleading if taken directly as a basis for predicting fertilizer needs. They are valuable, however, in providing a standard of reference or basis of correlation with soil nitrogen tests.

Microbiological Tests

Nitrification Test.   The nitrification test has been employed quite successfully by a number of investigators.[1, 6, 7, 8, 10] In this test a small sample of soil is usually incubated for a period of 2 to 4 weeks under controlled conditions of temperature, moisture, and aeration. The procedure proposed by Stanford and Hanway[16] and employed in the Iowa State Soil Testing Laboratory is given as follows:

(1) Place 10 gm of soil, mixed with approximately an equal volume of exfoliated vermiculite, in a tube through which water may be percolated.

(2) Leach the sample free of nitrates with 3 successive 20-ml portions of distilled water, allowing each portion to drain from the soil before adding the next.

(3) Apply suction to remove excess water.

(4) Place the sample in an incubator controlled at 35°C. Moisture loss during incubation is minimized by placing a one-hole rubber stopper or perforated plastic cap on the tube, and by maintaining a high relative humidity in the incubator.

(5) Following 2 weeks of incubation, leach the sample free of nitrates as in steps 2 and 3 above. Place a 2-ml aliquot of the leachate in a 50-ml beaker and evaporate to dryness following the addition of 1-ml of saturated $Ca(OH)_2$ solution. If the leachate requires filtering, add the $Ca(OH)_2$ prior to filtration or place on

the filter. Add 1 ml of phenoldisulphonic acid to the residue and let stand 10 to 15 min. Add 14 ml of water and 5 ml of 2:1 NH₄OH, and read intensity of the yellow color with a colorimeter.

Stanford and Hanway tested samples of 21 Iowa soils (7 types) by this method. They tested for total nitrogen, initial nitrate nitrogen, and for nitrogen released by boiling the sample with an alkaline permanganate solution as proposed by Truog, *et al.*[20] German millet was grown on the soils for fifty days in the greenhouse, and the amounts of nitrogen released were correlated with three nitrogen tests. The correlation coefficients (all significant at 1 per cent level) shown in Table 19.1 were obtained from the published paper and from information supplied by Black.[3] These results show clearly that the nitrogen removed by the crop was most closely related to the initial content of nitrate nitrogen and that released by a 2-week period of incubation. The authors ascribed little significance to the high correlation for initial nitrate nitrogen because they believed it to be appreciably higher than normal in the soils they studied. Favorable results for the nitrification test were also reported by Saunder, *et al.*,[14] with Southern Rhodesian soils and Synghal, *et al.*,[18] with Alberta soils.

***Aspergillus niger* Test.** Peterson, *et al.*,[11] grew two successive crops of tobacco in pots on soils from 37 tobacco fields, and correlated the uptake of nitrogen with various soil nitrogen tests. The procedure used for the *Aspergillus niger* test is given as follows:

Place a 50-gm sample of soil in a 250-ml beaker and add 50 ml of nutrient solution containing all the elements needed by the organism except nitrogen. After inoculation with the organism, incubate the culture at a temperature of about 35°C for three days, at which time the growth of the organism will be observed. If the supply of nitrogen is adequate, growth will be about 1 cm in thickness and will entirely cover the surface of the liquid, the fungus tissue being covered with jet-black conidia. Remove the tissue, dry, weigh, and translate the result from a standard curve to pounds per acre of available nitrogen in the soil. Make a standard curve from the growth of the organism on nutrient solutions with varied concentrations of nitrogen.

As indicated in Table 19.2 a high correlation (0.90) was obtained between this test and uptake of nitrogen by the first crop of tobacco, but

TABLE 19.1. CORRELATION BETWEEN AMOUNTS OF NITROGEN REMOVED BY GERMAN MILLET GROWN IN POTS OF 21 SOILS AND VARIOUS SOIL NITROGEN TESTS

Nitrogen Test	Correlation Coefficient
Initial NO₃-N	0.95
Nitrification rate	0.91
Total soil N	0.84
Alkaline permanganate N	0.70

TABLE 19.2. COEFFICIENTS OF CORRELATION FOR THE RELATION BETWEEN VARIOUS SOIL NITROGEN TESTS AND THE TOTAL NITROGEN CONTENT OF THE ABOVE GROUND PORTION OF TWO SUCCESSIVE CROPS OF TOBACCO GROWN IN POTS ON SOILS FROM 37 TOBACCO FIELDS

Nitrogen Test	Coefficient of Correlation	
	1st crop	2nd crop
Initial NO_3-N..........................	0.97**	−0.05
Nitrification rate.......................	−0.25	0.40*
Total soil N............................	−0.16	0.62**
Alkaline permanganate N...............	−0.10	0.61**
H_2SO_4 extraction.....................	−0.05	0.71**
Aspergillus niger test.................	0.90**	0.07

* Significant at 5 per cent level.
** Significant at 1 per cent level.

the correlation was nearly zero for the second crop. The highest correlation (0.97) was obtained for the initial content of NO_3-N before the first crop, but this was nearly zero for the second crop. Since there was a fairly good supply of this form of nitrogen in the soil at the start of the first crop but almost zero for the second crop, the results just noted might be expected. The close agreement between the results obtained with *Aspergillus niger* and the initial content of NO_3-N suggests that the growth of this organism was directly related to the amounts of NO_3-N present.

Chemical Tests

Nitrate Nitrogen. The content of nitrate nitrogen in the plow layer usually ranges between 5 and 75 ppm, but may exceed this under special circumstances where heavy applications of manure, high protein crop residues and nitrogen fertilizers have been made. It is normally low in the spring, but increases as the soil warms up, until crop removal or leaching limit further increases.

The content of nitrate nitrogen in the soil is usually determined by extraction of the sample with water and determination by the phenoldisulphonic acid method.[2] The NO_3-N content of the 21 soils reported in Table 19.1 varied from 12 to 71 ppm and 7 to 108 ppm for the 37 tobacco soils reported in Table 19.2. The data presented in both tables emphasize the importance of the initial content of NO_3-N as a basis for determining the amount of nitrogen fertilizer that should be applied. In the absence of appreciable amounts of NO_3-N for the second crop of tobacco (Table 19.2), total soil N, alkaline permanganate N, and NH_4-N extracted by H_2SO_4 gave the highest correlation. The reason for the lack of agreement between the Iowa and Wisconsin workers in regard to the results for the nitrification test is not clear, since the analyses for this test were all made in the Iowa State Soil Testing Laboratory. It seems possible, however, that greater variability among soil types and cultural practices was present in the Wisconsin soils.

Alkaline Permanganate Test. Truog, *et al.*,[20] proposed the following procedure for determining available soil nitrogen:

Place 1 gm of soil and 1 gm of a mixture of 20 parts of $KMnO_4$ and 80 parts of Na_2CO_3 in an 800-ml Kjeldahl flask. Then add 150 ml of water and attach a condenser. Catch in the distillate the nitrogen liberated from the soil as ammonia during 5 min of boiling, and Nesslerize. The results for available nitrogen thus determined are interpreted in terms of pounds per acre as follows: very low (0 to 75), low (75 to 150), medium (150 to 225), high (225 to 300), and very high (300 and more).

The results of this and other tests are presented in Tables 19.1, 19.2, and 19.3. In Table 19.1 the results for this test are less favorable than for the other three tests employed; for the second crop in Table 19.2 and the second experiment in Table 19.3, this test ranks as intermediate among the tests used. In most cases there was fairly good agreement between this test and that for total soil nitrogen. Subbiah and Asija[17] reported favorable results with this method.

H_2SO_4 Extraction. The data reported by Peterson, *et al.*,[11] in Table 19.2 for soil nitrogen extracted by H_2SO_4 were obtained by the following procedure:

Place 20 gm of soil and 50 ml of $1N$ H_2SO_4 in a 500-ml Erlenmeyer flask and shake in an end-over-end shaker for 30 min. Filter the sample with suction and wash twice with distilled water. Place the filtrate in an 800-ml Kjeldahl flask, and add sufficient NaOH to make it distinctly alkaline. Distill the ammonia into 4 per cent boric acid solution, and titrate with $0.018N$ H_2SO_4 .

The correlation data presented in Table 19.2 for this test relating to the second crop of tobacco are similar to those for total soil nitrogen and the alkaline permanganate tests. Tiurin and Kononova[19] found extraction of soil samples with $0.5N$ H_2SO_4 at room temperature gave more reliable results for available soil nitrogen than the other method used.

H_2SO_4 Digestion and Nitrate Reduction. Richard, *et al.*,[12] proposed a test for available nitrogen that takes into account both the amount of nitrogen hydrolyzed by boiling $0.25N$ H_2SO_4 and that present as NO_3-N. The procedure is given as follows:

Place 1 gm of soil in an 800-ml Kjeldahl flask, and add 0.6 gm metallic iron, 0.15 gm of salicylic acid, and 80 ml of $0.25N$ H_2SO_4 . Attach a condenser, and with an electric heater adjusted to bring to boiling in 3 min, boil for 5 min, and discard the distillate. Then add 22.5 ml of N NaOH, boil for 3 min, Nesslerize the distillate, and express the results as pounds per acre. The amount of nitrogen released by the dilute H_2SO_4 alone in this procedure was determined by subtracting the amount of nitrate nitrogen found in a separate sample by the phenoldisulphonic acid method from that found by the present procedure.

The data obtained for this test were compared with those for several other nitrogen tests in two experiments of 22 and 39 soils. In these experiments corn was grown in the greenhouse for 75 and 50 days, respectively, and the uptake of nitrogen by the crops was correlated with the values obtained for the various tests. The data presented in Table 19.3 for these tests further emphasize the importance of taking into account the initial content of NO_3-N where appreciable amounts are present and where leaching is not a serious problem. The average contents of this form was 15 and 10 ppm, respectively, for the two experiments. The results further show that the best estimates of nitrogen uptake by the crops were provided by test No. 3 (which takes into account both initial NO_3-N and that released by H_2SO_4 digestion) and by a combination of the separate texts, Nos. 2 and 5.

Total Soil N. Smith[15] and Woodruff[21] reported a fairly close relation between the uptake of nitrogen by crops and the total nitrogen content of Missouri soils. Their data showed that within certain limits a fairly definite percentage of the total soil nitrogen was mineralized and thus became available in the course of a growing season. They calculated that $1\frac{1}{2}$ to 3 per cent of the total became available for silt loams, $1\frac{1}{2}$ to $2\frac{1}{2}$ per cent for

TABLE 19.3. COEFFICIENTS OF CORRELATION FOR THE RELATION BETWEEN NITROGEN UPTAKE RESPONSE BY CORN GROWN ON SOIL IN POTS AND THE RESULTS OF VARIOUS SOIL TESTS

Soil Test Number	Soil Nitrogen Test	1st Experiment (22 soils)	2nd Experiment (39 soils)
		Linear correlation coefficients	
1	alkaline permanganate N	0.37	0.65**
2	H_2SO_4 digestion	—	0.63**
3	same as (2) except NO_3-N reduced and included	0.86**	0.82**
4	total soil N	0.45*	0.65**
5	initial NO_3-N	0.74**	0.77**
6	nitrification rate	0.16	—
7	*Aspergillus niger* test	0.64**	—
		Multiple correlation coefficient	
2 and 5	H_2SO_4 digestion N and NO_3-N	—	0.87**

* Significant at 5 per cent level.
** Significant at 1 per cent level.

clays and clay loams, and 4 to 6 per cent for sands and sandy loams. Total nitrogen was determined by the Kjeldahl method.[2] The results of the tests presented in all three tables suggest that the test for total soil nitrogen compares favorably with extraction with H_2SO_4 and with digestion with H_2SO_4 or alkaline permanganate solutions.

SELECTION AND INTERPRETATION OF SOIL TESTS

On the basis of the data presented, there is good evidence that the content of NO_3-N should be taken into account if appreciable amounts are present (possibly 10 ppm or more) and if leaching is not likely to be a serious problem between the time of sampling and uptake of the nitrogen by the crop. Where serious leaching is likely to occur or in the absence of appreciable amounts of NO_3-N, tests for total nitrogen or some fraction of the total as obtained by nitrification rate, alkaline permanganate digestion, or acid extraction or digestion, can prove satisfactory. Tests which take into account both NO_3-N already present in the soil and that which is likely to become available in the course of a growing season should prove to be superior. One advantage of the chemical tests over the microbiological tests is the short time required for their completion.

For proper interpretation of nitrogen soil test values, it is highly important that the results of the test be correlated with crop response to added nitrogen on a number of agriculturally important soil types. Also, the amounts of nitrogen supplied by manure, crop residues, or legume sods often need to be taken into account. For example, in a corn-wheat rotation Smith[15] found the addition of 8 tons of manure per acre to corn plots receiving 400 lb per acre of 0-12-12 fertilizer increased the yield of corn by about 10 bu/acre. An increase of 19 bu/acre was obtained by plowing down a crop of sweet clover in place of the manure. His findings also emphasize the great importance of adding adequate amounts of phosphate and potash fertilizers if corn is to make a full response to applications of nitrogen fertilizer.

Several items should be taken into account in recommending nitrogen fertilizer based on soil tests. These include the total amount of nitrogen required by the crop and the amount to be supplied by manure, crop residues, and the soil itself. It is generally known that a 100-bu/acre crop of corn requires about 200 lb of nitrogen. If the above sources of nitrogen are inadequate to supply this amount, the balance must be supplied in the form of fertilizer. According to Smith,[15] barnyard manure may be expected on the average to supply about 4 lb of nitrogen per ton for the first crop of corn and 2 lb for the second. Marriott[9] found red clover sod plowed under for corn on Miami silt loam supplied the equivalent of about 60 lb/

acre of nitrogen, alfalfa 80 lb and red clover-timothy and alfalfa-timothy 40 lb each. An application of 10 tons/acre of manure plowed under together with a red clover sod would therefore be expected to provide about 100 lb of nitrogen for the corn crop. Assuming a soil test value of 60 lb/acre of available nitrogen, the difference between the total amount of nitrogen (200 lb) required by the crop and the total amount (160 lb) to be supplied by the soil, manure, and red clover would be 40 lb, the amount to be supplied as commercial fertilizer. This amount could be supplied by 120 lb of ammonium nitrate, 50 lb of anhydrous ammonia or 200 lb of ammonium sulfate.

REFERENCES

1. Allison, F. E., and Sterling, L. D., "Nitrate Formation from Soil Organic Matter in Relation to Total Nitrogen and Cropping Practices," *Soil Sci.,* **67,** 239-252 (1949).
2. Association of Official Agricultural Chemists, "Methods of Analysis," 7th ed., Washington, D. C., 1950.
3. Black, C. A., "Soil-Plant Relationships," New York, John Wiley & Sons, Inc., 1957.
4. Bremner, J. M., "Studies on Soil Organic Matter. Part 1. The Chemical Nature of Soil Organic Nitrogen," *J. Agr. Sci.,* **39,** 183-193 (1949).
5. Bremner, J. M., "The Nature of Soil Nitrogen Complexes," *J. Sci. Food Agr.,* **3,** 497-500 (1952).
6. Fitts, J. W., Bartholomew, W. V., and Heidel, H., "Predicting Nitrogen Fertilizer Needs of Iowa soils: I. Evaluation and Control of Factors in Nitrate Production and Analysis," *Soil Sci. Soc. Amer. Proc.,* **19,** 69-73 (1955).
7. Fraps, G. S., "Relation of Soil Nitrogen, Nitrification and Ammonification to Pot Experiments," *Texas Agr. Exp. Sta. Bul.,* **283** (1921).
8. Hanway, G., and Dumenil, L., "Predicting Nitrogen Fertilizer Needs of Iowa soils. III. Use of Nitrate Production Together with Other Information as a Basis of Making Nitrogen Fertilizer Recommendations for Corn in Iowa." *Soil Sci. Soc. Amer. Proc.,* **19,** 77-80 (1955).
9. Marriott, L. F., "Nitrogen Supplied by Legume and Grass Residues on Miami Silt Loam in Relation to Grain Response to Commercial Nitrogen," Ph.D. Thesis, Madison, University of Wisconsin, 1955.
10. Munson, R. D., and Stanford, G., "Predicting Nitrogen Fertilizer Needs for Iowa Soils. IV. Evaluation of Nitrate Production as a Criterion of Nitrogen Availability," *Soil Sci. Soc. Amer. Proc.,* **19,** 464-468 (1955).
11. Peterson, L. A., Attoe, O. J., and Ogden, W. B., "Correlation of Nitrogen Soil Tests with Nitrogen Uptake by the Tobacco Plant," *Soil Sci. Soc. Amer. Proc.,* **24,** 205-208 (1960).
12. Richard, T. A., Attoe, O. J., Moskal, S. and Truog, E., "A Chemical Method for Determining Available Soil Nitrogen," Trans., 7th Intern. Cong. of Soil Sci. II: 28-35, 1960.
13. Russell, E. W., "Soil Conditions and Plant Growth," 9th ed., New York, John Wiley & Sons Inc., 1961.
14. Saunder, D. H., Ellis, B. S., and Hall, A., "Estimation of Available Nitrogen for Advisory Purposes in Southern Rhodesia," *J. Soil Sci.,* **8,** 301-312 (1957).

15. Smith, G. E., Soil Fertility and Corn Production," *Missouri Agr. Exp. Sta., Bul.,* **583,** (1952).

16. Stanford, G., and Hanway, J., "Predicting Nitrogen Fertilizer Needs of Iowa soils: II. A Simplified Technique for Determining Relative Nitrate Production in Soils," *Soil Sci. Soc. Amer. Proc.,* **19,** 74–77 (1955).

17. Subbiah, B. V., and Asija, G. L. A., "A Rapid Procedure for the Estimation of Available Nitrogen in Soils," *Current Sci.,* **25,** 259–260 (1956).

18. Synghal, K. N., Toogood, J. A., and Bentley, C. F., "Assessing Nitrogen Requirements of Some Alberta Soils," *Canad. J. Soil Sci.,* **39,** 120–128 (1959)

19. Tiurin, I. V., and Kononova, M. M., "Methods of Determining the Requirements of Soils for Nitrogen Fertilizer," *Trans. Dokiechaiev Soil Inst.,* **25,** 159–180 (1935).

20. Truog, E., Hull, H. H., and Shihata, M. M., "A Test for Available Soil Nitrogen," Paper presented before 1953 Annual Meeting Amer. Soc. Agron., Dallas, Texas, 1953.

21. Woodruff, C. M., "Estimating the Nitrogen Delivery of Soil from the Organic Matter Determination as Reflected by Sanborn Field," *Soil Sci. Soc. Amer. Proc.,* **14,** 208–212 (1949).

20

Safety Precautions in Fertilizer Processing Plants

ELMER C. PERRINE

Nitrogen Division, Allied Chemical Corporation, New York, New York

Since men must use and service the tools of their civilization, the intransigency of man in a changing world continues to be a problem. For example, in 1961 the average frequency rate of disabling injuries in the fertilizer industry was about ten per million man hours of work. For the forty-one industries which reported to the National Safety Council (for comparative data see Figure 20.1), the average frequency rate was about six.

The use of nitrogen (or ammoniating) solution, anhydrous ammonia, and acid is associated with a number of accidents each year. Moreover, the production of nitrogen solutions involves the making and handling of large quantities of highly active nitric acid and anhydrous ammonia. Yet, some nitrogen-producing plants have completed three million (or more) man hours of work without a disabling injury. The interests of safety are not well served by thinking that accidents are to be expected.

In the average plant, safety was probably an important consideration when the initial professional decisions were made concerning equipment and processes. Therefore, no change should be made or allowed to develop without thorough investigation. Nevertheless, the design and condition of equipment frequently create hazards. Much of the equipment is well made, but often suffers obsolescence before being worn out, which may lead to risky improvisation and inadequate maintenance. Furthermore, some of the operations performed are sensitive in themselves. A typical example is the combining of concentrated sulfuric acid with nitrogen solution in the

Work Accidents, 1961

....some facts from NSC's AC-
CIDENT FACTS (1962 edition)

1961 injury rates, reporters to National Safety Council

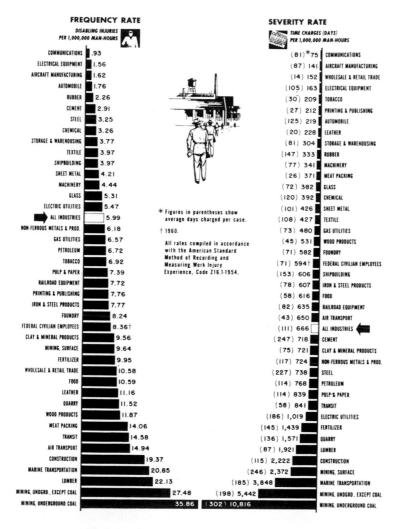

FREQUENCY RATE
DISABLING INJURIES
PER 1,000,000 MAN-HOURS

Industry	Rate
COMMUNICATIONS	.93
ELECTRICAL EQUIPMENT	1.56
AIRCRAFT MANUFACTURING	1.62
AUTOMOBILE	1.76
RUBBER	2.26
CEMENT	2.91
STEEL	3.25
CHEMICAL	3.26
STORAGE & WAREHOUSING	3.77
TEXTILE	3.97
SHIPBUILDING	3.97
SHEET METAL	4.21
MACHINERY	4.44
GLASS	5.31
ELECTRIC UTILITIES	5.47
ALL INDUSTRIES	5.99
NON-FERROUS METALS & PROD.	6.18
GAS UTILITIES	6.57
PETROLEUM	6.72
TOBACCO	6.92
PULP & PAPER	7.39
RAILROAD EQUIPMENT	7.72
PRINTING & PUBLISHING	7.76
IRON & STEEL PRODUCTS	7.77
FOUNDRY	8.24
FEDERAL CIVILIAN EMPLOYEES	8.36†
CLAY & MINERAL PRODUCTS	9.56
MINING, SURFACE	9.64
FERTILIZER	9.95
WHOLESALE & RETAIL TRADE	10.58
FOOD	10.59
LEATHER	11.16
QUARRY	11.52
WOOD PRODUCTS	11.87
MEAT PACKING	14.06
TRANSIT	14.58
AIR TRANSPORT	14.94
CONSTRUCTION	19.37
MARINE TRANSPORTATION	20.85
LUMBER	22.13
MINING, UNDGRD., EXCEPT COAL	27.48
MINING, UNDERGROUND COAL	35.86

* Figures in parentheses show
average days charged per case.

† 1960.

All rates compiled in accordance
with the American Standard
Method of Recording and
Measuring Work Injury
Experience, Code Z16.1-1954.

SEVERITY RATE
TIME CHARGES (DAYS)
PER 1,000,000 MAN-HOURS

Days	Industry
(81) *75	COMMUNICATIONS
(87) 141	AIRCRAFT MANUFACTURING
(14) 152	WHOLESALE & RETAIL TRADE
(105) 163	ELECTRICAL EQUIPMENT
(30) 209	TOBACCO
(27) 212	PRINTING & PUBLISHING
(125) 219	AUTOMOBILE
(20) 228	LEATHER
(81) 304	STORAGE & WAREHOUSING
(147) 333	RUBBER
(77) 341	MACHINERY
(26) 371	MEAT PACKING
(72) 382	GLASS
(120) 392	CHEMICAL
(101) 426	SHEET METAL
(108) 427	TEXTILE
(73) 480	GAS UTILITIES
(45) 531	WOOD PRODUCTS
(71) 582	FOUNDRY
(71) 594†	FEDERAL CIVILIAN EMPLOYEES
(153) 606	SHIPBUILDING
(78) 607	IRON & STEEL PRODUCTS
(58) 616	FOOD
(82) 635	RAILROAD EQUIPMENT
(43) 650	AIR TRANSPORT
(111) 666	ALL INDUSTRIES
(247) 718	CEMENT
(75) 721	CLAY & MINERAL PRODUCTS
(117) 724	NON-FERROUS METALS & PROD.
(227) 738	STEEL
(114) 768	PETROLEUM
(114) 839	PULP & PAPER
(58) 841	TRANSIT
(186) 1,019	ELECTRIC UTILITIES
(145) 1,439	FERTILIZER
(136) 1,571	QUARRY
(87) 1,921	LUMBER
(115) 2,222	CONSTRUCTION
(246) 2,372	MINING, SURFACE
(185) 3,848	MARINE TRANSPORTATION
(198) 5,442	MINING, UNDGRD., EXCEPT COAL
(302) 10,816	MINING, UNDERGROUND COAL

Figure 20.1. (*Reproduced Courtesy the National Safety Council*)

presence of potassium chloride in the ordinary continuous or rotary batch mixer. For safety and other reasons, the prereactor, or preneutralizer, was developed to isolate desirable from undesirable actions. The use of water in this arrangement is an excellent control.

Against the desires of sales departments for the ideal fertilizer stands the over-riding problem of economics. Opposed to the highest rates of ammoniation are the problems of maintenance and the possibility of air pollution. It should be noted that either the intended or accidental use of exessive amounts of an ingredient may change a process into a hazardous one or result in an inferior product.

In the fertilizer industry, there are signs that point to impending danger. Thus without help, many operators quickly learn to control ammonia fumes, or granulation, by increasing the amount of sulfuric acid, although they may not be aware of the other consequences of this measure. Of course, it cannot be expected that the average operator will understand why it requires precisely 3.09 lb of 66° Bé sulfuric acid to neutralize 1.0 lb of ammonia, while the utilization of from 3.0 to 6.5 lb of ammonia per unit of P_2O_5 in 20 per cent superphosphate is safe and practical. On the other hand, operators frequently know that excessive heat in the dryer, in storage, and the mixer can be dangerous. They will learn to check regularly the performance of meters, furnaces, and pumps, and to be otherwise alert to any changes necessary to insure safety. The operating staff should be instructed to recognize and heed all signs of impending trouble. Increased respect for properties of materials and some understanding of their reactions can greatly improve a safety record. It is hoped that this chapter will inspire alertness to possibilities in handling chemicals. Not all of these are discussed, and, of course, no guarantee of results can be given for those which are.

THE MATERIALS

Anhydrous ammonia has a comparatively good safety record even with its relatively high vapor pressure and great destructiveness upon escape. There has been much effective education in the handling of anhydrous ammonia and some other chemicals.

Good equipment of low cost carbon steel of heavy construction is readily available for handling ammonia, and the temptations for substituting and improvising do not exist to the extent that they do in the handling of nitrogen solutions and the acids. The fact that ammonia is often transferred by its own vapor pressure eliminates what hazards may be entailed in the use of pumps and compressors. The end products derived from combining ammonia with superphosphates, sulfuric, and phosphoric acid create no serious problems of subsequent handling or storage.

Aqua ammonia is usually a by-product and contains from 25 to 30 per cent ammonia. It is sometimes made in plants with anhydrous ammonia to contain as much as 50 per cent ammonia. The vapor pressure of 30 per cent aqua ammonia is so low that fumes in handling are not a serious problem. For practical reasons, however, it must be assumed that any ammoniating medium will very probably create an explosive mixture inside of all tanks and mixers.

Nitrogen solutions, also termed ammoniating solutions, are employed in nearly every fertilizer mixing plant. They are used in some formulas in amounts that closely approach the highest expectations of the nitrogen producers. They contain from about 50 to 75 per cent ammonium nitrate when this is the only nitrogen-bearing salt, and some contain from about 32 to 45 per cent urea as the one nitrogen bearing salt. The ammonia content ranges from about 16 to 34 per cent and even more. Water content ranges from less than 1.0 to about 18 per cent in the ammonium nitrate–ammonia solutions. It is about 30 per cent in the urea–ammonia solutions.

The complexities which lead to these desirable features complicate the problems of safely handling the nitrogen solutions. They have vapor pressures ranging from 1 psig at 104°F to 57 psig or more. Therefore, handling them involves some of the problems of handling anhydrous ammonia (such as fumes, vapor locking of pumps, and metering problems), but to a milder degree. The nitrogen salts add the problems of corrosion of ordinary steel and some other metals. Salting out sometimes becomes a problem when the choice of solution is ill-advised. The points at which salting out begin range from −52°F for one solution to as high as 61°F for another.

Phosphoric acid in the low cost, wet-process form and in the furnace grade with its special properties have become important sources of P_2O_5 because of their efficient reactions with ammonia and high total plant food. One combination of nitrogen solution and phosphoric acid will yield about 22.4 per cent N and 40 per cent P_2O_5 (dry basis).

As with other acids, the problems of handling phosphoric acid are those of deterioration of equipment and the destruction of human tissue which, however, is not as severe as is such destruction by sulfuric acid. The original equipment as recommended by the acid suppliers or by most equipment makers is usually adequate. Some problems arise from poor maintenance; others, from lack of appreciation of the effects of acids on human tissue.

Sulfuric acid is highly destructive to human tissue. It is also destructive to carbon steel in concentrations below 60° Bé (about 77 per cent acid).

One problem derives from the fact that small amounts of moisture in the air can dilute the acid at its surface enough to cause severe corrosion of carbon steel. Carbon steel is ordinarily an acceptable low cost material of construction.

The viscosity of sulfuric acid increases at low temperature particularly if there is some dilution. This creates some problems in metering and handling which are often solved by applying greater pressure. This in turn somewhat raises the chances of accidents.

Very large amounts of sulfuric acid are employed safely in many formulas when the equipment and controls are in good order. However, when large amounts are used with poor control in the presence of little water and with large amounts of ammonium nitrate and potassium chloride, flash fires and explosions may occur in the mixers.

HANDLING THE MATERIALS

Physiological Effects

Physiological effects are too often discounted by workers until they become victims of an accident. No human tissue can resist the strong destructive power of sulfuric acid, the eyes being particularly vulnerable. The affected areas should be flushed immediately, preferably with clean running water, although any water will do in an emergency.

Under some conditions, sulfuric acid has the ability to raise the temperature of its mixture with water to a degree that it can be a serious problem. Questions may be raised about the effects of this temperature rise with its accompanying fumes when the eyes begin to tear excessively. The eyes should be flushed for 15 min with low pressure water; a drinking fountain makes a good emergency eye bath. A small squeeze bottle of distilled or clean water carried in a pocket should be readily available, even when the victim of an accident is temporarily blinded. Thus each man can assure himself that the vital first few seconds are employed to the best advantage. Indeed, these initial seconds can mean the difference between permanent blindness and temporary pain. Competent medical service should, of course, be obtained immediately after first aid treatment. Even a slight consideration of the problems of handling accidents involving sulfuric acid in the eyes should convert the most flagrant violator into a habitual wearer of goggles or a face mask.

Data from the Compressed Gas Association pamphlet G2 indicate that ammonia fumes can be detected by smell in concentrations as low as about 50 ppm of air. The maximum tolerance for working conditions is stated to be about 100 ppm and about 700 ppm will cause eye irritation. More than 5000 ppm can cause death from spasms in a short time or inflammation of the larynx. The ordinary cartridge type of ammonia or the universal gas mask is rated to protect the wearer from concentrations up to about 3 per cent in air, which is 33,000 ppm of air. Damage to the skin can be severe, even though a mask may protect the respiratory system and the eyes. Further safety information may be obtained from "Dangerous Properties of Industrial Materials," Second Edition, by N. I. Sax (Reinhold, 1963).

Unlike such gases as the common and deadly carbon monoxide, ammonia nearly always gives some warning in time for workers to escape or for corrective measures to be started. However, when there is a sudden failure of equipment, particularly with anhydrous ammonia, the situation can become serious very rapidly. In addition to releasing very heavy concentrations of gas, anhydrous ammonia can cause severe injury or death from freezing. Liquid ammonia at atmospheric pressure has a temperature of $-28°F$.

As in the emergency treatment for accidents with acids, the recommended first aid procedure is immediately to flush the affected parts with copious amounts of running water, then to have the services of a doctor. Artificial respiration may be required. However, never force an unconscious person to drink any liquid.

Two escape routes should be always available. Quick accounting for all persons will greatly simplify rescue efforts.

CORROSION AND DETERIORATION OF EQUIPMENT

Corrosion and deterioration of equipment lead to accidents as well as to inefficient operations.

In addition to using the liquids to the best advantage, there is much safety built in the designs of some of the distribution pipes for the nitrogen solutions and acids used in the mixing equipment. Corrosion and abrasion in the presence of heat and moisture are severe. Inspection is often difficult and dangerous, so that inspection is often sadly neglected.

In regard to the use and arrangement of distributor pipes, good operators and engineers will experiment with and discuss the merits of 15 or 50 holes, $\frac{1}{16}$ or $\frac{1}{8}$ in. in size, as well as the proper spacing required to insure delivery of acids and solutions in correct proportions. Through failure of proper maintenance, these distributor pipes quite often degenerate to a point where practically all of the liquids are pouring through the first two or three holes. They have become so enlarged that less than one-fifth of the length of the distributor is being used. Some distributor pipes are

ORIGINAL PATTERN OF 3/15" HOLES AT INLET END OF DISTRIBUTOR PIPE

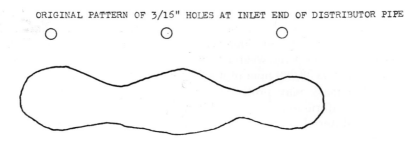

Figure 20.2. Effects of corrosion in 3 months on extra heavy black steel pipe.

replaced only after they break off. Figure 20.2 shows the effects of corrosion on one nitrogen solution distributor. This represents a fairly common situation.

The poor distribution of nitrogen solutions leads some operators to apply more and more acid to control the fumes from a formula which originally released little, if any, fumes.

Even if the formula is not changed, the pouring together of the correct total amounts of solution and sulfuric acid in large streams deprives the system of the safe controlling effects that were originally provided in the designs. These conditions also cause balling of the mass, and the mixer no longer can really mix. Even after years of publicity for the principles of good ammoniation, some present distributor pipes still do not remotely meet the requirements.

Failure of recycle in the continuous system and poor distributor pipes result in quite a few flash fires and explosions in the mixers. Unobserved failure of dry materials to enter the rotary batch mixer sometimes yield the same results even when the distributor pipes are in good condition.

When moisture from air or from cleaning the system has diluted sulfuric acid, even some stainless steel indicators in the flowmeters may become so reduced in size by corrosion that the excess amount of sulfuric acid delivered can result in explosion in the mixer. In one such case, the amount of sulfuric acid used was so great for so long that a good materials inventory should actually have inspired an investigation in ample time.

The initial result of the action of sulfuric acid on ordinary black steel is the depositing of a coating of iron sulfate on the inside surface. At velocities below about 2 ft/sec, this coating provides protection against further rapid corrosion. Above this velocity, this coating is flushed off and corrosion is rapid in pipes and greater at elbows. In schedule 80 (extra heavy) steel pipe, a velocity of 2 ft/sec will deliver about the following number of gallons per minute:

Nominal Pipe Size (inches)	Actual Inside Diameter of Extra Heavy Pipe (inches)	Square Inch Area	Approx. Gal/Min at Velocity of 2 Ft/Sec
1	0.95	.071	4.4
1½	1.49	1.75	10.9
2	1.93	2.94	18.4

The capacity for trouble from the effects of sulfuric and phosphoric acids on various materials needs more understanding in fertilizer processing plants.

Because hydrogen gas will be released when the acids react with steel, provisions must be made to prevent the build-up of pressures in the piping and tanks. Because hydrogen is explosive over the extremely wide range of from about 4 to 75 per cent in air, it is imperative that all precautions be taken against forming it and against igniting it once it is produced. Only one other common gas, acetylene, has a wider explosive range (2.5 to 81 per cent). Acetylene is well respected for its explosive possibilities. Hydrogen should be given the same wholesome respect.

In one known case, galvanized pipe was installed from the storage tank to the pump and then for a considerable distance to the meters. The release of hydrogen was so great that it vapor-locked the pump.

The use of air pressure is not advised for handling acids in fertilizer plants for several good reasons. Where there is air, there is usually moisture, and more is present when the air is compressed because more air is involved. This leads to corrosion, locally or generally, particularly with sulfuric acid. If there is a failure of equipment, such as a broken pipe or valve, it is difficult to stop the flow quickly if the force is air compressed in the supply tank. However, the flow from electrically driven pumps can be stopped immediately from any of several safe points. For added safety, air pressure should not remain in an acid tank during an idle period.

Rubber and plastic hoses, fittings, and tanks should be adopted only after consulting the makers of the materials to be handled and also the acid or nitrogen solution suppliers. Use the correct materials in the diaphragms of valves, in gaskets, gauge glass packing, and pump packings.

There have been failures of plastic hoses which were not properly chosen. Carbon steel bands or clamps will be quickly corroded even outside fertilizer plants. Use stainless steel clamps. More than one hose has slipped from fittings and created severe hazards to the personnel. Even the warmer atmospheric temperatures considerably reduce the strength of some plastic materials. There are suitable plastic materials made for most of the services in normal fertilizer plants. Competent advice is highly desirable for making the correct choices and for installing the piping.

Explosive mixtures of ammonia and air range from about 11 to 28 per cent ammonia in air. This is about the widest range considered. However, men are quickly forced away from concentrations of 0.5 per cent because of the inability to breathe freely. It is, therefore, an academic question whether an explosive mixture exists in a working area, for the lowest point in the explosive range is some twenty times greater than the maximum concentration in which man can stay for any length of time. However, with poor ventilation, it is conceivable that explosive mixtures could exist near an area in which the personnel could be present for a time.

It is impractical to determine the exact concentration of ammonia inside the tanks, mixers, and over masses of fertilizer. As the concentrations doubtless often enter the explosive range, particularly inside of tanks, the only safe assumption is that the range exists at all times. Personnel should be so governed in their use of heats.

CONTAINED NITROGEN SALTS

Contained nitrogen salts need be of little concern even in cold climates. The correct choice of the nitrogen solution and good judgment in its use will avoid salting out in the equipment. Most tank cars are well insulated, and the nitrogen solution can be shipped warm. Many tank cars which seem badly plugged with deposits can be quickly freed of blockage by pouring hot water over the solution valve of the car.

Maiming and fatal results have occurred when high heats have been applied to equipment containing deposits of salts from nitrogen solutions. The welding or acetylene cuttings of piping which had been on outdoor scrap piles for years has caused explosions with serious consequences. High heats are safe only when the equipment has been completely freed of all deposits. This usually requires much flushing with water, wire brushing, preferably by hand, followed by more flushing. Many explosions are recorded which resulted from the use of blow torches or the burning of oil soaked rags employed to free piping blocked with salted-out material.

VAPOR PRESSURES

Vapor pressures, except in anhydrous ammonia, are generally low enough not to be a serious hazard in the usual low pressure equipment. Anhydrous ammonia equipment in usually well-made and of good design. The force exerted by the expansion of liquid ammonia is very great when a vessel is completely filled with the liquid. The expansion increases the volume about

1 per cent for each 8°F increase in the temperature of liquid anhydrous ammonia. When it is 100 per cent full of liquid ammonia, almost any vessel or piping system can fail from the force of this expansion unless protected with an adequate pressure release. The piping and metering systems are sometimes not equipped with this needed protection. Gauge glasses are not advised for measuring anhydrous ammonia. If they are used, they should be equipped with automatic check valves and hand valves. If excess flow valves are present in a system, *never* pound on them to restart the flow.

Vapor pressures do present problems at times in transfering and metering all of the volatile materials including anhydrous ammonia, aqua ammonia, and the ammoniating solutions which contain any uncombined ammonia. One of these problems is the complete unloading of tank cars whether by pumps or by the more popular air-pressure method.

Vapor pressures vary with the nitrogen solutions, ranging from practically no gauge pressure to 50 lb or more at 104°F. All nitrogen producers supply temperature and pressure data covering their products. Without enough air pressure to overcome the vapor pressure in the car, the rush of ammonia gas will reduce, and often stop completely the flow of liquid. The flow of ammonia gas in a large volume will cause rumbling sounds in the car or storage tank and jerking of the hose. When these symptoms are caused by the flow of large volumes of air, they serve as reliable indications that essentially all the liquid has actually been removed. This principle applies equally to the use of pumps. The suction on the piping created by the pumps will release ammonia gas from the liquid unless the air pressure on the tank is high enough or the temperature of the liquid is low enough to prevent this condition from developing.

When the popular centrifugal pump operates against low discharge pressure, it has great volume capacity, and this is reflected in considerable suction, or relative vacuum in the suction piping. Under the conditions of temperature and pressures that frequently exist, the suction is sufficient to strip or pull ammonia gas from the liquid. The flow is then greatly reduced or completely stopped as the pump becomes "vapor locked." More air pressure on the supply tank is the best answer to this problem. Another answer is to throttle down the *discharge* flow enough to lower the suction to a workable level. Unless the conditions are severe, the throttled pump may still have enough capacity to perform the service satisfactorily for an emergency.

One common malpractice in unloading tank cars is to permit the air pressure to dwindle as the operations reduce the contents of a storage tank or tank car to a low point. The minimum air pressure required for moving liquid from a nearly empty tank will actually be greater than the air pressure needed when the supply tank is full. The vertical lift will be greater. It can be hazardous when even small quantities of some liquids exist under pressure in any equipment which is supposed to be empty.

Failure to cope with vapor pressures can result in off-analysis fertilizer. Vapor in meters will usually destroy their accuracy. When much sulfuric acid is being used, an imbalance of materials may leave too much acid free to work on any potassium chloride and ammonium nitrate present for maximum safety in the process or in the storage of the finished product.

CHEMICAL ACTIONS IN FERTILIZER MIXTURES

Chemical actions in fertilizer mixtures are calculated to yield the desired analysis economically and safely with good physical conditions. There must be a wide margin for safety in most of these calculations, since many of the accidents occur after the theoretical limits for safety have been violated quite badly for some time. The desirable quick actions for stability and conditioning of fertilizers are those involving ammonia with superphosphates and often with sulfuric or phosphoric acids. Even the most violent of these actions are conducted in most plants with almost complete safety. It is where the process runs wild that troubles develop, such as flash fires and sometimes explosions in the mixers, fires with dangerous fumes in the dryer, and troublesome heats in the storage pile.

Some factors causing the process to run wild are failure of any of the meters through breakdowns, corrosion, or by vapor pressure; failure of flow of nitrogen solutions or acids; corrosion, abrasion, or plugging of distribution pipes as well as bad original design; failure of supply of recycle or of dry process materials; failure of the mixer to actually mix the liquids and dry materials.

Since the final results of unsafe acts or unsafe conditions can develop after some time in unexpected quarters, it is desirable to consider what is produced when ammoniating solutions and acids are improperly handled.

PROCESSES AND FORMULAS

Processes and formulas have evolved through the forces of economics, chemistry, convenience, and abilities of the personnel. As originally arranged, they are generally practical and safe. Each new demand, however, seems to trim a little more from the margin of safety. For a time, after starting up, much dependence is placed on one or two men to detect and correct any trend that may be unsatisfactory. At times, the corrective measures reflect more of convenience than of knowledge and safety. Because communications are short of perfect in most fertilizer plants, management may only assume that its original idea is safe and is being applied as intended.

The processes employed in full scale granulating plants are usually slow and involve much costly equipment. It is good business to force all possible tonnage through this equipment. Much of the quality of the product, however, is determined by the length of time of contact among the chemicals; the period of granulating, drying and cooling; the temperature and moisture at several points including storage; and the kind, amount, and regularity of recycle. Soon after a plant is in operation, adjustments are often made, using the full potential of several of the aspects of the system. As all units are interdependent, an increase in the rate at one point may overload to failure several points downstream resulting in costly delays and much off-grade product.

The liberties which some plant men take in adjusting the operations and formulas create one of the basic ingredients for accidents, i.e., unsafe conditions. Eventually, to these unsafe conditions may be added the other ingredient for an accident, namely, an unsafe act.

Operators have increased the use of sulfuric acid as much as 100 lb/ton of fertilizer beyond the well-balanced formula which management believed was being used. Some operators do this to control ammonia fumes without investigating why the original satisfactory formula is no longer performing.

In batch systems, some operators add the sulfuric acid after the nitrogen solution in the mistaken belief that this is the way to control ammonia fumes. To offset the nitrogen loss through fumes, more than the prescribed nitrogen is added, then more acid. This "vicious circle" sometimes culminates in an accident that has had a long-standing invitation.

To overcome the limitation of dryers, it is a common practice to develop more heat in the ammoniator by increasing the amount of sulfuric acid. This end is often achieved by also shifting to 66° Bé sulfuric acid, a drier superphosphate, and possibly to a nitrogen solution containing a minimum amount of water. Again, by this procedure, more of the safety margin (water in this case) is trimmed away.

This condition is pronounced in the semigranulation systems because the desired dryness in the product depends largely on just such provisions. Some semigranulation operators will use this method to extremes rather than obtain some of the drying by remilling because remilling adds to the cost and breaks down some of the granules.

Heating in drying has much influence on the quantity and quality of the product as well as in safety in the plant. Probably the most overloaded equipment in the granulating plant is the dryer, with the cooler a close second. Drying must be performed in such manner that it makes granules of the conditioned mass or preserves those of delicate structure which may have been made in the ammoniator.

For effective drying under granulating conditions, it is necessary to have a specific volume of air at specific temperatures traveling the full length of the dryer. These conditions are rarely achieved in countercurrent dryers because much air is bypassed through the material inlet chute, which is almost always very large to avoid fouling by the sticky mass. It is difficult to have an effective seal against air leaks at this point. However, where this situation has been even slightly alleviated, definite improvements have been realized. Cocurrent dryers do not face this trouble, since the seal is easily effected with the dried, free-flowing exit product.

Drying is a very important feature, but if it is attained at the cost of cooling, of penalties in the formula, or of operations ahead of dryer, then a close look at the drying operation is in order. In some cases of hard setting, the most probable cause of this malfunction is excess storage temperature. However, in the belief that the trouble is moisture, the operator sometimes performs more and more drying which usually means a yet higher storage temperature. Finally, when some grades of fertilizer are dried to very low levels, the material can catch fire in the dryer with bad consequences.

Equipment design is now generally quite good, but much of it is a compromise with practical problems and costs. In this respect, it is worth recalling the effects of the failure to provide an efficient seal for the feed into countercurrent dryers that has just been discussed. Moreover, about twice the proper tons per hour per foot of ammoniating distributor pipe is being passed through many continuous ammoniations. There are serious problems in the supporting of the interior mechanism in long continuous ammoniators. Also, a correctly proportioned long unit would be so large in diameter as to create problems of fitting it into existing buildings.

Many batch rotary mixers suffer badly from poor ammoniating and acid distributor pipes because it is difficult to support and to inspect correctly designed devices inside of them. The operating personnel have adjusted well to the demands of the changes, and have done much of it on their own. Any accident, however, is to be deplored. In the interests of efficiency and safety, which are often interlocked, much effort should be expended on the early training of at least the key men, followed by continuing close supervision.

WHY THESE MATERIALS ARE USED

The fertilizer industry can perform for itself several operations economically and safely. Present fertilizer formulas are favored because their materials are readily available in desired volumes.

Convenience of control is an important reason for using the ammoniating media and the acids in the fertilizer industry. The mixers and a few other devices are the only pieces of equipment peculiar to the industry; all of the others are well-proven standard items utilized in other industries. These include meters, scales, temperature and pressure recorders and controls, metals, and plastics.

Physical quality of the fertilizer is so important that even the economic considerations are sometimes submerged to permit the use of a particular material, or more of the same material. Technically, a desired amount of heat for drying can be obtained at much less cost with fuel oil employed in the dryer than with sulfuric acid used in the ammoniator. But heat in the mass while it is in the mixer and as it enters the dryer is considered worth the extra cost.

Chemical quality of the fertilizer influences the choice of materals, for much of the sales departments' efforts dwell on chemical as well as physical quality. Anhydrous ammonia is frequently employed to the maximum extent, sometimes supplying all of the nitrogen. Nitrogen solutions are favored for their effects on condition, the variety of types of nitrogen, and for economy.

SAFEGUARDS FOR HANDLING THE MATERIAL

Choice of the right material will simplify the problems of handling. Choosing a nitrogen solution that meets the production requirements and yet has a practical salting out point will eliminate the need for applying any heat to the material to bring it back into solution in cold weather. The correct choice of nitrogen solutions will also eliminate or greatly reduce the problems of vapor pressure in hot weather.

Because of its greater water content, 60° Bé sulfuric acid seems to be safer than 66° Bé acid for use in large quantities and in most mixing equipment. This practice, however, requires some adjustments in the operations, particularly in the dryer.

MATERIALS OF CONSTRUCTION

Materials of construction have an important bearing on the safe handling of the chemicals. Correct choice of materials will eliminate the need of acetylene cutting and welding for repairing equipment which has been weakened by corrosion. This eliminates one of the most dangerous practices in the fertilizer industry—the ill-advised use of temperature beyond those of hot water or low pressure steam on equipment for handling nitrogen solutions or ammonia.

Serious thought should be given before any change is made in materials or in the service of any equipment. For instance, rubber is recommended for handling phosphoric acid but not for sulfuric acid. Ordinary black or carbon steel, preferably schedule 80 (extra heavy), is generally suitable for handling 60° Bé and 66° Bé sulfuric acid but it is not suitable for more dilute sulfuric, nor for phosphoric acid.

Hastaloy C is used widely for distributor pipes in the mixers.

Design of construction usually includes generous safety provisions, yet the cost sometimes leads to short cuts. The fertilizer industry could stand much more guarding of glasses and meters as well as of gears, shafts, and belts. Only a few of the heavy hammers on mixers and dryers are protected from falling to work areas when they break loose.

The influence on safety of the design of the ammoniating and the acid distributor pipes has been discussed. The desirability of improved design in the arrangement for feeding materials into countercurrent dryers has also been discussed.

Plant layout and safety provisions are closely related to efficient production. Wide, well-lighted passages permit safe and fast movement of materials.

Where such critical areas as the mixing location and instrument panel are well laid out, operators can perform their duties efficiently and safely. When operations and the operating personnel can be freely observed for production reasons, the problems of safety are lessened.

The location of safety showers, drinking fountains, telephones, alarms, stairs and duplicate escape routes are important features in any industrial plant. Good housekeeping is an important aid to safety.

EQUIPMENT AND TRAINING OF PERSONNEL

Safety of the individual in a fertilizer plant is not always under full control of that individual. Quantities of acids, ammonia as such, and nitrogen solutions are now in use. Acids are being used with nitrogen solutions, and the resulting products are often heated with open flames. In the past, all heats were held to a minimum.

As previously noted, protection is needed for the worker. Eyes are vulnerable, for an accident with such strong chemicals as sulfuric acid can blind almost immediately and permanently. Ammonia, dust, and larger foreign objects can usually be kept from the eyes by proper goggles.

All persons who are regularly exposed to the possibility of getting acid, ammonia, or nitrogen solution in the eyes should wear goggles during all times of possible exposure. When repairs are made of acid equipment, the workers should wear full face masks in addition to the goggles.

Ammonia-type or universal-type full vision gas masks with speaking diaphragm should be worn by men while they are working on ammonia or nitrogen solution equipment. At least two gas masks should be available. Other personal equipment for repairmen are firm felt or hard hats with brims, elbow length rubber gloves, rubber suits, and rubber boots, which should be worn with the trouser legs outside of the boots.

TRAINING

Training of the personnel is one of the most important steps in developing a safe plant. Some of the most serious concerns for safety in fertilizer manufacturing plants stem from the fact that chemical actions are not seen by the operators and are little understood by them. Normally safe processes and equipment may gradually become hazardous because corrosion, abrasion, or breakage either gradually or suddenly alter the equipment, and thereby the process, from its original safe level.

Liberties taken by operators for their own convenience, or in the belief that they are improving the system, often are at the root of much trouble. For example, a maintenance worker may observe the fertilizer, which used a fourth of its weight in nitrogen solutions, while being exposed to direct flames in the dryer. An untrained man having observed this, may see no hazard in cutting, welding, or otherwise applying high heats to nitrogen solutions, ammonia, or acid equipment, as well as to equipment after it has been scrapped. He will not believe there is need of any preparation for safety.

Most operators have learned well the mechanics of their trade. Without attempting to make chemists of them, it is possible, in their training to impart to them some basic understanding of the properties of the individual chemicals. They can be taught the value of controlling the chemical combining of the materials, as well as the capacity for trouble in the processes when they run wild through neglect of equipment or unauthorized changes in the process.

The precautions are reasonable enough and the latitudes for safety generally are wide enough in the fertilizer industry that scare tactics are not called for. Training, explaining, education, and close supervision in the fertilizer industry have made the storing, handling, and usage of dynamite almost totally free of accidents. The same principles can also serve the industry well in its other activities.

THE HUMAN FACTOR

Suppliers of materials often recommend the use of their products below their full potential to meet the conditions of the far-flung fertilizer industry with its great range of processes, equipment, and personnel. It is not enough that the product in itself be safe, for some of the products are combined under questionable conditions beyond the control of the supplier. In order to avoid salting-out troubles and contamination through the deterioration of their equipment, suppliers have generally adopted corrosion-resistant, insulated tank cars capable of enough pressure to safely handle the materials.

Knowing the proclivity of the industry for improving and for finding "the better way" suppliers have many trained men on the alert for improved methods and put stress on doing the job safely.

SUPPLIERS OF EQUIPMENT

Suppliers of equipment face many of the same problems as suppliers of materials. Equipment is almost universally made quite safe for handling the materials and the processes as they originally exist. As in the case of materials, however, the equipment is subject to changes in physical structure and operating methods by the vagaries of the industry. Equipment is often at the mercy of the operating personnel.

It may be deemed too costly to make all equipment of materials which will resist for long all of the numerous corrosion and abrasion influences which come to bear. Provisions should be made, however, against the hazards introduced by failure of equipment. Obsolescence must also be considered when equipment is being evaluated, for the industry is continually progressing in its materials, designs, and processes.

THE RESPONSIBILITY OF MANAGEMENT

Management has a profound influence on safety. The decision to improve the safety record usually involves a willingness to invest money and effort initially which may be a long time in paying dividends. There may be doubt for some time whether the results justify the effort or the expenditure.

Management has usually cooperated fully when the safety program has been given the same sound consideration that is given to the other facets of a sucessful business. The problems encountered in handling the few chemicals which have been discussed show that safety cannot just happen. Everyone, certainly including management, must believe in a safety program in order for it to be fully effective.

THE RESPONSIBILITY OF SUPERVISORS

Supervisors are usually versatile enough to get the required knowledge of the processes and equipment to the variety of persons under their supervision. The same capability applied in the interest of doing their tasks safely will bring equally good results. The supervisor must, therefore, know the effects any changes may have on all phases of the process. He must keep the personnel always informed on the nature of the work. Many accidents occur to workers who have not been informed that any risks existed or who were never taught how to avoid them. Supervisors should thoroughly investigate every accident. Moreover, sometimes much can be learned about accident prevention by studying the near misses, and this route to safety is much more pleasant than the study of actual accidents.

THE RESPONSIBILITY OF THE WORKER

Workers have the highest stake in safety, for they pay the greatest price —the price of human misery for themselves and their families. The successful processes and pieces of equipment take into account the adaptability of the employees. The industry has performed remarkably well in its desire to retain existing personnel through the years to handle what are sometimes baffling developments. Employees have some responsibility to themselves and management to be flexible and receptive to the new ideas which seem to be coming in rapid succession. They must believe that their own safety depends on how well they know the processes and the equipment, not merely the visible moving parts.

SUMMARY

It is necessary to understand the nature of the materials, the principles of combining them, and the influence of equipment in maintainig safe conditions.

Anhydrous ammonia develops high vapor pressures and can develop destructive pressures when liquid ammonia fills a space completely without provision for releasing the pressure.

Even in small concentrations, fumes from any materials which contain uncombined ammonia can impair vision. Concentrations beyond about

500 ppm of air create bad working conditions. Ammonia in air in the range from about 11 to 28 per cent is an explosive mixture.

Nitrogen solutions contain substantial amounts of uncombined ammonia, as well as urea or ammonium nitrate. The solution, the vapor, and any deposited salts should never be subjected to temperatures which exceed those of low pressure steam or boiling water. This applies also to repair and salvage operations. Free the surfaces of equipment of all deposits before applying high heats.

The acids are violently destructive to human tissues, the eyes being particularly vulnerable. Apply running water, or any water, freely to affected areas for fifteen minutes, then obtain the services of a doctor.

Acids are destructive to many materials of construction, and corrosion may change a safe process into a questionable one. The release of hydrogen from corrosion of steel by acid creates an explosion hazard and can develop high pressure in a closed system. Before a person enters any tank, the tank should be thoroughly aired. Repairs to large tanks are best left to trained personnel.

Test periodically all hoses, meters, scales, gauges, distributor pipes, and safety devices. Check all gauge glass connections in tanks for any restriction of flow. Use cold water for testing tanks. Do not use air pressure. Be suspicious of all irregularities in rates of flows, physical condition of products, unusual temperatures at any place, and unnecessary fumes. Make sure that only the prescribed amounts of each material is actually being employed.

Keep at least two gas masks available. Make certain that workers are protected by personal equipment, including goggles or face shields. Train the workers. Know all of the causes of trouble and learn how to head off the possible consequences, surely and in time. Recognize and heed the signs.

Excellent additional information may be obtained from the following sources:

The Compressed Gas Association, Inc., 500 Fifth Ave., New York 36, N. Y. Pamphlet 6-2, Anhydrous Ammonia

National Plant Food Institute, 1700 K St., N. W., Washington 6, D. C. Fertilizer Safety Guide ($0.50 each)

The National Safety Council, 425 N. Michigan Ave., Chicago 11, Ill.

Manufacturing Chemists' Association, Inc., 1825 Connecticut Ave., N. W., Washington 25, D. C.

Chemical Safety Data Sheet: SD-8, Anhydrous Ammonia; SD-13, Aqua Ammonia; SD-20, Sulfuric Acid; and SD-70, Phosphoric Acid ($0.30 each)

U. S. Department of Labor, Sup't of Documents, U. S. Gov't Printing Office Chem-

istry for the Safety of Man: **2**, Environmental Hazards; **222**, Safety in Industry
($0.15 each)

Sax, N. I., "Dangerous Properties of Industrial Materials", Second Ed., Reinhold,
1963.

Also, good information is available, usually free, from suppliers of materials and makers of equipment.

Index